Introduction to Engineering

Fall 2006

A Pearson Custom Publication

Pearson Prentice Hall
Vice President and Editorial Director, ECS: *Marcia J. Horton*
Executive Editor: *Eric Svendsen*
Associate Editor: *Dee Bernhard*
Vice President and Director of Production and Manufacturing, ESM: *David W. Riccardi*
Executive Managing Editor: *Vince O'Brien*
Managing Editor: *David A. George*
Production Editor: *Barbara A. Till*
Director of Creative Services: *Paul Belfanti*
Creative Director: *Carole Anson*
Art Director: *Jayne Conte*
Art Editor: *Greg Dulles*
Manufacturing Manager: *Trudy Pisciotti*
Manufacturing Buyer: *Lisa McDowell*
Marketing Manager: *Holly Stark*

Pearson Custom Publishing
Director of Database Publishing: *Michael Payne*
Executive Marketing Manager: *Nathan L. Wilbur*
Operations Manager: *Eric M. Kenney*
Editorial Assistant: *Victoria L. Ravin*
Project Specialist: *Zach LaRosa*
Cover Designer: *Renee Sartell*

Pearson Prentice Hall
Pearson Education, Inc.
Upper Saddle River, NJ 074588

ISBN: 0536196931
Package ISBN:

Excerpts taken from:

Design Concepts for Engineers, 2/e by Mark N. Horenstein
0-13-093430-5 © 2002 by Prentice-Hall, Inc., a Pearson Education Company

Engineering Design and Problem Solving, 2/e by Steven K. Howell
0-13-093399-6 © 2002 by Prentice-Hall, Inc., a Pearson Education Company

Engineering Ethics by Charles B. Fleddermann
0-13-784224-4 © 1999 by Prentice-Hall, Inc., a Pearson Education Company

Engineering with Excel by Ronald W. Larsen
0-13-017696-6 © 2002 by Prentice-Hall, Inc., a Pearson Education Company

Engineering Success, 2/e by Peter Schiavone
0-13-041827-7 © 2002 by Prentice-Hall, Inc., a Pearson Education Company

Exploring Engineering, 2/e by Joe King
0-13-093442-9 © 2002 by Prentice-Hall, Inc., a Pearson Education Company

Graphics Concepts by Richard M. Lueptow
0-13-030687-8 © 2000 by Prentice-Hall, Inc., a Pearson Education Company

Introduction to AutoCAD® 2000 by Mark Dix and Paul Riley
0-13-016732-0 © 2000 by Prentice-Hall, Inc., a Pearson Education Company

Introduction to Engineering Analysis by Kirk D. Hagen
0-13-016733-9 © 2000 by Prentice-Hall, Inc., a Pearson Education Company

Introduction to Excel 2002 by David C. Kuncicky
0-13-008175-2 © 2003 by Pearson Education, Inc.

Introduction to MathCad® 2000 by Ronald W. Larsen
0-13-020007-7 © 2001 by Prentice-Hall, Inc., a Pearson Education Company

Introduction to MatLab® 6 by Delores M. Etter and David C. Kuncicky with Doug Hull
0-13-032845-6 © 2002 by Prentice-Hall, Inc., a Pearson Education Company

Introduction to PowerPoint 2002 by Jack Leifer
0-13-008179-5 © 2003 by Pearson Education, Inc.

Introduction to Unix® by David I. Schwartz
0-13-095135-8 © 1999 by Prentice-Hall, Inc., a Pearson Education Company

Introduction to Word 2002 by David C. Kuncicky
0-13-008170-1 © 2003 by Pearson Education, Inc.

Power Programming with VBA/Excel by Steven C. Chapra
0-13-047377-4 © 2003 by Pearson Education, Inc.

About ESource

ESource—The Prentice Hall Engineering Source—www.prenhall.com/esource

ESource—The Prentice Hall Engineering Source gives professors the power to harness the full potential of their text and their first-year engineering course. More than just a collection of books, ESource is a unique publishing system revolving around the ESource website—www.prenhall.com/esource. ESource enables you to put your stamp on your book just as you do your course. It lets you:

Control You choose exactly what chapters are in your book and in what order they appear. Of course, you can choose the entire book if you'd like and stay with the authors' original order.

Optimize Get the most from your book and your course. ESource lets you produce the optimal text for your students needs.

Customize You can add your own material anywhere in your text's presentation, and your final product will arrive at your bookstore as a professionally formatted text. Of course, all titles in this series are available as stand-alone texts, or as bundles of two or more books sold at a discount. Contact your PH sales rep for discount information.

ESource ACCESS

Professors who choose to bundle two or more texts from the ESource series for their class, or use an ESource custom book will be providing their students with an on-line library of intro engineering content—ESource Access. We've designed ESource ACCESS to provide students a flexible, searchable, on-line resource. Free access codes come in bundles and custom books are valid for one year after initial log-on. Contact your PH sales rep for more information.

ESource Content

All the content in ESource was written by educators specifically for freshman/first-year students. Authors tried to strike a balanced level of presentation, an approach that was neither formulaic nor trivial, and one that did not focus too heavily on advanced topics that most introductory students do not encounter until later classes. Because many professors do not have extensive time to cover these topics in the classroom, authors prepared each text with the idea that many students would use it for self-instruction and independent study. Students should be able to use this content to learn the software tool or subject on their own.

While authors had the freedom to write texts in a style appropriate to their particular subject, all followed certain guidelines created to promote a consistency that makes students comfortable. Namely, every chapter opens with a clear set of **Objectives**, includes **Practice Boxes** throughout the chapter, and ends with a number of **Problems**, and a list of **Key Terms**. **Applications Boxes** are spread throughout the book with the intent of giving students a real-world perspective of engineering. **Success Boxes** provide the student with advice about college study skills, and help students avoid the common pitfalls of first-year students. In addition, this series contains an entire book titled ***Engineering Success*** by Peter Schiavone of the University of Alberta intended to expose students quickly to what it takes to be an engineering student.

Creating Your Book

Using ESource is simple. You preview the content either on-line or through examination copies of the books you can request on-line, from your PH sales rep, or by calling 1-800-526-0485. Create an on-line outline of the content you want, in the order you want, using ESource's simple interface. Insert your own material into the text flow. If you are not ready to order, ESource will save your work. You can come back at any time and change, re-arrange, or add more material to your creation. Once you're finished you'll automatically receive an ISBN. Give it to your bookstore and your book will arrive on their shelves four to six weeks after they order. Your custom desk copies with their instructor supplements will arrive at your address at the same time.

To learn more about this new system for creating the perfect textbook, go to www.prenhall.com/esource. You can either go through the on-line walkthrough of how to create a book, or experiment yourself.

Supplements

Adopters of ESource receive an instructor's CD that contains professor and student code from the books in the series, as well as other instruction aides provided by authors. The website also holds approximately **350 PowerPoint transparencies** created by Jack Leifer of University of Kentucky–Paducah. Professors can either follow these transparencies as pre-prepared lectures or use them as the basis for their own custom presentations.

Titles in the ESource Series

Design Concepts for Engineers, 2/e
0-13-093430-5
Mark Horenstein

Engineering Success, 2/e
0-13-041827-7
Peter Schiavone

Engineering Design and Problem Solving, 2E
ISBN 0-13-093399-6
Steven K. Howell

Exploring Engineering
ISBN 0-13-093442-9
Joe King

Engineering Ethics
0-13-784224-4
Charles B. Fleddermann

Introduction to Engineering Analysis
0-13-016733-9
Kirk D. Hagen

Introduction to Engineering Experimentation
0-13-032835-9
Ronald W. Larsen, John T. Sears, and Royce Wilkinson

Introduction to Mechanical Engineering
0-13-019640-1
Robert Rizza

Introduction to Electrical and Computer Engineering
0-13-033363-8
Charles B. Fleddermann and Martin Bradshaw

Introduction to MATLAB 6—Update
0-13-140918-2
Delores Etter and David C. Kuncicky, with Douglas W. Hull

MATLAB Programming
0-13-035127-X
David C. Kuncicky

Introduction to MATLAB
0-13-013149-0
Delores Etter with David C. Kuncicky

Introduction to Mathcad 2000
0-13-020007-7
Ronald W. Larsen

Introduction to Mathcad 11
0-13-008177-9
David W. Larsen

Introduction to Maple 8
0-13-032844-8
David I. Schwartz

Mathematics Review
0-13-011501-0
Peter Schiavone

Power Programming with VBA/Excel
0-13-047377-4
Steven C. Chapra

Introduction to Excel 2002
0-13-008175-2
David C. Kuncicky

Engineering with Excel
ISBN 0-13-017696-6
Ronald W. Larsen

Introduction to Word 2002
0-13-008170-1
David C. Kuncicky

Introduction to PowerPoint 2002
0-13-008179-5
Jack Leifer

Graphics Concepts
0-13-030687-8
Richard M. Lueptow

Graphics Concepts with SolidWorks 2/e
0-13-140915-8
Richard M. Lueptow and Michael Minbiole

Graphics Concepts with Pro/ENGINEER
0-13-014154-2
Richard M. Lueptow, Jim Steger, and Michael T. Snyder

Introduction to AutoCAD 2000
0-13-016732-0
Mark Dix and Paul Riley

Introduction to AutoCAD, R. 14
0-13-011001-9
Mark Dix and Paul Riley

Introduction to UNIX
0-13-095135-8
David I. Schwartz

Introduction to the Internet, 3/e
0-13-031355-6
Scott D. James

Introduction to Visual Basic 6.0
0-13-026813-5
David I. Schneider

Introduction to C
0-13-011854-0
Delores Etter

Introduction to C++
0-13-011855-9
Delores Etter

Introduction to FORTRAN 90
0-13-013146-6
Larry Nyhoff and Sanford Leestma

Introduction to Java
0-13-919416-9
Stephen J. Chapman

About the Authors

No project could ever come to pass without a group of authors who have the vision and the courage to turn a stack of blank paper into a book. The authors in this series, who worked diligently to produce their books, provide the building blocks of the series.

Martin D. Bradshaw was born in Pittsburg, KS in 1936, grew up in Kansas and the surrounding states of Arkansas and Missouri, graduating from Newton High School, Newton, KS in 1954. He received the B.S.E.E. and M.S.E.E. degrees from the University of Wichita in 1958 and 1961, respectively. A Ford Foundation fellowship at Carnegie Institute of Technology followed from 1961 to 1963 and he received the Ph.D. degree in electrical engineering in 1964. He spent his entire academic career with the Department of Electrical and Computer Engineering at the University of New Mexico (1961-1963 and 1991-1996). He served as the Assistant Dean for Special Programs with the UNM College of Engineering from 1974 to 1976 and as the Associate Chairman for the EECE Department from 1993 to 1996. During the period 1987-1991 he was a consultant with his own company, EE Problem Solvers. During 1978 he spent a sabbatical year with the State Electricity Commission of Victoria, Melbourne, Australia. From 1979 to 1981 he served an IPA assignment as a Project Officer at the U.S. Air Force Weapons Laboratory, Kirkland AFB, Albuquerque, NM. He has won numerous local, regional, and national teaching awards, including the George Westinghouse Award from the ASEE in 1973. He was awarded the IEEE Centennial Medal in 2000.

Acknowledgments: Dr. Bradshaw would like to acknowledge his late mother, who gave him a great love of reading and learning, and his father, who taught him to persist until the job is finished. The encouragement of his wife, Jo, and his six children is a never-ending inspiration.

Stephen J. Chapman received a B.S. degree in Electrical Engineering from Louisiana State University (1975), the M.S.E. degree in Electrical Engineering from the University of Central Florida (1979), and pursued further graduate studies at Rice University.

Mr. Chapman is currently Manager of Technical Systems for British Aerospace Australia, in Melbourne, Australia. In this position, he provides technical direction and design authority for the work of younger engineers within the company. He also continues to teach at local universities on a part-time basis.

Mr. Chapman is a Senior Member of the Institute of Electrical and Electronics Engineers (and several of its component societies). He is also a member of the Association for Computing Machinery and the Institution of Engineers (Australia).

Steven C. Chapra presently holds the Louis Berger Chair for Computing and Engineering in the Civil and Environmental Engineering Department at Tufts University. Dr. Chapra received engineering degrees from Manhattan College and the University of Michigan. Before joining the faculty at Tufts, he taught at Texas A&M University, the University of Colorado, and Imperial College, London. His research interests focus on surface water-quality modeling and advanced computer applications in environmental engineering. He has published over 50 refereed journal articles, 20 software packages and 6 books. He has received a number of awards including the 1987 ASEE Merriam/Wiley Distinguished Author Award, the 1993 Rudolph Hering Medal, and teaching awards from Texas A&M, the University of Colorado, and the Association of Environmental Engineering and Science Professors.

Acknowledgments: To the Berger Family for their many contributions to engineering education. I would also like to thank David Clough for his friendship and insights, John Walkenbach for his wonderful books, and my colleague Lee Minardi and my students Kenny William, Robert Viesca and Jennifer Edelmann for their suggestions.

Mark Dix began working with AutoCAD in 1985 as a programmer for CAD Support Associates, Inc. He helped design a system for creating estimates and bills of material directly from AutoCAD drawing databases for use in the automated conveyor industry. This system became the basis for systems still widely in use today. In 1986 he began collaborating with Paul Riley to create AutoCAD training materials, combining Riley's background in industrial design and training with Dix's background in writing, curriculum development, and programming. Mr. Dix received the M.S. degree in education from the University of Massachusetts. He is currently the Director of Dearborn Academy High School in Arlington, Massachusetts.

Delores M. Etter is a Professor of Electrical and Computer Engineering at the University of Colorado. Dr. Etter was a faculty member at the University of New Mexico and also a Visiting Professor at Stanford University. Dr. Etter was responsible for the Freshman Engineering Program at the University of New Mexico and is active in the Integrated Teaching Laboratory at the University of Colorado. She was elected a Fellow of the Institute of Electrical and Electronics Engineers for her contributions to education and for her technical leadership in digital signal processing.

Charles B. Fleddermann is a professor in the Department of Electrical and Computer Engineering at the University of New Mexico in Albuquerque, New Mexico. All of his degrees are in electrical engineering: his Bachelor's degree from the University of Notre Dame, and the Master's and Ph.D. from the University of Illinois at Urbana-Champaign. Prof. Fleddermann developed an engineering ethics course for his department in response to the ABET requirement to incorporate ethics topics into the undergraduate engineering curriculum. *Engineering Ethics* was written as a vehicle for presenting ethical theory, analysis, and problem solving to engineering undergraduates in a concise and readily accessible way.

Acknowledgments: I would like to thank Profs. Charles Harris and Michael Rabins of Texas A & M University whose NSF sponsored workshops on engineering ethics got me started thinking in this field. Special thanks to my wife Liz, who proofread the manuscript for this book, provided many useful suggestions, and who helped me learn how to teach "soft" topics to engineers.

Kirk D. Hagen is a professor at Weber State University in Ogden, Utah. He has taught introductory-level engineering courses and upper-division thermal science courses at WSU since 1993. He received his B.S. degree in physics from Weber State College and his M.S. degree in mechanical engineering from Utah State University, after which he worked as a thermal designer/analyst in the aerospace and electronics industries. After several years of engineering practice, he resumed his formal education, earning his Ph.D. in mechanical engineering at the University of Utah. Hagen is the author of an undergraduate heat transfer text.

Mark N. Horenstein is a Professor in the Department of Electrical and Computer Engineering at Boston University. He has degrees in Electrical Engineering from M.I.T. and U.C. Berkeley and has been involved in teaching engineering design for the greater part of his academic career. He devised and developed the senior design project class taken by all electrical and computer engineering students at Boston University. In this class, the students work for a virtual engineering company developing products and systems for real-world engineering and social-service clients.

Acknowledgments: I would like to thank Prof. James Bethune, the architect of the Peak Performance event at Boston University, for his permission to highlight the competition in my text. Several of the ideas relating to brainstorming and teamwork were derived from a

workshop on engineering design offered by Prof. Charles Lovas of Southern Methodist University. The principles of estimation were derived in part from a freshman engineering problem posed by Prof. Thomas Kincaid of Boston University.

Steven Howell is the Chairman and a Professor of Mechanical Engineering at Lawrence Technological University. Prior to joining LTU in 2001, Dr. Howell led a knowledge-based engineering project for Visteon Automotive Systems and taught computer-aided design classes for Ford Motor Company engineers. Dr. Howell also has a total of 15 years experience as an engineering faculty member at Northern Arizona University, the University of the Pacific, and the University of Zimbabwe. While at Northern Arizona University, he helped develop and implement an award-winning interdisciplinary series of design courses simulating a corporate engineering-design environment.

Douglas W. Hull is a graduate student in the Department of Mechanical Engineering at Carnegie Mellon University in Pittsburgh, Pennsylvania. He is the author of *Mastering Mechanics I Using Matlab 5*, and contributed to *Mechanics of Materials* by Bedford and Liechti. His research in the Sensor Based Planning lab involves motion planning for hyper-redundant manipulators, also known as serpentine robots.

Scott D. James is a staff lecturer at Kettering University (formerly GMI Engineering & Management Institute) in Flint, Michigan. He is currently pursuing a Ph.D. in Systems Engineering with an emphasis on software engineering and computer-integrated manufacturing. He chose teaching as a profession after several years in the computer industry. "I thought that it was really important to know what it was like outside of academia. I wanted to provide students with classes that were up to date and provide the information that is really used and needed."

Acknowledgments: Scott would like to acknowledge his family for the time to work on the text and his students and peers at Kettering who offered helpful critiques of the materials that eventually became the book.

Joe King received the B.S. and M.S. degrees from the University of California at Davis. He is a Professor of Computer Engineering at the University of the Pacific, Stockton, CA, where he teaches courses in digital design, computer design, artificial intelligence, and computer networking. Since joining the UOP faculty, Professor King has spent yearlong sabbaticals teaching in Zimbabwe, Singapore, and Finland. A licensed engineer in the state of California, King's industrial experience includes major design projects with Lawrence Livermore National Laboratory, as well as independent consulting projects. Prof. King has had a number of books published with titles including MATLAB, MathCAD, Exploring Engineering, and Engineering and Society.

David C. Kuncicky is a native Floridian. He earned his Baccalaureate in psychology, Master's in computer science, and Ph.D. in computer science from Florida State University. He has served as a faculty member in the Department of Electrical Engineering at the FAMU–FSU College of Engineering and the Department of Computer Science at Florida State University. He has taught computer science and computer engineering courses for over 15 years. He has published research in the areas of intelligent hybrid systems and neural networks. He is currently the Director of Engineering at Bioreason, Inc. in Sante Fe, New Mexico.

Acknowledgments: Thanks to Steffie and Helen for putting up with my late nights and long weekends at the computer. Finally, thanks to Susan Bassett for having faith in my abilities, and for providing continued tutelage and support.

Ron Larsen is a Professor of Chemical Engineering at Montana State University, and received his Ph.D. from the Pennsylvania State University. He was initially attracted to engineering by the challenges the profession offers, but also appreciates that engineering is a serving profession. Some of the greatest challenges he has faced while teaching have involved non-traditional teaching methods, including evening courses for practicing engineers and teaching through an interpreter at the Mongolian National University. These experiences have provided tremendous opportunities to learn new ways to communicate technical material. Dr. Larsen views modern software as one of the new tools that will radically alter the way engineers work, and his book *Introduction to MathCAD* was written to help young engineers prepare to meet the challenges of an ever-changing workplace.

Acknowledgments: To my students at Montana State University who have endured the rough drafts and typos, and who still allow me to experiment with their classes—my sincere thanks.

Sanford Leestma is a Professor of Mathematics and Computer Science at Calvin College, and received his Ph.D. from New Mexico State University. He has been the long-time co-author of successful textbooks on Fortran, Pascal, and data structures in Pascal. His current research interest are in the areas of algorithms and numerical computation.

Jack Leifer is an Assistant Professor in the Department of Mechanical Engineering at the University of Kentucky Extended Campus Program in Paducah, and was previously with the Department of Mathematical Sciences and Engineering at the University of South Carolina–Aiken. He received his Ph.D. in Mechanical Engineering from the University of Texas at Austin in December 1995. His current research interests include the analysis of ultra-light and inflatable (Gossamer) space structures.

Acknowledgments: I'd like to thank my colleagues at USC–Aiken, especially Professors Mike May and Laurene Fausett, for their encouragement and feedback; and my parents, Felice and Morton Leifer, for being there and providing support (as always) as I completed this book.

Richard M. Lueptow is the Charles Deering McCormick Professor of Teaching Excellence and Associate Professor of Mechanical Engineering at Northwestern University. He is a native of Wisconsin and received his doctorate from the Massachusetts Institute of Technology in 1986. He teaches design, fluid mechanics, an spectral analysis techniques. Rich has an active research program on rotating filtration, Taylor Couette flow, granular flow, fire suppression, and acoustics. He has five patents and over 40 refereed journal and proceedings papers along with many other articles, abstracts, and presentations.

Acknowledgments: Thanks to my talented and hard-working co-authors as well as the many colleagues and students who took the tutorial for a "test drive." Special thanks to Mike Minbiole for his major contributions to Graphics Concepts with SolidWorks. Thanks also to Northwestern University for the time to work on a book. Most of all, thanks to my loving wife, Maiya, and my children, Hannah and Kyle, for supporting me in this endeavor. (Photo courtesy of Evanston Photographic Studios, Inc.)

Larry Nyhoff is a Professor of Mathematics and Computer Science at Calvin College. After doing bachelor's work at Calvin, and Master's work at Michigan, he received a Ph.D. from Michigan State and also did graduate work in computer science at Western Michigan. Dr. Nyhoff has taught at Calvin for the past 34 years—mathematics at first and computer science for the past several years.

Acknowledgments: We thank our families—Shar, Jeff, Dawn, Rebecca, Megan, Sara, Greg, Julie, Joshua, Derek, Tom, Joan; Marge, Michelle, Sandy, Lory, Michael—for being patient and understanding. We thank God for allowing us to write this text.

Paul Riley is an author, instructor, and designer specializing in graphics and design for multimedia. He is a founding partner of CAD Support Associates, a contract service and professional training organization for computer-aided design. His 15 years of business experience and 20 years of teaching experience are supported by degrees in education and computer science. Paul has taught AutoCAD at the University of Massachusetts at Lowell and is presently teaching AutoCAD at Mt. Ida College in Newton, Massachusetts. He has developed a program, Computer-aided Design for Professionals that is highly regarded by corporate clients and has been an ongoing success since 1982.

Robert Rizza is an Assistant Professor of Mechanical Engineering at North Dakota State University, where he teaches courses in mechanics and computer-aided design. A native of Chicago, he received the Ph.D. degree from the Illinois Institute of Technology. He is also the author of *Getting Started with Pro/ ENGINEER*. Dr. Rizza has worked on a diverse range of engineering projects including projects from the railroad, bioengineering, and aerospace industries. His current research interests include the fracture of composite materials, repair of cracked aircraft components, and loosening of prostheses.

Peter Schiavone is a professor and student advisor in the Department of Mechanical Engineering at the University of Alberta, Canada. He received his Ph.D. from the University of Strathclyde, U.K. in 1988. He has authored several books in the area of student academic success as well as numerous papers in international scientific research journals. Dr. Schiavone has worked in private industry in several different areas of engineering including aerospace and systems engineering. He founded the first Mathematics Resource Center at the University of Alberta, a unit designed specifically to teach new students the necessary survival skills in mathematics and the physical sciences required for success in first-year engineering. This led to the Students' Union Gold Key Award for outstanding contributions to the university. Dr. Schiavone lectures regularly to freshman engineering students and to new engineering professors on engineering success, in particular about maximizing students' academic performance.

Acknowledgements: Thanks to Richard Felder for being such an inspiration; to my wife Linda for sharing my dreams and believing in me; and to Francesca and Antonio for putting up with Dad when working on the text.

David I. Schneider holds an A.B. degree from Oberlin College and a Ph.D. degree in Mathematics from MIT. He has taught for 34 years, primarily at the University of Maryland. Dr. Schneider has authored 28 books, with one-half of them computer programming books. He has developed three customized software packages that are supplied as supplements to over 55 mathematics textbooks. His involvement with computers dates back to 1962, when he programmed a special purpose computer at MIT's Lincoln Laboratory to correct errors in a communications system.

David I. Schwartz is an Assistant Professor in the Computer Science Department at Cornell University and earned his B.S., M.S., and Ph.D. degrees in Civil Engineering from State University of New York at Buffalo. Throughout his graduate studies, Schwartz combined principles of computer science to applications of civil engineering. He became interested in helping students learn how to apply software tools for solving a variety of engineering problems. He teaches his students to learn incrementally and practice frequently to gain the maturity to tackle other subjects. In his spare time, Schwartz plays drums in a variety of bands.

Acknowledgments: I dedicate my books to my family, friends, and students who all helped in so many ways.

Many thanks go to the schools of Civil Engineering and Engineering & Applied Science at State University of New York at Buffalo where I originally developed and tested my UNIX and Maple books. I greatly appreciate the opportunity to explore my goals and all the help from everyone at the Computer Science Department at Cornell.

John T. Sears received the Ph.D. degree from Princeton University. Currently, he is a Professor and the head of the Department of Chemical Engineering at Montana State University. After leaving Princeton he worked in research at Brookhaven National Laboratory and Esso Research and Engineering, until he took a position at West Virginia University. He came to MSU in 1982, where he has served as the Director of the College of Engineering Minority Program and Interim Director for BioFilm Engineering. Prof. Sears has written a book on air pollution and economic development, and over 45 articles in engineering and engineering education.

Michael T. Snyder is President of Internet startup Appointments123.com. He is a native of Chicago, and he received his Bachelor of Science degree in Mechanical Engineering from the University of Notre Dame. Mike also graduated with honors from Northwestern University's Kellogg Graduate School of Management in 1999 with his Masters of Management degree. Before Appointments123.com, Mike was a mechanical engineer in new product development for Motorola Cellular and Acco Office Products. He has received four patents for his mechanical design work. "Pro/ENGINEER was an invaluable design tool for me, and I am glad to help students learn the basics of Pro/ENGINEER."

Acknowledgments: Thanks to Rich Lueptow and Jim Steger for inviting me to be a part of this great project. Of course, thanks to my wife Gretchen for her support in my various projects.

Jim Steger is currently Chief Technical Officer and cofounder of an Internet applications company. He graduated with a Bachelor of Science degree in Mechanical Engineering from Northwestern University. His prior work included mechanical engineering assignments at Motorola and Acco Brands. At Motorola, Jim worked on part design for two-way radios and was one of the lead mechanical engineers on a cellular phone product line. At Acco Brands, Jim was the sole engineer on numerous office product designs. His Worx stapler has won design awards in the United States and in Europe. Jim has been a Pro/ENGINEER user for over six years.

Acknowledgments: Many thanks to my co-authors, especially Rich Lueptow for his leadership on this project. I would also like to thank my family for their continuous support.

Royce Wilkinson received his undergraduate degree in chemistry from Rose-Hulman Institute of Technology in 1991 and the Ph.D. degree in chemistry from Montana State University in 1998 with research in natural product isolation from fungi. He currently resides in Bozeman, MT and is involved in HIV drug research. His research interests center on biological molecules and their interactions in the search for pharmaceutical advances.

Reviewers

We would like to thank everyone who has reviewed texts in this series.

ESource Reviewers

Christopher Rowe, *Vanderbilt University*
Steve Yurgartis, *Clarkson University*
Heidi A. Diefes-Dux, *Purdue University*
Howard Silver, *Fairleigh Dickenson University*
Jean C. Malzahn Kampe, *Virginia Polytechnic Institute and State University*
Malcolm Heimer, *Florida International University*
Stanley Reeves, *Auburn University*
John Demel, *Ohio State University*
Shahnam Navee, *Georgia Southern University*
Heshem Shaalem, *Georgia Southern University*
Terry L. Kohutek, *Texas A & M University*
Liz Rozell, *Bakersfield College*
Mary C. Lynch, *University of Florida*
Ted Pawlicki, *University of Rochester*
James N. Jensen, *SUNY at Buffalo*
Tom Horton, *University of Virginia*
Eileen Young, *Bristol Community College*
James D. Nelson, *Louisiana Tech University*
Jerry Dunn, *Texas Tech University*
Howard M. Fulmer, *Villanova UniversityBerkeley*
Naeem Abdurrahman *University of Texas, Austin*
Stephen Allan *Utah State University*
Anil Bajaj *Purdue University*
Grant Baker *University of Alaska–Anchorage*
William Beckwith *Clemson University*
Haym Benaroya *Rutgers University*
John Biddle *California State Polytechnic University*
Tom Bledsaw *ITT Technical Institute*
Fred Boadu *Duke University*
Tom Bryson *University of Missouri, Rolla*
Ramzi Bualuan *University of Notre Dame*
Dan Budny *Purdue University*
Betty Burr *University of Houston*
Dale Calkins *University of Washington*
Harish Cherukuri *University of North Carolina –Charlotte*
Arthur Clausing *University of Illinois*
Barry Crittendon *Virginia Polytechnic and State University*
James Devine *University of South Florida*
Ron Eaglin *University of Central Florida*
Dale Elifrits *University of Missouri, Rolla*
Patrick Fitzhorn *Colorado State University*
Susan Freeman *Northeastern University*
Frank Gerlitz *Washtenaw College*
Frank Gerlitz *Washtenaw Community College*
John Glover *University of Houston*
John Graham *University of North Carolina–Charlotte*
Ashish Gupta *SUNY at Buffalo*
Otto Gygax *Oregon State University*
Malcom Heimer *Florida International University*
Donald Herling *Oregon State University*
Thomas Hill *SUNY at Buffalo*
A.S. Hodel *Auburn University*
James N. Jensen *SUNY at Buffalo*
Vern Johnson *University of Arizona*
Autar Kaw *University of South Florida*
Kathleen Kitto *Western Washington University*
Kenneth Klika *University of Akron*
Terry L. Kohutek *Texas A&M University*
Melvin J. Maron *University of Louisville*
Robert Montgomery *Purdue University*
Mark Nagurka *Marquette University*
Romarathnam Narasimhan *University of Miami*
Soronadi Nnaji *Florida A&M University*
Sheila O'Connor *Wichita State University*
Michael Peshkin *Northwestern University*
Dr. John Ray *University of Memphis*
Larry Richards *University of Virginia*
Marc H. Richman *Brown University*
Randy Shih *Oregon Institute of Technology*
Avi Singhal *Arizona State University*
Tim Sykes *Houston Community College*
Neil R. Thompson *University of Waterloo*
Dr. Raman Menon Unnikrishnan *Rochester Institute of Technology*
Michael S. Wells *Tennessee Tech University*
Joseph Wujek *University of California, Berkeley*
Edward Young *University of South Carolina*
Garry Young *Oklahoma State University*
Mandochehr Zoghi *University of Dayton*

Contents

1

Introduction to Engineering and Engineering Study

"How much do you know about engineering?

Why did you choose to study engineering?

What reasons lead you to believe that you are *ready* and *equipped* to study engineering?

What are the main differences between studying in college and studying in high school?

What new *success skills* do you need to succeed in engineering study?

Can you write down ten answers to each of these questions? Go ahead and try."

This is often how I begin my lecture to freshman engineering students enrolled in an *introductory engineering* class. After a little thought, most of them realize just how little they know about this subject called *engineering* and (often despite excellent high school averages) how ill-equipped they are to *study engineering.*

In this chapter, we address both issues. First, we ask the following questions:

1. What is engineering?
2. What do engineers do?
3. Why choose to study engineering?

SECTIONS

- What Is Engineering?
- What Do Engineers Do?
- Why Choose to Study Engineering?
- Equipping Yourself for Engineering Study
- Cooperative Education Programs (Co-ops) and Internships

OBJECTIVES

In this chapter you will:

- Be introduced to the engineering profession.
- Learn about different engineering disciplines and the areas of specialization within these disciplines.
- Learn about the different jobs that engineers do and the industries that employ them.
- Discover the rewards and opportunities offered by a career in engineering.
- Understand the main differences between studying in college or university and studying in high school.
- Learn new *skills* required to succeed in engineering study.
- Find out about cooperative education programs and internships.

The answers to these questions are not only interesting and informative but will help keep you motivated along the long, hard road to an engineering degree. Ability and hard work might get you through the initial stages but after that, you must have a driving force, something that will sustain you through the hard times.

You must develop a powerful motivation.

The best way to do this is to learn as much as possible about the rewards of an engineering degree. Perhaps write them out and pin them on your wall or paste them inside your calculus book. Keep them close at hand. They will keep you determined and strong. This is exactly what the most successful engineering students do; they remain focused by keeping in mind the reasons they chose engineering and the rewards associated with entering the engineering profession. Make it a priority to keep learning about engineering so that you will become aware of all the opportunities and rewards as they arise throughout your course of study. This will fuel your motivation and your desire to succeed. The more important it becomes for you to graduate, the more likely you are to do so.

Next, we address the question, "Are you prepared and equipped for engineering study?" In doing so, we examine the study skills required to succeed in the university environment. For many students, college is the next logical step after high school, the next academic challenge. Consequently, they expect their freshman year in engineering to be much like another year of high school—which, of course, it isn't. In engineering, such an expectation often manifests itself in unacceptably high first-year attrition rates. We address this issue by focusing on what you need to do to ensure the best possible start to earning your engineering degree. Essentially, you must develop the necessary:

Work strategies
Study strategies
Attitudes
Communication skills
Ability to work as part of a group
Time management skills

WHAT IS ENGINEERING?

What does *engineering* mean to you? Here are a few suggestions offered by freshman engineering students:

"A subject that reflects our understanding of things around us"

"The application of scientific knowledge to solve practical problems"

"The bridge between pure science and practical application"

"The application of scientific principles to provide goods to satisfy human needs"

"Creative problem solving"

"The use of technology to perform tasks"

"The study of how to build things"

"The study of how things work and how we can make them work better"

"Creating, designing, testing, and improving systems"

"A scholarly, yet practical, study of the physical applications of human beings' technology combined with nature's laws"

"A profession by which you utilize mathematical, scientific, and physical knowledge for the betterment of humankind"

"Applying math and science to life"

"The application of the simplest and least costly method to solving a problem"

"Being creative and facing new challenges every day"

In fact, engineering is all of these things. The activities included in its definition are complex and varied. It is an ever-expanding subject area. To me, engineering is

> The practical application of mathematics and science to create, design, test, improve, and develop knowledge, research, money, business, economics, and technology.

This is why engineering is such a challenging and demanding field of study: It involves areas of expertise that continue to evolve independently yet are required to perform together as part of the engineering process. Thus, an engineer must be expert in many areas, must know how to communicate knowledge between those areas, and must apply that knowledge to create, design, study, research, and invent all kinds of things. It is not uncommon for engineers to begin their careers as mathematicians, applied scientists, or even economists as I did.

The early stages of an engineering degree must be broad-based. The initial emphasis on mathematics, science, technology and language arts is no accident: these are the building blocks for what will follow in the later years of specialization within engineering.

> *Engineering is a process that applies mathematics and physical science to the design and manufacture of a product or service for the benefit of society.* This process is illustrated in the following diagram.

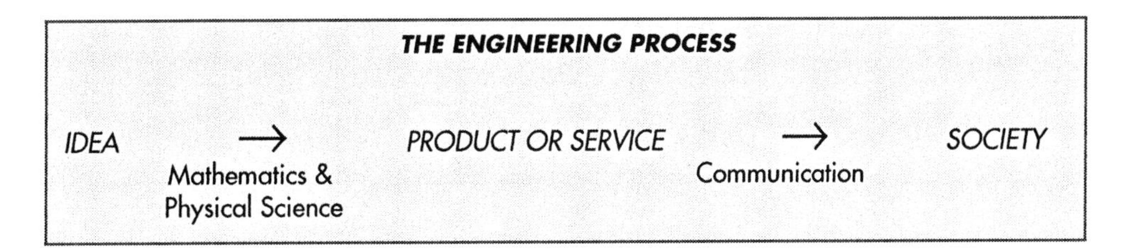

WHAT DO ENGINEERS DO?

Engineers are classified largely according to their areas of specialization. Traditionally, these areas have been:

Mechanical engineering

Electrical engineering

Civil engineering

Chemical engineering

Industrial engineering

Figure 1. What do engineers do?

More recently, the following areas have emerged as separate engineering disciplines:

Materials engineering
Computer engineering

Other areas of further specialization arising from advances in technology and the growth of related areas include the following:

- Biomedical engineering
- Environmental engineering
- Aerospace engineering
- Nuclear engineering
- Mining and petroleum engineering
- Agriculture and biosystems engineering
- Manufacturing engineering
- Ocean engineering/naval architecture

In what follows, we summarize the main features of each of these engineering disciplines and list the different occupations associated with each area of specialization.

Mechanical Engineering

Mechanical engineering is concerned with the analysis, design, and development of structures, machines, devices, and mechanical systems. Consequently, mechanical engineers work in areas related to:

The design and development of machinery and devices.

The analysis of mechanical systems and the vibrations of structures.

The design and development of manufacturing processes and energy conversion systems.

The design of heating, ventilation, and air-conditioning systems.

Mechanical engineering is perhaps the broadest of the engineering disciplines, covering a large number of technical fields broadly classified into the following four areas:

1. Solid mechanics
2. Fluid mechanics
3. Thermodynamics
4. Mechanical design

Solid mechanics Engineers working in solid mechanics are concerned with analyzing the behavior of solid bodies subjected to stresses and external loads. For example, in the design of a new bridge, it is necessary to predict how the bridge will react to high winds and the additional stresses caused by vibrations. Mathematical models are used to predict the behavior of the solid body. This information is then utilized in the design and manufacturing processes. For example, in the design of structures and mechanical components in engines, a stress analysis allows the designer to select materials and configurations for optimum performance. Applied mathematicians and physical scientists are equally at home in this area of mechanical engineering, allowing for interdisciplinary research and development.

Mechanical engineers specializing in solid mechanics find employment in many industries, including those related to bioengineering; tribology (the science of friction, lubrication, and wear); aerospace; the design and manufacture of advanced materials, textiles, and composite materials (e.g., ceramics and fiber-reinforced materials); the design and manufacture of engines; acoustics; management; nondestructive evaluation; the design and manufacture of pressure vessels; and dynamical systems and control.

Fluid mechanics Fluid mechanics is concerned with the behavior of *liquids and gases* and the design and development of machinery, such as pumps, pipes, fans, and turbines, responsible for that behavior. For example, in the aerodynamics industry, mechanical engineers specializing in fluid mechanics apply their expertise to the flow of air around aerofoils to design and develop many of the major components of aircraft, including jet engines.

Mechanical engineers specializing in fluid mechanics find employment in many industries: meteorology, oceanography, acoustics and noise control, fluid power systems, aerodynamics, and the design and manufacture of pressure vessels, to name just a few.

Thermodynamics Thermodynamics is concerned with the conversion of one form of energy to another, as in, for example, the production of electricity. Here, energy from the combustion of fuels such as coal, oil or natural gas is converted to mechanical energy, which drives a generator. Mechanical engineers in this area apply their expertise to the design and development of devices such as power plants, engines, heat exchangers, and cold-storage facilities.

Specific examples of employment in the area of thermodynamics are in: environmental control; heating, ventilation and air-conditioning systems; alternative fuel sources; pollution control; and solar energy, among others.

Mechanical design Mechanical design can be described as a process that translates an idea, demand, or identified need into a working prototype of a product or service. Accordingly, mechanical design engineers are involved in many different aspects of the engineering process. For example, they must gather all available information on the proposed product or service, perform the necessary analysis, optimization, and evaluation, and, finally, produce a working prototype. The availability of many different designs (solutions) for a given set of requirements (problems) makes the task of finding the best design extremely challenging, yet this is one of the most rewarding aspects of mechanical engineering. Design engineers find employment in any area that develops, improves, and manufactures products or services, for example, everything from the manufacture and development of automobiles and aircraft to the production of office equipment (e.g., photocopiers, fax machines, pens, pencils, etc.), computers, and kitchen and home appliances.

Electrical Engineering

Electrical engineering embodies the study of all things electrical—in particular, electrical devices, electrical systems, and electrical energy. Consider for a moment the extent to which electrical phenomena are present in our everyday lives, as computers, cars, televisions, stereos, machines used in manufacturing, automatic banking machines, and communications devices (cellular phones, fax machines, etc.). Soon you will begin to see the importance of the work of electrical engineers. As a graduating electrical engineer, you will find no shortage of employment opportunities in every sector of the economy.

There are five major specialities within electrical engineering:

1. Electric power engineering
2. Communications
3. Control systems engineering
4. Digital systems engineering
5. Electronics

Electric Power Engineering Electric power engineers or simply power engineers design, develop, and maintain systems and devices for the generation, transmission, and distribution of electric power. A strong background in mathematics, circuit analysis, control systems, electric machines, and computing allows the power engineer to be involved in all aspects of the planning, transmission, utilization, and control of electrical energy.

Communications Communications engineering is concerned with the transmission of information using wires, coaxial cable, fiber optics, or radio. Communications engineers must be familiar with various methods of transmitting, routing, and receiving both analog and digital signals, as well as methods for processing these signals. A strong background in network analysis and statistical analysis is required for the design of complete communication systems, while an in-depth knowledge of digital and analog circuit design, signal processing, and electronics is essential for the design of individual elements making up such systems. Recent technological advances in fiber optics and lasers, together with the revolution in personal communications (e.g., cellular phones, the Internet, etc.) mean that there are extensive opportunities in this area of engineering.

Control Systems Engineering Control systems engineering is concerned with the design and development of machines or systems that control automated processes. The control of physical systems is very much an interdisciplinary area involving many engineering specializations; consequently the control systems engineer will find employment in many areas, including robotics, manufacturing, the aerospace industry, offshore oil and gas extraction, power systems, and the manufacture of automobiles and household appliances.

Digital Systems Engineering Digital systems engineers draw on expertise in the areas of digital system design and digital electronics to design hardware for a broad range of applications, including digital signal processing, communications, computers, and instrumentation. For example, a digital systems engineer might design an electronic device to measure, process, store, and transmit data. The need for this kind of expertise is widespread in such areas as commercial aviation, oil exploration, telecommunications, and banking, allowing for extensive employment opportunities in these industries.

Electronics Electronics is an area of electrical engineering that is concerned with the design and development of electronic devices and electrical circuits for the production, detection, and control of electrical signals. Electronic engineers use knowledge in the areas of solid-state devices, integrated circuits, semiconductors, and computer-aided design to design and analyze systems used in a wide variety of applications from microwave systems to instrumentation. Consider the impact that recent advances in electronics have had on your everyday life. For example, personal computers, cars and trucks, household appliances and personal stereo equipment are commonplace in many households.

Civil Engineering

Civil engineers plan, design, construct, operate, and maintain many of the structures and facilities around us, for example, airports, buildings, bridges, harbors, highways, transit systems, offshore drilling platforms, waste collection structures, water supply facilities, and other public works. Civil engineering offers vast employment opportunities in a wide variety of technical fields ranging from planning, design, and construction to research, teaching, sales, and management. There are seven major specialities within civil engineering:

1. Construction engineering
2. Environmental engineering
3. Geotechnical engineering
4. Structural engineering
5. Surveying
6. Transportation engineering
7. Water resources engineering

Construction Engineering Construction engineers combine engineering and management skills to plan and complete projects designed by architects and consulting engineers. Such projects might include the construction of a bridge, building, or shopping mall. The construction engineer will be responsible for the entire project, from start to finish. He or she will lead a team of financial planners, technicians, tradespeople, and professional engineers from many specialities to ensure that the project is completed on time, within budget, and in accordance with the designer's specifications. The construction engineer will be responsible also for the choice of construction methods, materials, and equipment. He or she also ensures that the work is performed safely.

Environmental Engineering Environmental engineers provide technical solutions to environmental problems, such as those associated with the prevention and control of pollution in water and air and on land. In the latter regard, the environmental engineer will work in areas related to the provision of safe drinking water; disposal and recycling of waste (including hazardous waste); provision of municipal services such as sewer, water mains, and garbage disposal; air pollution control; reclamation of industrial land and cleanups at sea (e.g., from oil spills).

Geotechnical Engineering This branch of civil engineering is concerned with the analysis of the properties of soils and rock that support and influence the behavior of structures, pavements, and underground facilities. Geotechnical engineers evaluate the potential settlement of buildings, the stability of slopes and fills, the potential for groundwater seepage, the potential for landslides, and the effects of earthquakes. They work closely with structural engineers in the design and construction of dams, tunnels, and building foundations.

Structural Engineering Structural engineers are responsible for the planning and design of all types of structures, from bridges and containment facilities to buildings, high towers and drilling platforms. They analyze the forces that each structure must withstand, select the appropriate construction materials, and configure all members and connections to produce a safe, stable, effective, and economical structure.

Surveying A surveyor makes precise measurements to obtain reliable information, which is used to locate and design engineering projects. For example, surveyors' maps give accurate information for the construction of tunnels, highways, and dams. Modern-day surveying makes use of the most up-to-date technology, including satellites, aerial and terrestrial photogrammetry, and computers.

Transportation Engineering Civil engineers working in the area of transportation plan, design, construct, and manage all types of transportation facilities, including streets and highways, transit systems, airports, railroads, ports, and harbors. They are also involved in the provision of safe methods for transporting goods, such as oil and gas and hazardous materials.

Water Resources Engineering This area of specialization is concerned with the control and use of water, including flood control and protection, water distribution systems, wastewater collection systems, irrigation, drainage, hydroelectric power, harbor and river development, and road and pipeline river crossings. Water resources engineers draw from a strong background in hydraulics, hydrology, fluid mechanics, mathematics, and computer analysis.

Chemical Engineering

Many of the products we use in our everyday lives (e.g., food products, building materials, plastics, oil, gas, and electricity) are conceived and developed by scientists working in laboratories. Chemical engineers are responsible for translating these *small-scale* successes into *large-scale* commercial realities for the benefit of society as a whole. Chemical engineers design, build, maintain, and develop the complex systems required to convert the laboratory experiment into an industrial operation capable of large-scale production. They apply principles from chemistry, physics, and mathematics in order to understand and overcome problems associated with, for example, heating or cooling large quantities of materials or moving these same materials from one section of the plant to another. Equipment used inside the plant is designed and built by the chemical engineer to withstand the necessary high temperatures and pressures, as well as the inevitable corrosion and wear.

Graduates in chemical engineering find employment in many industries, including the chemical, petrochemical, food-processing, forestry, and pharmaceutical industries.

There are six major specialities within chemical engineering:

1. Polymer engineering
2. Biotechnology
3. Process control engineering
4. Environmental engineering
5. Engineering management
6. Oil and natural gas

Polymer Engineering Polymer engineering is an area of materials engineering in which advanced materials composed of chainlike polymer molecules are designed. Examples of such materials are plastics, rubbers, fibres, films, and composites.

Biotechnology New biotechnology industries produce a range of products for medical, agricultural, food, and chemical applications. Chemical engineers apply principles from the life sciences—in particular, molecular biology—to design, develop, and operate complex processes for the manufacture of these new products. For example, chemical engineers develop processes for the economic production of fertilizers. One use of these fertilizers would be eliminating famine in developing nations.

Process Control Engineering Process control is concerned with the design and development of control systems to maintain the efficient operation of large-scale industrial processes. Process control is necessary to account for changes in any of the process parameters, such as a change in raw materials. Control systems range from schemes that use simple instruments to sophisticated digital computer systems.

Environmental Engineering Many chemical engineers are involved in designing and developing technical and economically feasible solutions to environmental pollution problems in an effort to protect and improve our environment.

Engineering Management Chemical engineers often assume the responsibilities of technical managers by becoming involved in the design and implementation of optimal operating conditions inside a complex, large-scale industrial plant. In this case, both technical and managerial skills are required for the smooth operation of the process.

Oil and Natural Gas Chemical engineers are frequently employed in industries that produce, process and refine natural gas and petroleum and in those industries that manufacture petroleum products, including soaps and cosmetics.

Industrial Engineering

Industrial Engineering is concerned with efficiency, or, more precisely, how to design, organize, implement, and operate the basic factors of production (materials, equipment, people, information, and energy) in the most efficient manner possible. Because of this orientation, industrial engineers are concerned with related issues, such as optimum performance, reliability, cost efficiency, quality control, plant design, and management of human resources. Opportunities for industrial engineers are extensive. They may find employment in many areas, from the financial sector (banks, insurance companies, etc.) to the medical profession and the public sector.

The major areas of specialization within industrial engineering are:

1. Manufacturing
2. Work Design
3. Ergonomics (Human Factors)
4. Management Decision Making
5. Quality Control
6. Facility Design
7. Engineering Management

Manufacturing Industrial engineers working in the area of manufacturing are engaged in the continuing development of efficient systems for the production of goods and services. For example, industrial engineers determine:

- The most effective and efficient use of equipment and human resources to build high quality products with minimal cost (in terms of time and money).
- Procedures to be followed by workers in order to manufacture products most efficiently.
- The optimal arrangement of buildings and equipment for efficient production.
- The capacity of the production system while establishing and maintaining quality control systems.

Positions often held by industrial engineers working in the area of manufacturing include: line manager, production engineer, manufacturing engineer, plant manager, and operations manager.

Work Design Industrial engineers also design the jobs individual workers do in performing the work of the organization. In doing so, the industrial engineer will determine the objectives to be accomplished by an individual employee and the skills, abilities, and knowledge the employee must possess to do the job. Human resource analysts use this information to determine the qualifications required for a particular position within the organization. In addition, work design is used to determine production capabilities, improve efficiencies, and to determine pay scales and salaries. Positions often held by industrial engineers working in the area of work design include production and manufacturing engineer, operations engineer, management engineer, and work measurement engineer.

Ergonomics or Human Factors Industrial engineers study human physiology and psychology in order to understand the interface between workers and their environments (the building, workspace, equipment, etc.). The objective here is to design the workplace to better accommodate the human factor. Good ergonomic design assists workers in using equipment more efficiently, resulting in fewer mistakes and errors (thereby, improving quality) and fewer accidents and injuries. Positions often held by industrial engineers working in this area include ergonomist, design engineer, and safety engineer. Many industrial engineers interested in ergonomics also specialize in the extremely important area of occupational health and safety.

Management Decision Making Industrial engineers often analyze data in order to develop information about a company, its customers or a product/service, to help managers make decisions on, for example, improving competitiveness. For example, statistical analysis of data relating to defects found in a company's product may be used to determine which set of actions should be taken to improve the quality of the product. In many cases, industrial engineers use operations research techniques to determine efficient scheduling of operations, the optimal location of a new facility or to answer routine questions such as the number of cashiers needed in a new grocery store.

Quality Control Industrial engineers use a variety of quality control techniques (including statistical analysis) to continually evaluate the quality of products and services provided by an organization. This may result in changes as simple as tightening loose bolts and screws on equipment or as complex as replacing an existing configuration with a new state-of-the-art system. Positions often held by industrial engineers working in the area of quality control include quality control engineer, quality assurance engineer, and quality manager.

Facility Design Industrial engineers such as facility engineers and facility planners commonly help design the facilities required by an organization in order to carry out its objectives. This includes analyzing and predicting the size and shape of the physical space required to house the organization's employees, equipment, and materials and designing any special facilities (e.g. restrooms, loading docks, special storage vaults, etc.). This information is then used by, for example, architects as the basis for the design of the facility.

Engineering Management Industrial engineers can also be found in management positions such as plant manager, production manager, or vice-president of operations. Specializing in this area often requires that you earn a graduate degree (normally a Master's degree) in Engineering Management. This degree provides the graduate engineer with the additional managerial-related skills required to manage people (often groups of other engineers, usually of varying backgrounds and specialities) and resources.

The newer engineering disciplines are materials engineering and computer engineering, discussed briefly in the next two sections.

Materials Engineering

Materials engineering has evolved as a separate discipline mainly because of the production and engineering applications of new, advanced materials (polymers, ceramics, composites, and electronic materials). Materials engineers are involved with materials production, materials processing, and materials application and design. They find employment in all sectors of the economy that involve the materials cycle, including raw materials processing (steel production, aluminum smelting, and mineral processing), the manufacturing sector (the aerospace, automotive, electronics, and petrochemical industries), and the service sector (tribology, fracture mechanics, failure analysis, and recycling).

Computer Engineering

The use of computers in today's society is pervasive. Computer engineering, once considered part of electrical engineering, has evolved as a separate discipline in response to the demand for, and widespread use of, computers. Computer engineers utilize knowledge from both electrical engineering and computer science to design and implement computer systems in which the hardware and software components are both intimately connected with and critical to the success of the design. Examples of such systems can be found in control processes and in the communications industry. Graduates find work in areas ranging from software design and systems analysis to electronics design and the design of specialized electronic devices. Examples of specific areas of employment for computer engineers are in industries related to the design and production of automobiles, biomedical equipment, communications equipment, and chemical plant control systems.

Areas of Further Specialization

Biomedical Engineering Biomedical engineering is concerned with the application of engineering concepts and technologies to solve biological and medical problems. Biomedical engineers work with biologists and medical doctors as part of interdisciplinary teams to design and develop new technologies such as artificial organs, prosthetic devices, and medical equipment. They are employed in both the private and public sectors, from small consulting companies to large pharmaceutical companies, medical device manufacturers, and government agencies.

Environmental Engineering Environmental engineering deals with issues concerning the environment, such as urban, regional, and global air quality; water supply and water quality control; hazardous waste treatment; global environmental change; the maintenance of stable ecosystems; prevention and control of air pollution; wastewater management; and hazardous waste management. Environmental engineers work in both the private and public sectors. For example, oil companies will employ environmental engineers to ensure that oil and gas resources are extracted with minimum impact on the environment. On the other hand, local municipalities will employ environmental engineers to oversee the management of drinking water and waste disposal systems.

Aerospace Engineering Aerospace engineers design, develop, and implement new and existing technologies in both civil and military aviation, including the design and development of all types of commercial and military aircraft, such as vehicles used for space exploration. In addition, aerospace engineering is concerned with the development of systems that support the safe and efficient operation of all types of aircraft. For example, aerospace engineers are involved in control and guidance systems, information systems, and instruments used for navigation. There are many specialities within aerospace engineering. For example, the more theoretically inclined may specialize in aerodynamics, in which mathematical models are used to predict the behavior of different materials and new designs in the construction of aircraft. On the other hand, the more practically minded may be involved in the manufacture of commercial and military aircraft. Other areas of specialization include acoustics, rocket technology, computational fluid dynamics, and thermodynamics.

Nuclear Engineering Nuclear engineers deal with all aspects of nuclear power, from the design, development, and implementation of different forms of nuclear power (e.g., nuclear power plants for the generation of electricity and nuclear engines in submarines and spacecraft) to the handling and safe disposal of nuclear fuels used in the commercial and military sectors of the economy. In addition, nuclear engineers may specialize in areas related to medical applications (e.g., radiation sciences) where the use of radioactive materials is prominent. Radioactive materials can be found in hospitals, medical clinics, and laboratories, as well as in military establishments, where they are used in the construction of advanced weapon systems.

Mining Engineering and Petroleum Engineering Mining engineering is concerned with the extraction of minerals and hydrocarbons from the earth and the processing of these minerals in preparation for further use. Mining engineering is a broad field that includes specialities such as: methods for estimating ore reserves; geostatistics; geology; underground and surface mine design; the design and development of mining equipment; rock and soil mechanics; and mineral processing. Petroleum engineering is also a speciality within mining engineering in which the primary focus is on oil and gas. Mining engineers work all over the world, in both developed and developing nations. They are employed by a range of companies in both the private and public sectors, including mining companies, oil companies, government and industry research facilities, and even financial institutions, which invest heavily in these types of industries. A mining or petroleum engineer might be employed to design mines and mining equipment, supervise and manage mining operations, manage and design blasting operations, or research occupational health and safety in the workplace.

Agriculture and Biosystems Engineering Agricultural engineering is concerned with efficient food production while maintaining or improving the environmental quality of the agro-ecosystem. Agricultural engineers deal with the design, development, construction, and operation of systems for food production, storage, handling, and processing. They are trained in biological and agricultural sciences, and they use their skills not only to improve the efficiency of food production, but also to decrease or eliminate environmental hazards and reduce the consumption and waste of natural resources. The role of the modern-day agricultural engineer has changed dramatically with the ever-expanding field of biotechnology. For example, agricultural engineers now provide specialized services in areas such as the genetic manipulation of plants and animals, the development and implementation of environmentally friendly pesticides, and the production of enzymes in the enhancement of food processing. In addition, they continue to provide expertise in traditional areas, including farm equipment and structures such as tractors, barns, drainage systems, harvesters, and processing units. Agriculture and biosystems engineers are employed by consulting companies, government agencies, small businesses, and academic institutions all over the world.

Manufacturing Engineering Manufacturing engineering is concerned with the design, development, and implementation of all aspects of manufacturing operations, from product, equipment, and inventory to quality management, on-time delivery, capacity, and manufacturing cost. Consequently, manufacturing engineers are involved in many of the things that we use in our everyday lives, from the clothes we wear to the vehicles we drive. Both the private and public sectors employ manufacturing engineers in any operation that involves the manufacture of a product or service.

Ocean Engineering and Naval Architecture Ocean engineering and naval architecture are concerned with the application of ocean science and engineering design to the ocean environment. Ocean engineering differs from conventional land-based engineering mainly as a result of additional factors that must be taken into account in designing and manufacturing for the ocean environment. Examples of such factors are wave motion, currents, significant temperature variations, and chemical and biological factors. Ocean engineers and naval architects design offshore drilling platforms, harbors, and the corresponding equipment required for their maintenance. These engineers also apply their engineering expertise to the design and development of ships and other water-based vessels, as well as to help solve problems related to, for example, beach erosion. Ocean engineers and naval architects find employment in both the private and public sectors. For example, in consulting firms, environmental agencies, finance, shipbuilding, government, and on offshore drilling platforms.

Engineering Job Classifications

Engineers are classified not only by an *area* of specialization but also by the *type* of engineering they perform within that area. For example, a mechanical engineer, could also be classified as an analyst, an experimentalist, a design engineer, or a research engineer. Your own particular strengths and preferences will determine which of these you choose to be.

Analytical Engineer The analytical engineer is concerned mainly with the mathematical modeling and analysis of engineering problems. It is often far too expensive to build and test real, *physical* prototypes (e.g., an aircraft wing). Instead, analysts often build and analyze less expensive *mathematical models* for the preliminary investigations of the viability of a new idea, design, or concept. Analytical engineers have a strong background in applied mathematics, the physical sciences, engineering science, and computer applications.

Experimental Engineer In contrast to the analytical engineer, the experimental engineer is concerned mainly with physical prototypes. He or she will use actual *hands-on* experience to evaluate a particular new idea. The experimental engineer is more comfortable in the laboratory or out in the field than in the office.

Design Engineer The design engineer is involved in all aspects of the design process. He or she will use ideas and relevant information to produce a detailed plan, or *design*, from which an actual product can be assembled. The key word in design engineering is *detail.* Often, plans and specifications are read by a nonexpert who will require precise instructions. Also, the most technically brilliant design is not necessarily the best one, because of cost considerations or the unavailability of materials. Hence, in achieving the optimum design, the design engineer must also consider other factors, such as efficiency, cost control, and ease of production.

Research Engineer The research engineer is concerned with the development of *new* products, designs, and processes. The research is usually *applied,* in the sense that it is directed towards a fixed goal rather than being open ended, as in the case of curiosity-driven research. Most industries employ at least a small number of research engineers, if only to ensure that their products and services remain at the leading edge of technology. Research skills include the ability to find and assimilate *relevant* information and use that information in conjunction with engineering skills to develop new products or improve existing ones.

Test Engineer Test engineers *test* new and existing (quality control) products and processes to see whether they comply with the required design specifications. For example, a test engineer might test a new braking system on a car or a new control system to see if it is reliable.

Consulting Engineer The consulting engineer works as an independent professional, selling his expertise to clients, usually on a contract basis. Consulting engineers are required to be registered as professional engineers (licensed engineers) before undertaking any form of consulting. This assures clients of the engineer's expertise and professionalism. Typical services offered by consulting engineers include design, analysis, investigations for insurance companies, professional witness services (e.g., testifying in vehicle accident cases), research and development, management, construction, and environmental research. In fact, professional engineers can be found working in every engineering speciality.

Engineering Management Engineering managers are engineers (from any of the engineering specializations) who *combine* engineering skills with managerial abilities to *direct* resources towards the efficient production of goods and services. They can manage whole projects or different parts of projects. The chief objective of an engineering manager is no different from that of any other manager: to see that a project or task is completed according to the required specifications, on time and within budget. Engineers usually move into this area through promotion, having demonstrated solid leadership and technical ability.

Engineering Professor Engineering professors are employed by colleges and universities as teachers and researchers. A Ph.D. degree is the minimum qualification required to enter an engineering faculty. As with professional engineers, engineering professors are classified according to their particular speciality. For example, there are professors of mechanical engineering, of electrical engineering, and so on. On the instruction side, professors develop and teach different engineering courses at various levels (junior undergraduate, senior undergraduate, and graduate), improve and update curricula, and supervise graduate students. Their research activities include discovering and developing new information, publishing new findings in scientific and engineering journals or books, soliciting research funds from both private and public sources, presenting information at conferences, and collaborating with scholars from other institutions. Engineering professors also undertake what is known as *community service* by participating in professional societies, consulting, and serving on education or various other government boards.

WHY CHOOSE TO STUDY ENGINEERING?

What are your reasons for choosing to study engineering? Write down as many as you can. You'll find it an interesting and rewarding exercise. The following are some of the reasons offered by my freshman engineering students:

> "It's really interesting."

"Engineering is practical."
"[It's] useful in life."
"I get to make a difference in society."
"To please my parents."
"I like to think."
"The money."
"[The] variety of challenging and exciting problems."
"[You] get to travel and meet lots of interesting people."
"If you can finish an engineering degree, you can do anything."
"Prestige."
"Respect."
"[There's a] wide range of careers available within the engineering profession."
"My parents told me I had to because it would get me a stable, secure job."
"To learn how to make practical and significant decisions."
"To train my mind and to give me confidence."
"Job security."
"Engineering is an international subject. I can work anywhere in the world."
"I really enjoy applying math to physical, practical problems."
"Status in society."
"[It has a] well-defined career path and options."
"[There are] so many different types of study under the same umbrella."
"I have a knack for making things and understanding how things work."
"[You can] work on a team with other engineers."
"It's a dynamic subject—new fields of engineering are created every day!"
"My mom and dad are both engineers—it seemed the natural thing for me to do."
"I love applying math and physics."
"[It gives me] a chance for personal development."
"I want to do something more than my parents did."
"I enjoy being creative."

How many reasons did you find? Twenty? Thirty? Forty? The explanation for this variety of reasons is that the rewards, benefits, and opportunities offered by an engineering education are vast. A career in the engineering profession is just one of them. Priorities may be different (e.g., some may prefer the high standard of living that comes with an engineering career, while others might enjoy the challenges and the variety that are a part of studying engineering), but most engineering students agree on the following list of major reasons they chose to study engineering (in no particular order):

- Engineering is interesting and enjoyable.
- Engineering offers personal and intellectual development.
- Engineering is challenging—not just now and again but every day.
- Engineering offers a variety of career opportunities.
- Engineering offers financial security.

- Engineering is being able to apply math and science to solve real-world problems and understand how things work.
- The engineering profession is respected and prestigious.
- Engineering offers the opportunity to be creative.
- Engineering offers the opportunity to do something good for society.

Your own personal preferences will dictate how you rank these different items. Most students agree, however, that the number-one reason for choosing a career in engineering is job satisfaction. Many of my former students (now practicing engineers) have returned to tell me the same story: After the honeymoon period of a new job (i.e., after the initial euphoria associated not only with obtaining an excellent salary and the corresponding increase in standard of living but also with meeting new people, working in new surroundings, etc.), the number-one factor in sustaining them in their employment (and therefore in their careers) is job satisfaction—how much they enjoy their jobs daily. Bright, inquisitive, intelligent people need to be challenged; they cannot spend their working lives in boring, routine, mundane occupations, no matter how high the material rewards. A career in engineering challenges talented people to use all of their skills on a daily basis.

Apart from the rewards, benefits, and opportunities afforded by a career in engineering, you will find that an engineering education will increase your confidence, your general analytical skills, your ability to communicate with people on all levels, and perhaps most of all, your ability to adapt to almost any new situation. You see, as with all good education,

> Engineering education is a training of the mind!

You can go on and do almost anything after an engineering education. You can become a politician, a movie actor, a teacher, a physician, an entrepreneur, a lawyer, a consulting engineer, or a manager. Look around you. I'll bet you can find at least ten examples of people who began their careers with an engineering education and ended up being extremely successful in a completely different career.

EQUIPPING YOURSELF FOR ENGINEERING STUDY

There are certain key strategies—commitment, application, strategy, perseverance, and associations—that are vital for performance throughout your pursuit of an engineering degree. In this section, we focus on what you should do to ensure the best possible start to your engineering degree.

Many of you were high school students only a few months ago. As recent graduates, you are equipped with attitudes, work ethics, and strategies that worked well in high school. Now you are freshman engineering students. Does it follow that you can continue to operate as you did in high school? The answer is a resounding "no." There is a huge (social and academic) gap between high school and college and it seems to be growing bigger. This gap exists primarily because of the following reasons:

1. ***Attending a university is a different ballgame.*** A university is not equivalent to the next year of high school. It's a life change. There are new pressures, new people, new competitors, and new standards. All of a sudden you will find yourself surrounded by people as bright as, if not brighter than, you are. Standards previously accepted as excellent become good or average.

You find out quickly that high school routines, attitudes, and philosophies don't work anymore. You might be homesick, you might have financial problems (perhaps it's the first time you've left home), and your parents might even be pressuring you to be the best student out of the 500 or so in your freshman class. Everything is different—a whole new world.

2. ***You probably don't have the required skills to be successful in a university.*** Engineering is a demanding curriculum. If you've come straight from high school, then you've likely never done anything like this before. Consequently, you have to learn a whole new set of skills, skills that you were not taught in high school, mainly because you never had any reason to use them there. For example, you need to develop appropriate:
   - Study skills and strategies
   - Attitudes
   - Communication skills
   - Team skills—the ability to work as part of a team
   - Time management skills

Figure 2. "I didn't realize the gap was THIS big."

These are absolutely essential to manage the hectic, often crazy, pace associated with the freshman year in engineering.

3. ***What professors assume you know is often not what you've been taught in high school prerequisites.*** Universities ask that you satisfy certain prerequisites before they allow you to register for a particular course or program. In doing so, they assume that on Day 1 of the university course, you are ready to take up where you left off at the prerequisite level. In the freshman year in engineering, the prerequisites are usually high school courses. Sometimes the curricula of high school courses change and no one tells the professors. Thus, a situation arises in which the professor assumes that you know what you don't know and you're in trouble right from the start.
4. ***What professors assume you can do is often not what you really can do.*** You forget things. The summer between high school and university is three months long. Worse still, you may have had a significant period of absence from school. In either case, your prerequisite skills will not be as fluent as they should be (indeed, as your professor will assume they are) and you probably won't be ready to use them on the first day of classes. I like to compare this situation to that of a long-distance runner who has had three months off and then tries to run a marathon without any training. What are his or her chances of even finishing? Not very high! As with most challenges, you have to be in shape to take on a new engineering course. You must be fluent in the prerequisites (have them at your fingertips) and be ready to build on existing knowledge.

Most first-year engineering students begin to feel the effect of the gap between high school and college around midterm time, when grades begin to tumble and expectations are far from realized. Recovering from this point is not easy: It takes a lot of effort to change your study habits and lifestyle amid the usual chaos associated with five or six courses in full-steam-ahead mode. Make sure you don't find yourself in this position by preparing ahead of time. The gap is not necessarily your fault but the responsibility for filling it rests with you. The good news is that it's not difficult to do so: Successful engineering students have been doing it for years. The key is to learn what the best students have done and to follow the same procedures yourself. For example, the most successful freshman-engineering students use the following strategies continually. Try them yourself. They will help you to prepare for engineering study.

1. ***Expect changes and adapt.*** Unfortunately, most freshman engineering students don't find out that they lack the necessary success skills until well into the first semester, when it's too late. You can avoid this scenario by accepting the fact that you will have to learn a whole new set of skills and preparing to change the way you do things before the semester begins. If you expect things to change, you will be ready for change and that's an advantage. Use the initial few days and weeks of the semester to adapt your study habits and your everyday routine to the demands of the engineering curriculum. After all, the latter should be your first priority—make it so.
2. ***Ask.*** Make it a goal to find out as much as you can about how to be most effective in your freshman year. Talk to professors, advisors, and any second-year students who have had a successful first year, and find out as much as you can about how to maximize your performance. This is an excellent investment of time and effort.

3. ***Get together with other first-year students.*** Share problems, concerns and information with your peers. Not only will this help alleviate stress and foster friendships but it will lay strong foundations for the inevitable group work that comes with engineering study.
4. ***Get organized and manage your time effectively.*** In the initial stages of an engineering degree, it is of the utmost importance to get and stay organized. Use a notebook or calendar to write down your appointments, commitments, and obligations. Don't try to remember everything: There is just far too much information to remember. Make lists of things to do for short-term (e.g., daily) and long-term (e.g., weekly) goals and cross off each item on the list as soon as it has been achieved (this part is extremely satisfying). In addition, you must learn to manage your time. Schedule blocks of time for studying and blocks of time for other things (e.g., recreation or family responsibilities) and stick to your schedule! Decide beforehand what you will do during a particular period of time and where you will do it (e.g., in the library, at home, etc.). There is nothing worse than spending half the allocated study time deciding what and where to study, so always do this well in advance. For example, you might reserve the period from 2:00 P.M. to 4:00 P.M. on Thursday afternoon to complete the statics assignment in the library. Alternatively, you might reserve the period from 11:00 A.M. to 11:30 A.M. to see your professor regarding some problems with the calculus lecture. Again, write it down in your calendar or planner. Be meticulous and soon you will become a master planner, making the most effective use of your time. You will establish routines that will greatly improve your effectiveness and you'll have much more fun!
5. ***Before a course begins, know what your instructor assumes you know.*** One of the main reasons why many well-qualified students do not do well in engineering is that they approach new courses from the cold-start position, not realizing that most courses simply pick up from the end of the prerequisite course (usually the previous semester). These students spend the first half of the new course relearning the material from the prerequisite course. It has been shown time and time again that a few hours' review of the most important prerequisite skills before the course begins will significantly improve your performance during the course. Consequently, ask your instructor to identify the most important prerequisite skills necessary to make an effective start in the (new) course. Make sure those skills are fluent and in working order. You may have forgotten the most important prerequisite techniques (particularly if they were covered last semester), so practice with some warm-up exercises if necessary. For example, in calculus, you might practice some factoring, trigonometric identities, or the algebra of functions; in engineering mechanics, you might recall equations of motion and practice drawing some free-body diagrams. Remember, most engineering subjects are cumulative: One part usually depends heavily on a knowledge of the previous part. Consequently, it pays to ensure that your prerequisite skills actually work. (Your instructor will assume that they do.)

COOPERATIVE EDUCATION PROGRAMS (CO-OPS) AND INTERNSHIPS

Most engineering schools offer two types of degree programs: a traditional program and a cooperative education program. In the cooperative education program (co-op), students complement their academic studies with relevant and productive paid work experience from employers in business, industry, and government. Typically, in a co-op program, you would alternate periods of work with periods of study. In most cases, because of the alternating periods of work, co-op programs are longer than traditional engineering programs, lasting perhaps one more year than the traditional program.

Since cooperative education programs are degree programs in their own right, they require separate registration and administration. These are usually handled by the engineering school's own *cooperative education center* which gives assistance to co-op students in all aspects of the co-op program including assistance in finding relevant work-term employment for the duration of the program.

Internships are also career-related work opportunities. They are usually sponsored by companies working in a range of engineering disciplines. Internships, however, may be paid or unpaid and are most often one time, rather than alternating, work experiences occurring usually over the summer months. Some companies however, may also offer part-time internships during the Fall and Spring semesters. Most companies insist that you have completed a minimum number of course credits before considering an internship. Usually this means that you can apply for internships from the summer of your sophomore year until graduation. Unlike co-op programs, internships generally carry no academic course credit and do not require course registration (although there can be exceptions—check with your particular engineering school). Information on internships in your area of speciality can be found in your career services office or in the administrative offices of your engineering school.

The advantages of taking career-related work opportunities during your time in engineering study are many and varied. They include:

Advantages of a Cooperative Education Program/Internship

- You gain valuable real work experience which prepares you for the future job market.
- You learn on-the-job skills that you cannot learn in the classroom.
- You have improved employment opportunities upon graduation.
- You get a foretaste of the work-world allowing you to bridge the gap between academia and the workplace.
- You get to apply theory learned in class to real world problems.
- You learn to work in groups and interdisciplinary teams.
- You gain motivation and enthusiasm for your training as an engineer.
- They allow you to make informed decisions when it comes to deciding your career path.
- You make valuable contacts for networking inside the engineering and business professions.
- You get the opportunity to sample different working environments.

Employers also gain from co-ops and internships having access to a year-round supply of well-trained and highly motivated student employees for short-term projects.

SUMMARY OF IMPORTANT POINTS FROM THIS CHAPTER

In this chapter we focused first on an introduction to the field of engineering. Specifically, you:

- Were introduced to the engineering profession.
- Learned about different engineering disciplines and the areas of specialization within these disciplines.
- Learned about the different jobs that engineers do and the industries that employ them.
- Discovered some of most important rewards and opportunities offered by a career in engineering.

Secondly, you learned about studying engineering in college and how to make yourself as effective an engineering student as possible. In particular, you:

- Learned about the main differences between studying in college and studying in high school.
- Learned new *skills* required to succeed in engineering study—skills that were never required in high school.
- Found out about cooperative education programs and internships and how these allow you to gain valuable relevant work experience as you study towards your engineering degree.

The information in this chapter will help keep you motivated as you become aware of the rewards and opportunities that await you both during your time of study and following your graduation. In addition, this information will assist you in becoming an effective engineering student by informing you of the things you need to do to make a successful transition from high school to the college learning environment.

EXERCISES

1. What is engineering? Write down your definition of *engineering* and what you think the subject is all about. Give some examples to justify your conclusions.
2. Write a paper (of maybe 500 words) on the engineering discipline that appeals to you most. Include the most important features of the *discipline* that led to your choice.
3. What kind of engineer do you hope to become—for example, an analytical engineer, an experimentalist, a professor of engineering, a test engineer or one of the other kinds of engineer described in this Chapter? Why?
4. What strengths and qualities do you think would be required to become a design engineer? An analytical engineer? A research engineer? An engineering manager? A test engineer?
5. Write a one-page paper describing the work of mechanical engineers as opposed to that of civil engineers.
6. What are the newest engineering disciplines? How did they emerge? Write a one-page paper to answer these questions.
7. Write a 500-word paper on what you believe to be new emerging areas of engineering.
8. Complete the following table by listing five jobs typically associated with each type of engineer:

MECHANICAL	ELECTRICAL	CIVIL	CHEMICAL	INDUSTRIAL	MATERIALS	COMPUTER

9. Which of the specialities within mechanical engineering would be of most interest to you? Why?
10. Repeat Exercise 9 for each of the engineering disciplines heading the table in Exercise 8.
11. Why did you choose to study engineering? Make a list of ten reasons used to arrive at your decision.
12. Why do you think that someone with an ability in math and science might choose an engineering education?
13. Write down at least 20 rewards associated with a career in engineering. Rank the top ten in order of importance to you.
14. Write a 500-word paper on why you want to be an engineer.
15. Get together with a couple of fellow engineering students and think of a product that would do well in today's economy. Write down what kind of engineering would be required to bring the product to reality and then to the marketplace. For example, what would be the role of the design engineer? The mechanical engineer? The test engineer, etc.? (You do not need to include all the different engineering disciplines.)
16. Which people influenced you the most in your decision to pursue an engineering education? How? Compare your answers with the reasons given in Exercise 11.
17. Write down answers to each of the following questions:

    - What reasons lead you to believe that you are *ready* and *equipped* to study engineering?
    - What are the main differences between studying at a university and studying in high school?
    - What new *success skills* do you need to succeed in engineering study?

18. Consider the following first-year engineering courses:

    Chemistry
    Engineering Mechanics
    Calculus
    Physics

    (i) Revise this list to include core courses required in first-year engineering by your particular engineering college.
    (ii) Look in the catalog for the course descriptions of each of the courses you wrote down in Part (i).
    (iii) List the formal prerequisites required to register for each of the courses in Part (i).

(iv) Identify what you regard as the most important (*working*) prerequisite *skills* you learned in each of the prerequisite courses listed in Part (iii).
(v) Ask the professor from each of the courses in Part (i) to identify the most important (*working*) prerequisite skills he or she *requires* right from the beginning of the course.
(vi) How long has it been since you studied each of these prerequisite courses?
(vii) Do you anticipate having any problems as a result of your answers to Parts (iv)–(vi)?

19. Interview a second-year engineering student. Find out the following:

(i) What new study skills did he or she have to learn that were never taught in high school?
(ii) What did he or she do to manage his or her time effectively in the first year?
(iii) What does he or she think of group work or collaborating with fellow students?
(iv) Ask the student to give you the benefit of his or her experience of first-year engineering, and list the most vital skills required to *survive* first-year engineering.

20. The word *calculus* often evokes images of fear and pain in many students. Much of this reaction can be attributed to a lack of *preparation* and a lack of *fluency* in the skills required before entering the course (e.g., students lack or have forgotten skills related to factoring, algebra, functions, trigonometry, etc.). Consider the following questions from *precalculus,* which identify some of the skills I *require* from my students on the first day of a beginning calculus course:

a. Is $2x^2 + x + 1$ always positive, always negative, or sometimes negative and sometimes positive?
b. Can you rationalize the denominator of the expression $1/(x^{1/3} - 8)$?
c. When is the expression $(x - 4)/(x^2 - 8)$ positive, negative, zero, or undefined?
d. If $f(x) = 3$, what is $f(x + h)$ and $f(x^2)$?
e. Factor the expression $6(x - 2)^{-1/3}(2x + 1)^{1/3} - 2(x - 2)^{2/3}(2x + 1)^{-2/3}$.
f. What is the domain of $f(x) = \sqrt{(x^2 - 3x + 2)}$?
g. If $\cos 2x = 2\cos^2 x - 1$, write down formulas for $\cos 4x$ and $\cos 20x$?

You should be able to answer all of these questions correctly in approximately 15 minutes to consider yourself well-prepared for first-year calculus. See if you can answer the questions correctly in that amount of time and then take action to ensure that you have the relevant prerequisite skills (i.e., review the necessary concepts).

21. Talk to your engineering professors and devise assessment tests similar to the one in Exercise 20 for each of the first-year engineering subjects listed in Exercise 18(i). The tests should be designed to gauge your level of preparedness for each of the courses; they should thus cover the required working prerequisite skills in an appropriate time.

22. Get together with a group of fellow first-year engineering students and devise an assessment test for high school graduates about to enter first-year engineering at your institution. The test should investigate whether the students have the necessary success skills and academic (working) prerequisites required for first-year engineering. Imagine how valuable such a test would be if it could be taken by high school students *before* arriving at your institution.
23. Write a 750-word paper on what a high school student considering studying engineering in the Fall should know about being successful in first-year engineering. You should use the information obtained in Exercise 22.
24. Go to your local career services office and find out any information about possible internships in your engineering speciality.
25. Write a one page paper outlining why you might benefit from work experience while you are studying engineering.

2

The Role of Analysis in Engineering

SECTIONS

OBJECTIVES

After reading this chapter, you will have learned

- What engineering analysis is
- That analysis is a major component of the engineering curriculum
- How analysis is used in engineering design
- How analysis helps engineers prevent and diagnose failures

1 INTRODUCTION

What is **analysis**? A dictionary definition of analysis might read something like this:

> *The separation of a whole into its component parts. An examination of a complex system, its elements, and their relationships.*

Based on this general definition, analysis may refer to everything from the study of a person's mental state (psychoanalysis) to the determination of the amount of certain elements in an unknown metal alloy (elemental analysis). *Engineering analysis*, however, has a specific meaning. A concise working definition of **engineering analysis** is the

> *Analytical solution of an engineering problem, using mathematics and principles of science.*

Engineering analysis relies heavily on **basic mathematics** such as algebra, geometry, trigonometry, calculus, and statistics. **Higher level mathematics** such as linear algebra, differential equations and complex variables may also be used. Principles and laws from the **physical sciences**, particularly physics and chemistry, are key ingredients of engineering analysis.

Engineering analysis involves more than searching for an equation that fits a problem, plugging numbers into the equation, and "turning the crank" to generate an answer. It is not a simple "plug and chug" procedure. Engineering analysis requires logical and systematic thinking about the engineering problem. The engineer must first be able to state the problem clearly, logically, and concisely. The engineer must understand the physical behavior of the system being analyzed and know which scientific principles to apply. He or she must recognize which mathematical tools to use and how to implement them by hand or on a computer. The engineer must be able to generate a solution that is consistent with the stated problem and any simplifying assumptions. The engineer must then ascertain that the solution is reasonable and contains no errors.

Engineering analysis may be regarded as a type of **modeling** or *simulation*. For example, suppose that a civil engineer wants to know the tensile stress in a cable of a suspension bridge that is being designed. The bridge exists only on paper, so a direct stress measurement cannot be made. A scale model of the bridge could be constructed, and a stress measurement taken on the model, but models are expensive and very time-consuming to develop. A better approach is to create an analytical model of the bridge or a portion of the bridge containing the cable. From this model, the tensile stress can be calculated.

Engineering courses that focus on analysis, such as statics, dynamics, strength of materials, thermodynamics, and electrical circuits, are considered *core* courses in the engineering curriculum. Because you will be taking many of these courses, it is vital that you gain a fundamental understanding of what analysis is and, more importantly, how to do analysis properly. As the bridge example illustrates, analysis is an integral part of engineering design. Analysis is also a key part of the study of engineering failures.

Engineers who perform engineering analyses on a regular basis are referred to as *engineering analysts* or *analytic engineers*. These functional titles are used to differentiate analysis from the other engineering functions such as research and development (R&D), design, testing, production, sales, marketing, etc. In some engineering companies, clear distinctions are made between the various engineering functions and the people who work in them. Depending on the organizational structure and the type of products involved, large companies may dedicate a separate department or group of engineers as analysts. Engineers whose work is dedicated to analysis are considered specialists. In this capacity, the engineering analyst usually works in a support role for design engineering. It is not uncommon, however, for design and analysis functions to be combined in a single department because design and analysis are so closely related. In small firms that employ only a few engineers, the engineers often bear the responsibility of many technical functions, including analysis.

PROFESSIONAL SUCCESS: CHOOSING AN ENGINEERING MAJOR

Perhaps the biggest question facing the new engineering student (besides "How much money will I make after I graduate?") is "In which field of engineering should I major?" Engineering is a broad area, so the beginning student has numerous options. The new engineering student should be aware of a few facts. First, all engineering majors have the potential for preparing the student for a satisfying and rewarding engineering career. As a profession, engineering has historically enjoyed a fairly stable and well-paid market. There have been fluctuations in the engineering market in recent decades, but the demand for engineers in all the major disciplines is high, and the future looks bright for engineers. Second, all engineering majors are academically challenging, but some engineering majors are more challenging than others. Study the differences between the various engineering programs. Compare the course requirements of each program by examining the course listings in your college or university catalog. Ask department chairs to discuss the similarities and differences between their engineering programs and the programs in other departments. (Just keep in mind that professors, like everyone else, are biased and will probably tell you that *their* engineering discipline is the best.) Talk with people who are practicing engineers in the various disciplines, and ask them about their educational experiences. Learn all you can from as many sources as you can about the various engineering disciplines. Third, and this is the most important point, try to answer the following question: "What kind of engineering will be the most gratifying for me?" It makes little sense to devote four or more years of intense study of X engineering just because it happens to be the highest paid discipline, just because your uncle Vinny is an X engineer, just because X engineering is the easiest program at your school, or just because someone tells you that they are an X engineer, so you should be one too.

Engineering disciplines may be broadly categorized as either mainstream or narrowly focused. Mainstream disciplines are the broad-based, traditional disciplines that have been in existence for decades (or even centuries) and in which degrees are offered by most of the larger colleges and universities. Many colleges and universities do not offer engineering degrees in some of the narrowly focused disciplines. Chemical, civil, computer, electrical, and mechanical engineering are considered the core mainstream disciplines. These mainstream disciplines are broad in subject content and represent the majority of practicing engineers. Narrowly focused disciplines concentrate on a narrow engineering subject by combining specific components from the mainstream disciplines. For example, biomedical engineering may combine portions of electrical and mechanical engineering plus components from biology. Construction engineering may combine elements from civil engineering and business or construction trades. Other narrowly focused disciplines include materials, aeronautical and aerospace, environmental, nuclear, ceramic, geological, manufacturing, automotive, metallurgical, corrosion, ocean, and cost and safety engineering.

Should you major in a mainstream area or a narrowly focused area? The safest thing to do, especially if you are uncertain about which discipline to study, is to major in one of the mainstream disciplines. By majoring in a mainstream area, you will graduate with a general engineering education that will make you marketable in a broad engineering industry. On the other hand, majoring in a narrowly focused discipline may lead you into an extremely satisfying career, particularly if your area of expertise, narrow as it may be, is in high demand. Perhaps your decision will be largely governed by geographical issues. The narrowly focused majors may not be offered at the school you wish to attend. These are important issues to consider when selecting an engineering major.

2 ANALYSIS AND ENGINEERING DESIGN

Design is the heart of engineering. In ancient times, people recognized a need for protection against the natural elements, for collecting and utilizing water, for finding and growing food, for transportation, and for defending themselves against other people with unfriendly intentions. Today, even though our world is much more advanced and complex than that of our ancestors, our basic needs are essentially the same. Throughout history, engineers have designed various devices and systems that met the changing needs of society. The following is a concise definition of **engineering design**:

> *A process of devising a component, system or operation that meets a specific need.*

The key word in this definition is *process*. The design process is like a road map that guides the designer from need recognition to problem solution. Design engineers make decisions based on a thorough understanding of engineering fundamentals, design constraints, cost, reliability, manufacturability, and human factors. A knowledge of design *principles* can be learned in school from professors and books, but in order to become a good design engineer, you must *practice* design. Design engineers are like artists and architects who harness their creative powers and skills to produce sculptures and buildings. The end products made by design engineers may be more functional than artistic, but their creation still requires knowledge, imagination, and creativity.

Design has always been a part of engineering programs in colleges and universities. Historically, design courses have been taught in the junior or senior years. At some schools, design courses have even been postponed until the senior year when the students would do a "senior design project" or a "capstone design project." In recent years, the traditional practice of placing design courses in the latter half of the curriculum has been scrutinized. Recognizing that design is indeed the heart of engineering and that students need an earlier introduction to the subject, colleges and universities have revised their engineering programs to include design experiences early in the curriculum, perhaps as early as the introductory course. By introducing design courses at the level that introductory mathematics and science courses are taught, students benefit from a more integrated approach to their engineering education. Students gain a better understanding of *how* mathematics and science are used to design engineering systems when they study these courses concurrently. Analysis is becoming embedded in design to teach engineering students more practical, real-world applications of mathematics and science.

What is the relationship between engineering analysis and engineering design? As we defined it earlier, engineering analysis is the *analytical solution of an engineering problem, using mathematics and principles of science*. The false notion that engineering is merely mathematics and applied science is widely held by many beginning engineering students. Because design is the heart of engineering, this notion may lead a student to believe that engineering design is the equivalent of a "story problem" found in high school math books. Hence, engineering design is merely a math problem posed in word form, right? Wrong! Unlike math problems, design problems are "open ended." This means, among other things, that design problems do not have a single "correct" solution. Design problems have many possible solutions, depending on the *decisions* made by the design engineer. The main goal of engineering design is to obtain the *best* or *optimum* solution within the specifications and constraints of the problem.

So, how does analysis fit in? One of the steps in the design process is to obtain a preliminary concept of the *design*. (Note that the word *design* here refers to the actual component, system, or operation that is being created.) At this point, the engineer begins to investigate design alternatives. Alternatives are different approaches, or options, that the design engineer considers to be viable at the conceptual stage of the design. For example, some of these concepts may be used to design a better mousetrap:

- use a mechanical or an electronic sensor
- insert cheese or peanut butter as bait
- construct a wood, plastic, or metal cage
- install an audible or a visible alarm
- kill or catch and release the mouse

Analysis is a *decision-making tool* for evaluating a set of design alternatives. By performing analysis, the design engineer zeroes in on the alternatives that yield the optimum solution, while eliminating alternatives that either violate design constraints or yield inferior solutions. In the mousetrap design, a dynamics analysis may show that a mechanical sensor is too slow, resulting in delaying the closing of a trap door and therefore freeing the mouse. Thus, an electronic sensor is chosen because it yields a superior solution.

The application that follows illustrates how analysis is used to design a machine component.

APPLICATION: DESIGNING A MACHINE COMPONENT

One of the major roles for mechanical engineers is the design of machines. Machines can be very complex systems consisting of numerous moving components. In order for a machine to work properly, each component must be designed so that it performs a specific function in unison with the other components. The components must be designed to withstand specified forces, vibrations, temperatures, corrosion, and other mechanical and environmental factors. An important aspect of machine design is determining the *dimensions* of the mechanical components.

Consider a machine component consisting of a 20-cm-long circular rod, as shown in Figure 1. As the machine operates, the rod is subjected to a 100-kN tensile force. One of the design constraints is that the axial deformation (change in length) of the rod cannot exceed 0.5 mm if the rod is to interface properly with a mating component. Taking the rod length and the applied tensile force as given, what is the minimum diameter required for the rod?

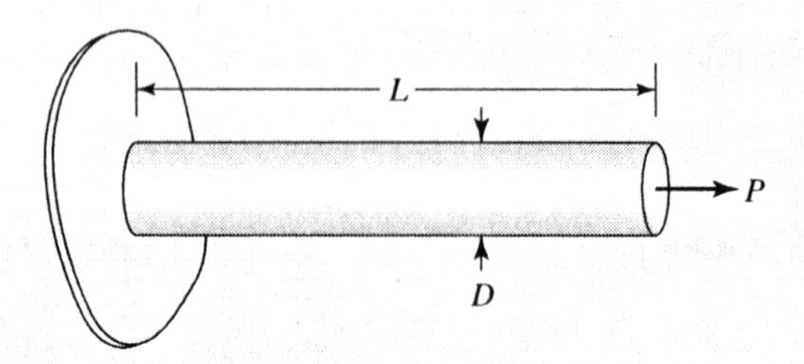

Figure 1. A machine component.

To solve this problem, we use a familiar equation from mechanics of materials,

$$\delta = \frac{PL}{AE}$$

where

δ = axial deformation (m)

P = axial tensile force (N)

L = original length of rod (m)

$A = \pi D^2/4$ = cross-sectional area of rod (m^2)

E = modulus of elasticity (N/m^2)

The use of this equation assumes that the material behaves elastically (i.e., it does not undergo permanent deformation when subjected to a force). Upon substituting the formula for the rod's cross-sectional area into the equation and solving for the rod diameter, D, we obtain

$$D = \sqrt{\frac{4\,PL}{\pi \delta E}}$$

We know the tensile force, P, the original rod length, L, and the maximum axial deformation, δ. But to find the diameter, D, we must also know the modulus of elasticity, E. The modulus of elasticity is a material property, a constant defined by the ratio of stress to strain. Suppose we choose 7075-T6 aluminum for the rod. This material has a modulus of elasticity of E = 72 GPa. Substituting values into the equation gives the following diameter:

$$D = \sqrt{\frac{4(100 \times 10^3 \text{ N})(0.20 \text{ m})}{\pi(0.0005 \text{ m})(72 \times 10^9 \text{ N/m}^2)}}$$
$$= 0.0266 \text{ m} = 26.6 \text{ mm}$$

As part of the design process, we wish to consider other materials for the rod. Let's find the diameter for a rod made of structural steel (E = 200 GPa). For structural steel, the rod diameter is

$$D = \sqrt{\frac{4(100 \times 10^3 \text{ N})(0.20 \text{ m})}{\pi(0.005 \text{ m})(200 \times 10^9 \text{ N/m}^2)}}$$
$$= 0.0160 \text{ m} = 16.0 \text{ mm}.$$

Our analysis shows that the minimum diameter for the rod depends on the material we choose. Either 7075-T6 aluminum or structural steel will work as far as the axial deformation is concerned, but other design issues such as weight, strength, wear, corrosion, and cost should be considered. The important point to be learned here is that analysis is a fundamental step in machine design.

As the application example illustrates, analysis is used to ascertain what design features are required to make the component or system *functional*. Analysis is used to size the cable of a suspension bridge, to select a cooling fan for a computer, to size the heating elements for curing a plastic part in a manufacturing plant, and to design the solar panels that convert solar energy to electrical energy for a spacecraft. Analysis is a crucial part of virtually every design task because it guides the design engineer through a sequence of decisions that ultimately lead to the optimum design. It is important to point out that in design work, it is not enough to simply produce a *drawing* of the component or system. A drawing by itself, while revealing the visual and dimensional characteristics of the design, may say little, or nothing, about the functionality of the design. Analysis must be included in the design process if the engineer is to know whether the design will actually work when it is placed into service. Also, once a working prototype of the design is constructed, testing is performed to validate analysis and to aid in the refinement of the design.

3 ANALYSIS AND ENGINEERING FAILURE

With the possible exception of farmers, engineers are probably the most taken for granted people in the world. Virtually all the man-made products and devices that people use in their personal and professional lives were designed by engineers. Think for a moment. What is the first thing you did when you arose from bed this morning? Did you hit the snooze button on your alarm clock? Your alarm clock was designed by engineers. What did you do next, go into the bathroom, perhaps? The bathroom fixtures—the sink, bathtub, shower, and toilet—were designed by engineers. Did you use an electrical appliance to fix breakfast? Your toaster, waffle maker, microwave oven, refrigerator and other kitchen appliances were designed by engineers. Even if you ate cold cereal for breakfast, you still took advantage of engineering because engineers designed the processes by which the cereal and milk were produced, and they even designed the cereal box and milk container! What did you do after breakfast? If you brushed your teeth, you can thank engineers for designing the toothpaste tube and toothbrush and even formulating the toothpaste. Before leaving for school, you got dressed. Because our society does not look favorably upon public nudity, you can thank engineers for designing the textiles from which your clothing is made and the machines that manufactured them. Did you drive a car to school or ride a bicycle? In either case, engineers designed both transportation systems. What did you do when you arrived at school? You sat down in your favorite chair in a classroom, removed a pen or pencil and a note pad from your backpack, and began another day of learning. The chair you sat in, the writing instrument you used to take notes, the note pad you wrote on, and the bulging backpack you use to carry books, binders, paper, pens, and pencils, plus numerous other devices were designed by engineers.

We take engineers for granted, but we expect a lot from them. We expect everything they design, including alarm clocks, plumbing, toasters, automobiles, chairs, and pencils, to work and to work all the time. Unfortunately, they don't. We experience a relatively minor inconvenience when the heating coil in our toaster burns out, but when a bridge collapses, a commercial airliner crashes, or a space shuttle explodes, and people are injured or die, the story makes headline news, and engineers are suddenly thrust into the spotlight of public scrutiny. Are engineers to blame for every failure that occurs? Some failures occur because people misuse the products. For example, if you persist in using a screwdriver to pry lids off cans, to dig weeds from the garden, and to chisel masonry, it may soon stop functioning as a screwdriver. Engineers try to design products that are "people proof." The types of failures that engineers take primary responsibility for are those caused by various types of errors during the design phase. After all, engineering is a human enterprise, and humans make mistakes.

Whether we like it or not, **failure** is part of engineering. It is part of the design process. When engineers design a new product, it seldom works exactly as expected the first time. Mechanical components may not fit properly, electrical components may be connected incorrectly, software glitches may occur, or materials may be incompatible. The list of potential causes of failure is long, and the cause of a specific failure in a design is probably unexpected because otherwise the design engineer would have accounted for it. Failure will always be part of engineering, because engineers cannot anticipate every mechanism by which failures *can* occur. Engineers make every concerted effort to design systems that do not fail. If failures do arise, hopefully they are revealed during the design phase and can be ironed out before the product goes into service. One of the hallmarks of a good design engineer is one who turns failure into success.

The role of analysis in engineering failure is twofold. First, as discussed earlier, analysis is a crucial part of engineering design. It is one of the main decision-making tools the design engineer uses to explore alternatives. Analysis helps establish the functionality of the design. Analysis may therefore be regarded as a *failure prevention* tool. People expect kitchen appliances, automobiles, airplanes, televisions, and other systems to work as they are supposed to work, so engineers make every reasonable attempt to design products that are reliable. As part of the design phase, engineers use analysis to ascertain what the physical characteristics of the system must be in order to prevent system failure within a specified period of time. Do engineers ever design products to fail on purpose? Surprisingly, the answer is yes. Some devices rely on failure for their proper operation. For example, a fuse "fails" when the electrical current flowing through it exceeds a specified amperage. When this amperage is exceeded, a metallic element in the fuse melts, breaking the circuit, thereby protecting personnel or a piece of electrical equipment. Shear pins in transmission systems protect shafts, gears, and other components when the shear force exceeds a certain value. Some utility poles and highway signs are designed to safely break away when struck by an automobile.

The second role of failure analysis in engineering pertains to situations where design flaws escaped detection during the design phase, only to reveal themselves after the product was placed into service. In this role, analysis is utilized to address the questions "Why did the failure occur?" and "How can it be avoided in the future?" This type of detective work in engineering is sometimes referred to as *forensic engineering*. In failure investigations, analysis is used as a diagnostic tool of reevaluation and reconstruction. Following the explosion of the Space Shuttle Challenger in 1986, engineers at Thiokol used analysis (and testing) to reevaluate the joint design of the solid rocket boosters. Their analyses and tests showed that, under the unusually cold conditions on the day of launch, the rubber O-rings responsible for maintaining a seal between the segments of one of the solid rocket boosters lost resiliency and therefore the ability to contain the high-pressure gases inside the booster. Hot gases leaking past the O-rings developed into an impinging jet directed against the external (liquid hydrogen) tank and a lower strut attaching the booster to the external tank. Within seconds, the entire aft dome of the tank fell away, releasing massive amounts of liquid hydrogen. Challenger was immediately enveloped in the explosive burn, destroying the vehicle and killing all seven astronauts. In the aftermath of the Challenger disaster, engineers used analysis extensively to redesign the solid rocket booster joint.

APPLICATION: FAILURE OF THE TACOMA NARROWS BRIDGE

The collapse of the Tacoma Narrows Bridge was one of the most sensational failures in the history of engineering. This suspension bridge was the first of its kind spanning the Puget Sound, connecting Washington State with the Olympic Peninsula. Compared with existing suspension bridges, the Tacoma Narrows Bridge had an unconventional design. It had a narrow two-lane deck, and the stiffened-girder road structure was not very deep. This unusual design gave the bridge a slender, graceful appearance. Although the bridge was visually appealing, it had a problem: It oscillated in the wind. During the four months following its opening to traffic on July 1, 1940, the bridge earned the nickname "Galloping Gertie" from motorists who felt as though they were riding a giant roller coaster as they crossed the 2800-ft center span. (See Figure 2.) The design engineers failed to recognize that their bridge might behave more like the wing of an airplane subjected to severe turbulence than an earth-bound structure subjected to a steady load. The engineers' failure to consider the aerodynamic aspects of the design led to the destruction of the bridge on November 7, 1940, during a 42-mile-per-hour wind storm. (See Figure 3.) Fortunately, no people were injured or killed. A newspaper editor, who lost control of his car between the towers due to the violent undulations, managed to stumble and crawl his way to safety, only to look back to see the road rip away from the suspension cables and fall, along with his car and presumably his dog, which he could not save, into the Narrows below.

Figure 2. The Tacoma Narrows Bridge twisting in the wind.

Even as the bridge was being torn apart by the wind storm, engineers were testing a scale model of the bridge at the University of Washington in an attempt to understand the problem. Within a few days following the bridge's demise, Theodore von Karman, a world renown fluid dynamicist, who worked at the California Institute of Technology, submitted a letter to *Engineering News-Record* outlining an aerodynamic analysis of the bridge. In the analysis, he used a differential equation for an idealized bridge deck twisting like an airplane wing as the lift forces of the wind tend to twist the deck one way, while the steel in the bridge tends to twist it in another way. His analysis showed that the Tacoma Narrows Bridge should indeed have exhibited an aerodynamic instability more pronounced than any existing suspension bridge. Remarkably, von Karman's "back of the envelope" calculations predicted dangerous levels of vibration for a wind speed not 10 miles per hour over the wind speed measured on the morning of November 7, 1940. The dramatic failure of Galloping Gertie forever established the importance of aerodynamic analysis in the design of suspension bridges.

The bridge was eventually redesigned with a deeper and stiffer open-truss structure that allowed the wind to pass through. The new and safer Tacoma Narrows Bridge was reopened on October 14, 1950.

Figure 3. The center span of the Tacoma Narrows Bridge plunges into Puget Sound.

PROFESSIONAL SUCCESS: LEARN FROM FAILURE

The Tacoma Narrows Bridge and countless other engineering failures teach engineers a valuable lesson:

> *Learn from your own failures and the failures of other engineers.*

Unfortunately, the designers of the Tacoma Narrows Bridge did not learn from the failures of others. Had they studied the history of suspension bridges dating back to the early 19th century, they would have discovered that 10 suspension bridges suffered severe damage or destruction by winds.

NASA and Thiokol learned that the pressure-seal design in the solid rocket-booster joint of the Space Shuttle Challenger was overly sensitive to a variety of factors such as temperature, physical dimensions, reusability, and joint loading. Not only did they learn some hard-core technical lessons, they also learned some lessons in engineering judgment. They learned that the decision-making process culminating in the launch of Challenger was flawed. To correct both types of errors, during the two-year period following the Challenger catastrophe, the joint was redesigned, additional safety-related measures were implemented and the decision-making process leading to shuttle launches was improved.

In another catastrophic failure, NASA determined that fragments of insulation that broke away from the external fuel tank during the launch of the Space Shuttle Columbia impacted the left wing of the vehicle, severely damaging the wing's leading edge. The damage caused a breach in the wing's surface, which, upon reentry of Columbia, precipitated a gradual burn-through of the wing, resulting in a loss of vehicle control. Columbia broke apart over the southwestern part of the United States, killing all seven astronauts aboard.

If we are to learn from engineering failures, the *history* of engineering becomes as relevant to our education as design, analysis, science, mathematics, and the liberal arts do. Lessons learned not only from our own experiences, but also from those who have gone before us, contribute enormously to the constant improvement of our technology and the advancement of engineering as a profession. Errors in judgement made by Roman and Egyptian engineers have been repeated in modern times, notwithstanding a greatly improved chest of scientific and mathematical tools. Engineers have and will continue to make mistakes. Learn from them.

KEY TERMS

analysis
basic mathematics
engineering analysis
engineering design
failure
higher level mathematics
modeling
physical sciences

REFERENCES

Adams, J.L., *Flying Buttresses, Entropy and O-rings: The World of an Engineer*: Cambridge, MA: Harvard University Press, 1991.

Ferguson, E.S., "How Engineers Lose Touch," *Invention and Technology*, Vol. 8 (3), Winter 1993, pp. 16–24.

Fogler, H.S. and S.E. LeBlanc, *Strategies for Creative Problem Solving*, Upper Saddle River, NJ: Prentice Hall, 1995.

French, M., *Invention and Evolution: Design in Nature and Engineering*, 2d ed., Cambridge, UK: Cambridge University Press, 1994.

Horenstein, M.N., *Design Concepts for Engineers*, 2d ed., Upper Saddle River, NJ: Prentice Hall, 2002.

Howell, S.K., *Engineering Design and Problem Solving*, 2d ed., Upper Saddle River, NJ: Prentice Hall, 2002.

Hyman, B., *Fundamentals of Engineering Design*, 2d ed., Upper Saddle River, NJ: Prentice Hall, 2002.

Laithwaite, E., *An Inventor in the Garden of Eden*, Cambridge, UK: Cambridge University Press, 1994.

Petroski, H., *Design Paradigms: Case Histories of Error and Judgement in Engineering*, Cambridge, UK: Cambridge University Press, 1994.

Petroski, H., *To Engineer is Human: The Role of Failure in Successful Design*, NY: Vintage Books, 1992.

Wright, P.H., *Introduction to Engineering*, 3d ed., NY: John Wiley and Sons, 2003.

Problems

1. The following basic devices are commonly found in a typical home or office. Discuss how analysis might be used to design these items.

   a. staple remover
   b. scissors
   c. fork
   d. mechanical pencil
   e. door hinge
   f. paper clip
   g. toilet
   h. incandescent light bulb
   i. cereal box
   j. coat hanger
   k. three-ring binder
   l. light switch
   m. doorknob

n. stapler
o. can opener
p. water faucet
q. kitchen sink
r. electrical outlet
s. window
t. door
u. dinner plate
v. chair
w. table
x. plastic CD case
y. drawer slide
z. bookend

2. A 1-m-long beam of rectangular cross section carries a uniform load of $w = 15$ kN/m. The design specification calls for a 5-mm maximum deflection of the end of the beam. The beam is to be constructed of fir ($E = 13$ GPa). By analysis, determine at least five combinations of beam height, h, and beam width, b, that meet the specification. Use the equation

$$y_{max} = \frac{wL^4}{8EI}$$

where

y_{max} = deflection of end of beam (m)
w = uniform loading (N/m)
L = beam length (m)
E = modulus of elasticity of beam (Pa)
$I = bh^3/12$ = area moment of inertia of beam (m^4)

Note: 1 Pa = 1 N/m^2, 1 kN = 10^3 N and 1 GPa = 10^9 Pa.

What design conclusions can you draw about the influence of beam height and width on the maximum deflection? Is the deflection more sensitive to h or b? If the beam were constructed of a different material, how would the deflection change? See Figure 2 for an illustration of the beam.

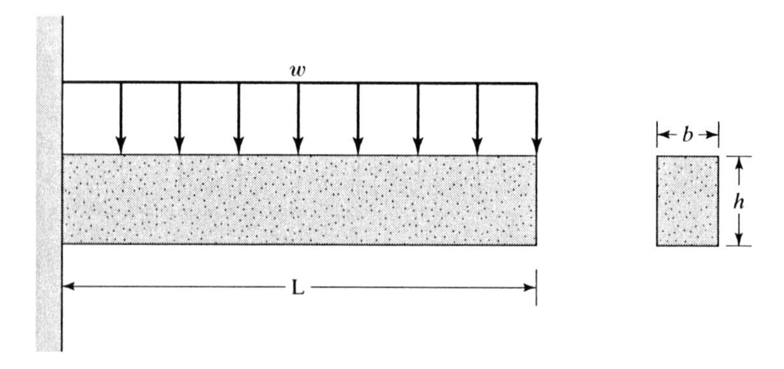

Figure 2.

3. Identify a device from your own experience that has failed. Discuss how it failed and how analysis might be used to redesign it.

4. Research the following notable engineering failures. Discuss how analysis was used or could have been used to investigate the failure.

   a. Hyatt Hotel, Kansas City, 1981
   b. Titanic, North Atlantic, 1912
   c. Chernobyl Nuclear Power Plant, Soviet Union, 1986
   d. Three Mile Island Nuclear Power Plant, Pennsylvania, 1979
   e. Hartford Civic Center, Connecticut, 1978
   f. Union Carbide Plant, India, 1984
   g. Hindenburg airship, New Jersey, 1937
   h. Hubble Space Telescope, 1990
   i. Highway I-880, Loma Prieta, California earthquake, 1989
   j. American Airlines DC-10, Chicago, 1979
   k. Skylab, 1979
   l. Apollo I capsule fire, Cape Canaveral, Florida, 1967
   m. Dee Bridge, England, 1847
   n. Green Bank radio telescope, West Virginia, 1989
   o. Boiler explosions, North America, 1870–1910
   p. ValuJet Airlines DC-9, Miami, 1996
   q. Ford Pinto gas tanks, 1970s
   r. Teton dam, Idaho, 1976
   s. Apollo 13, 1970
   t. Mars Climate Orbiter, 1999
   u. Space Shuttle Challenger, 1986
   v. Space Shuttle Columbia, 2003

3

Dimensions and Units

1 INTRODUCTION

Suppose for a moment that someone asks you to hurry to the grocery store to buy a few items for tonight's dinner. You get in your car, turn the ignition on, and drive down the road. Immediately you notice something strange. There are no numbers or divisions on your speedometer! As you accelerate and decelerate, the speedometer indicator changes position, but you do not know your speed because there are no markings to read. Bewildered, you notice that the speed limit and other road signs between your house and the store also lack numerical information. Realizing that you were instructed to arrive home with the groceries by 6 P.M., you glance at your digital watch only to discover that the display is blank. Now you are really spooked, but you drive on. Upon arriving at the store, you check your list: 1 pound of lean ground beef, 4 ounces of fresh mushrooms, and a 12-ounce can of tomato paste. You go to the meat counter first. As you scan the meat counter, you can't believe your eyes. The label on each package does not indicate the weight of the product. "This can't be," you mutter under your breath. You hastily grab what appears to be a 1-pound package and scurry to the produce section. Scooping up a bunch of mushrooms, you place them on the scale to weigh them. "Oh no! The scale looks like my speedometer:—It has no markings either!" Once again, you estimate. One item is left: the tomato paste. The canned goods aisle is very large and contains many types of canned items: soup, juice, and fruit. Finally, you locate the tomato paste. "Not again!" you exclaim. The label on the can has no numerical information—no weight, no volume, nothing to let you know the amount of tomato paste in the can. Being mystified and shaken by this whole experience, you still make your purchase, drive home, and deliver the items. Later, you somehow manage to consume a large plate of spaghetti.

SECTIONS

OBJECTIVES

After reading this chapter, you will have learned

- How to check equations for dimensional consistency
- The physical standards on which units are based
- Rules for proper usage of SI units
- Rules for proper usage of English units
- The difference between mass and weight
- How to do unit conversions between the SI and English unit systems

The preceding Twilight Zone-like story is, of course, fictitious, but it dramatically illustrates how strange our world would be without measures of physical quantities. Speed is a physical quantity that is measured by the speedometers in our automobiles and the radar gun of a traffic officer. Time is a physical quantity that is measured by the watch on our wrist and the clock on the wall. Weight is a physical quantity that is measured by the scale in the grocery store or at the health spa. The need for measurement was recognized by the ancients, who based standards of length on the breadth of the hand or palm, the length of the foot, or the distance from the elbow to the tip of the middle finger (referred to as a cubit). Such measurement standards were both changeable and perishable because they were based on human dimensions. In modern times, definite and unchanging standards of measurement have been adopted to help us quantify the physical world. These measurement standards are used by engineers and scientists to analyze physical phenomena by applying the laws of nature such as conservation of energy, the second law of thermodynamics, and the law of universal gravitation. As engineers design new products and processes by utilizing these laws, they use dimensions and units to describe the physical quantities involved. For instance, the design of a bridge primarily involves the dimensions of length and force. The units used to express the magnitudes of these quantities are usually either the meter and newton or the foot and pound. The thermal design of a boiler primarily involves the dimensions of pressure, temperature, and heat transfer, which are expressed in units of pascal, degrees Celsius, and watt, respectively. Dimensions and units are as important to engineers as the physical laws they describe. It is vitally important that engineering students learn how to work with dimensions and units. Without dimensions and units, analyses of engineering systems have little meaning.

2 DIMENSIONS

To most people, the term dimension denotes a measurement of length. Certainly, length is one type of dimension, but the term dimension has a broader meaning. A **dimension** is a *physical variable that is used to describe or specify the nature of a measurable quantity.* For example, the mass of a gear in a machine is a dimension of the gear. Obviously, the diameter is also a dimension of the gear. The compressive force in a concrete column holding up a bridge is a structural dimension of the column. The pressure and temperature of a liquid in a hydraulic cylinder are thermodynamic dimensions of the liquid. The velocity of a space probe orbiting a distant planet is also a dimension. Many other examples could be given. Any variable that engineers use to specify a physical quantity is, in the general sense, a dimension of the physical quantity. Hence, there are as many dimensions as there are physical quantities. Engineers always use dimensions in their analytical and experimental work. In order to specify a dimension fully, two characteristics must be given. First, the *numerical value* of the dimension is required. Second, the appropriate *unit* must be assigned. A dimension missing either of these two elements is incomplete and therefore cannot be fully used by the engineer. If the diameter of a gear is given as 3.85, we would ask the question, "3.85 what? Inches? Meters?" Similarly, if the compressive force in a concrete column is given as 150,000, we would ask, "150,000 what? Newtons? Pounds?"

Dimensions are categorized as either *base* or *derived*. A **base dimension**, sometimes referred to as a *fundamental* dimension, is a dimension that cannot be broken down or subdivided into other dimensions or a dimension that has been internationally accepted as the most basic dimension of a physical quantity. There are seven base dimensions that have been formally defined for use in science and engineering:

1. length [L]
2. mass [M]

3. time [t]
4. temperature [T]
5. electric current [I]
6. amount of substance [N]
7. luminous intensity [i]

A **derived dimension** is obtained by any combination of the base dimensions. For example, volume is length cubed, density is mass divided by length cubed, and velocity is length divided by time. Obviously, there are numerous derived dimensions. Table 1 lists some of the most commonly used derived dimensions in engineering, expressed in terms of base dimensions.

TABLE 1 Derived Dimensions Expressed in Terms of Base Dimensions.

Quantity	Variable Name	Base Dimensions
Area	A	$[L]^2$
Volume	V	$[L]^3$
Velocity	v	$[L][t]^{-1}$
Acceleration	a	$[L][t]^{-2}$
Density	ρ	$[M][L]^{-3}$
Force	F	$[M][L][t]^{-2}$
Pressure	P	$[M][L]^{-1}[t]^{-2}$
Stress	σ	$[M][L]^{-1}[t]^{-2}$
Energy	E	$[M][L]^2[t]^{-2}$
Work	W	$[M][L]^2[t]^{-2}$
Power	P	$[M][L]^2[t]^{-3}$
Mass flow rate	$\dot{m}$	$[M][t]^{-1}$
Specific heat	c	$[L]^2[t]^{-2}[T]^{-1}$
Dynamic viscosity	μ	$[M][L]^{-1}[t]^{-1}$
Molar mass	M	$[M][N]^{-1}$
Voltage	V	$[M][L]^2[t]^{-3}[I]^{-1}$
Resistance	R	$[M][L]^2[t]^{-3}[I]^{-2}$

The single letters in brackets in Table 1 are symbols that designate each base dimension. These symbols are useful for checking the dimensional consistency of equations. Every mathematical relation used in science and engineering must be **dimensionally consistent**, or *dimensionally homogeneous*. This means that the dimension on the left side of the equal sign must be the same as the dimension on the right side of the equal sign. The equality in any equation denotes not only a numerical equivalency but also a dimensional equivalency. To use a simple analogy, you cannot say that five apples equals four apples, nor can you say that five apples equals five oranges. You can only say that five apples equals five apples.

The following examples illustrate the concept of dimensional consistency:

EXAMPLE 1

Dynamics is a branch of engineering mechanics that deals with the motion of particles and rigid bodies. The straight-line motion of a particle, under the influence of gravity, may be analyzed by using the equation

$$y = y_0 + v_0 t - \frac{1}{2} g t^2$$

where

y = height of particle at time t
y_0 = initial height of particle (at $t = 0$)
v_0 = initial velocity of particle (at $t = 0$)
t = time
g = gravitational acceleration

Verify that this equation is dimensionally consistent.

SOLUTION

We check the dimensional consistency of the equation by determining the dimensions on both sides of the equal sign. The heights, y_0 and y, are one-dimensional coordinates of the particle; so these quantities have a dimension of length, [L]. The initial velocity, v_0, is a derived dimension consisting of a length, [L], divided by a time, [t]. Gravitational acceleration, g, is also a derived dimension consisting of a length, [L], divided by time squared, $[t]^2$. Of course, time, [t], is a base dimension. Writing the equation in its dimensional form, we have

$$[L] = [L] + [L][t]^{-1}[t] - [L][t]^{-2}[t]^2$$

Note that the factor, ½, in front of the gt^2 term is a pure number, and therefore has no dimension. In the second term on the right side of the equal sign, the dimension [t] cancels, leaving length, [L]. Similarly, in the third term on the right side of the equal sign, the dimension [t] cancels, leaving length, [L]. This equation is dimensionally consistent because all terms have the dimension of length, [L].

EXAMPLE 2

Aerodynamics is the study of the performance of bodies moving through air. An aerodynamics analysis could be used to determine the lift force on an airplane wing or the drag force on an automobile. A commonly used equation in aerodynamics relates the total drag force acting on a body to the velocity of the air approaching it. This equation is

$$F_D = \frac{1}{2} C_D A \rho U^2$$

where

F_D = drag force
C_D = drag coefficient
A = frontal area of body
ρ = air density
U = upstream air velocity

Determine the dimensions of the drag coefficient, C_D.

SOLUTION

The dimension of the drag coefficient, C_D, may be found by writing the equation in dimensional form and simplifying the equation by combining like dimensions. Using the information in Table 1, we write the dimensional equation as

$$[M][L][t]^{-2} = C_D[M][L]^{-3}[L]^2[t]^{-2}[L]^2$$
$$= C_D[M][L][t]^{-2}$$

Compare the combination of base dimensions on the left and right sides of the equal sign. They are identical. This can only mean that the drag coefficient, C_D, has no dimension. If it did, the equation would not be dimensionally consistent. Thus, we say that C_D

is *dimensionless*. In other words, the drag coefficient, C_D, has a numerical value, but no dimensional value. This is not as strange as it may sound. In engineering, there are many instances, particularly, in the disciplines of fluid mechanics and heat transfer, where a physical quantity is dimensionless. Dimensionless quantities enable engineers to form special ratios that reveal certain physical insights into properties and processes. In this instance, the drag coefficient is physically interpreted as a "shear stress" at the surface of the body, which means that there is an aerodynamic force acting on the body parallel to its surface that tends to retard the body's motion through the air. If you take a course in fluid mechanics, you will learn more about this important concept.

EXAMPLE 3

For the following dimensional equation, find the dimensions of the quantity k:

$$[M][L][t]^{-2} = k[L][t]$$

SOLUTION

To find the dimensions of k, we multiply both sides of the equation by $[L]^{-1}[t]^{-1}$ to eliminate the dimensions on the right side of the equation, leaving k by itself. Thus, we obtain

$$[M][L][t]^{-2}[L]^{-1}[t]^{-1} = k$$

which, after applying a law of exponents, reduces to

$$[M][t]^{-3} = k$$

A closer examination of the given dimensional equation reveals that it is Newton's second law of motion:

$$F = ma$$

Here F is force, m is mass, and a is acceleration. Referring to Table 1, force has dimensions of $[M][L][t]^{-2}$, which is a mass $[M]$ multiplied by acceleration, $[L][t]^{-2}$.

PRACTICE!

1. For the following dimensional equation, find the base dimensions of the parameter k:

$$[M][L]^2 = k[L][t][M]^2$$

Answer: $[L][M]^{-1}[t]^{-1}$

2. For the following dimensional equation, find the base dimensions of the parameter g:

$$[T]^{-1}[t][L] = g[L]^{-2}$$

Answer: $[L]^3[t][T]^{-1}$

3. For the following dimensional equation, find the base dimensions of the parameter h:

$$[I][t]^{-1}h = [N]$$

Answer: $[I][N]^{-1}[t]^{-1}$

4. For the following dimensional equation, find the base dimensions of the parameter f:

$$[M][M]^{-3} = \cos(f[L])$$

Answer: $[L]^{-1}$

5. For the following dimensional equation, find the base dimensions of the parameter p:

$$[T] = [T]\log([T]^{-2}[t]p)$$

Answer: $[T]^2[t]^{-1}$

3 UNITS

A **unit** is an *arbitrarily chosen size subdivision by which the magnitude of a dimension is expressed*. For example, the dimension length, [L], may be expressed in units of meter (m), feet (ft), mile (mi), millimeter (mm), and many others. The dimension temperature, [T], is expressed in units of degrees Celsius (°C), degrees Fahrenheit (°F), degrees rankine (°R), or kelvin (K). (By convention, the degree symbol (°) is not used for the Kelvin temperature scale.) In the United States, there are two unit systems commonly in use. The first unit system, and the one that is internationally accepted as the standard, is the **SI** (System International d'Unites) **unit system**, commonly referred to as the *metric* system. The second unit system is the **English** (or **British**) **unit system**, sometimes referred to as the *United States Customary System (USCS)*. With the exception of the United States, most of the industrialized nations of the world use the SI system exclusively. The SI system is preferred over the English system, because it is an internationally accepted standard and is based on simple powers of 10. To a limited extent, a transition to the SI system has been federally mandated in the United States. Unfortunately, this transition to total SI usage is a slow one, but many American companies are using the SI system to remain internationally competitive. Until the United States makes a complete adaptation to the SI system, U.S. engineering students need to be conversant in both unit systems and know how to make unit conversions.

The seven base dimensions are expressed in terms of SI units that are based on **physical standards**. These standards are defined such that, the corresponding SI units, except the mass unit, can be reproduced in a laboratory anywhere in the world. The reproducibility of these standards is important, because everyone with a suitably equipped laboratory has access to the same standards. Hence, all physical quantities, regardless of where in the world they are measured, are based on identical standards. This universality of physical standards eliminates the ancient problem of basing dimensions on the changing physical attributes of kings, rulers, and magistrates who reigned for a finite time. Modern standards are based on constants of nature and physical attributes of matter and energy.

The seven base dimensions and their associated SI units are summarized in Table 2. Note the symbol for each unit. These symbols are the accepted conventions for science and engineering. The discussion that follows outlines the physical standards by which the base units are defined.

TABLE 2 Base Dimensions and Their SI Units.

Quantity	Unit	Symbol
Length	meter	m
Mass	kilogram	kg
Time	second	s
Temperature	kelvin	K
Electric current	ampere	A
Amount of substance	mole	mol
Luminous intensity	candela	cd

Length

The unit of length in the SI system is the *meter* (m). As illustrated in Figure 1, the meter is defined as the distance traveled by light in a vacuum, during a time interval of 1/299,792,458 s. The definition is based on a physical standard: the speed of light in a vacuum. The speed of light in a vacuum is 299,792,458 m/s. Thus, light travels one

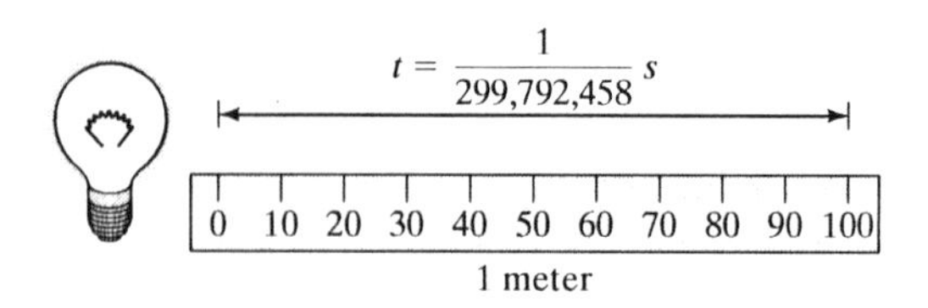

Figure 1. The physical standard for the meter is based on the speed of light in a vacuum.

meter during a time interval of the reciprocal of this number. Of course, the unit of time, the *second* (s), is itself a base unit.

Mass

The unit of mass in the SI system is the *kilogram* (kg). Unlike the other units, the kilogram is not based on a reproducible physical standard. The standard for the kilogram is a cylinder of platinum-iridium alloy, which is maintained by the International Bureau of Weights and Measures in Paris, France. A duplicate of this cylinder is kept in the United States by the National Institute of Standards and Technology (NIST). (See Figure 2.)

Mass is the only base dimension that is defined by an artifact. An artifact is a man-made object, not as easily reproduced as the other laboratory-based standards.

Figure 2. A duplicate of the kilogram standard is a platinum-iridium cylinder maintained by NIST. (© Copyright Robert Rathe. Courtesy of the National Institute of Standards and Technology, Gaithersburg, MD)

Time

The unit of time in the SI system is the *second* (s). The second is defined as the duration of 9,192,631,770 cycles of radiation corresponding to the transition between the two hyperfine levels of the ground state of the cesium133 atom. An atomic clock incorporating this standard is maintained by NIST. (See Figure 3.)

Figure 3. The seventh generation atomic clock maintained by NIST keeps time with an accuracy of five parts in 10^{15}, equivalent to about one second in six million years. (Courtesy of the National Institute of Standards and Technology, Boulder, CO.)

Temperature

The unit of temperature in the SI system is the *kelvin* (K). The kelvin is defined as the fraction 1/273.16 of the temperature of the triple point of water. The triple point of water is the combination of pressure and temperature at which water exists as a solid, liquid, and gas at the same time. (See Figure 4.) This temperature is 273.16 K, 0.01°C, or 32.002°F. Absolute zero is the temperature at which all molecular activity ceases and has a value of 0 K.

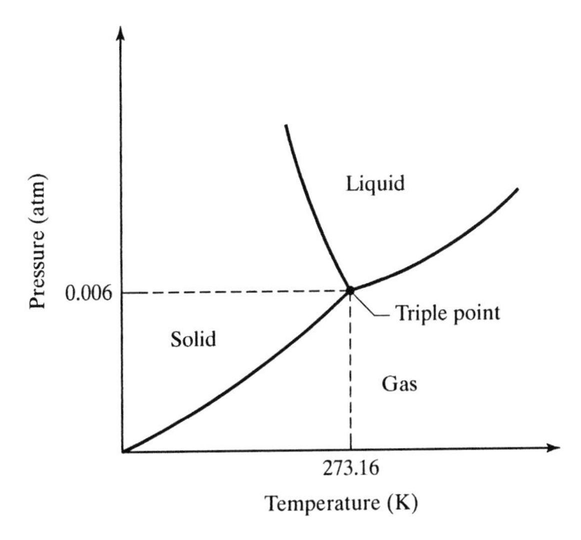

Figure 4. A phase diagram for water shows the triple point on which the kelvin temperature standard is based.

Electric Current

The unit of electric current in the SI system is the *ampere* (A). As shown in Figure 5, the ampere is defined as the steady current, which, if maintained in two straight parallel wires of infinite length and negligible circular cross section and placed one meter apart in a vacuum, produces a force of 2×10^{-7} newton per meter of wire length. Using Ohm's law, $I = V/R$, one ampere may also be denoted as the current that flows when one volt is applied across a 1-ohm resistor.

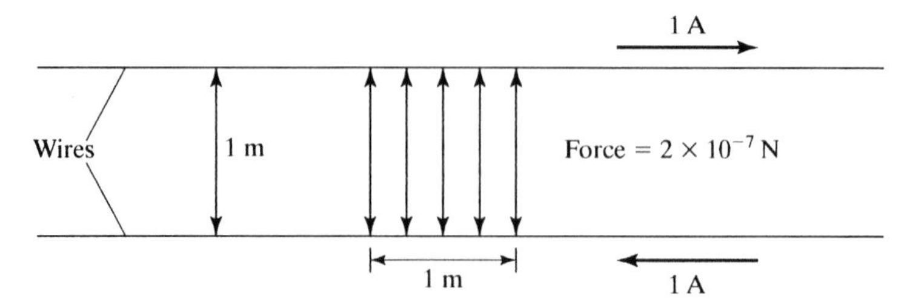

Figure 5. The standard for the ampere is based on the electrical force produced between two parallel wires, each carrying 1 A, located 1 m apart.

Amount of Substance

The unit used to denote the amount of substance is the *mole* (mol). One mole contains the same number of elements as there are atoms in 0.012 kg of carbon-12. This number is called Avogadro's number and has a value of approximately 6.022×10^{23}. (See Figure 6.)

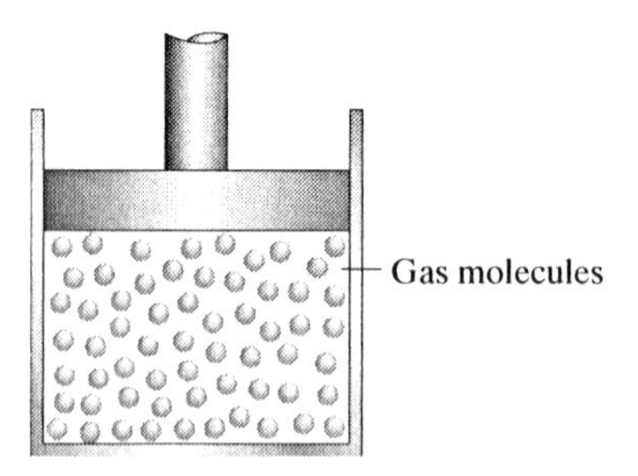

Figure 6. A mole of gas molecules in a piston-cylinder device contains 6.022×10^{23} molecules.

Luminous Intensity

The unit for luminous intensity is the *candela* (cd). As illustrated in Figure 7, one candela is the luminous intensity of a source emitting light radiation at a frequency of 540×10^{12} Hz that provides a power of 1/683 watt (W) per steradian. A steradian is a solid angle, which, having its vertex in the center of a sphere, subtends (cuts off) an area of the sphere equal to that of a square with sides of length equal to the radius of the sphere.

The unit for luminous intensity, the candela, utilizes the steradian, a dimension that may be unfamiliar to most students. The *radian* and *steradian* are called *supplementary*

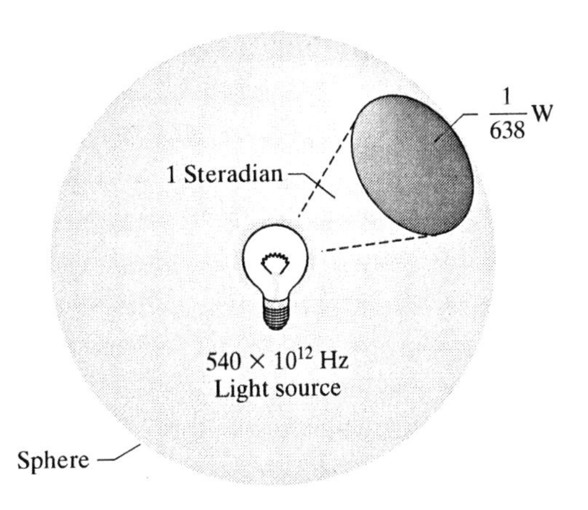

Figure 7. The candela standard for luminous intensity.

dimensions. These quantities, summarized in Table 3, refer to plane and solid angles, respectively. The radian is frequently used in engineering, and it is defined as the plane angle between two radii of a circle that subtends on the circumference an arc equal in length to the radius. From trigonometry, you may recall that there are 2π radians in a circle (i.e., 2π radians equals 360°). Thus, one radian equals approximately 57.3°. The steradian, defined earlier, is used primarily for expressing radiation quantities such as light intensity and other electromagnetic parameters.

TABLE 3 Supplementary Dimensions.

Quantity	Unit	Symbol
Plane angle	radian	rad
Solid angle	steradian	sr

4 SI UNITS

Throughout the civilized world there are thousands of engineering companies that design and manufacture products for the benefit of man. The international buying and selling of these products is an integral part of a global network of industrialized countries, and the economic health of these countries, including the United States, depends to a large extent on international trade. Industries such as the automotive and electronics industries are heavily involved in international trade, so these industries have readily embraced the SI unit system in order to be economically competitive. The general adoption of the SI unit system by U.S. companies has been slow, but global economic imperatives are driving them to fall into step with the other industrialized nations of the world. SI units are now commonplace on food and beverage containers, gasoline pumps, and automobile speedometers. The SI unit system is the internationally accepted standard. In the United States, however, the English unit system is still widely used. Hopefully, it is only a matter of time before all U.S. companies use SI units exclusively. Until that time, the burden is upon you, the engineering student, to learn both unit systems. You will gladly discover, however, that most engineering textbooks emphasize SI units, but provide a list of unit conversions between the SI and English systems.

Table 2 summarizes the seven base dimensions and their SI units, and Table 3 summarizes the supplementary dimensions and their units. Derived dimensions consist of a combination of base and supplementary dimensions. Sometimes, the units of a derived dimension are given a specific name. For example, the derived dimension *force* consists of the SI base units kg • m • s^{-2}. This combination of SI base units is called a *newton* and is abbreviated N. Note that the unit name, in honor of Isaac Newton, is not capitalized when spelled out as a unit name. The same rule applies to other units named after people such as hertz (Hz), kelvin (K), pascal (Pa), etc. Another example is the *joule*, the SI unit for energy, work, and heat. The joule unit is abbreviated J and consists of the SI base units kg • m^2 • s^{-2}. A summary of the most commonly used SI derived dimensions and the corresponding SI unit names is given in Table 4.

Most derived dimensions do not have specific SI unit names, but their units may contain specific SI unit names. For example, the dimension, *moment of force*, usually

TABLE 4 Derived Dimensions and SI Units with Specific Names.

Quantity	SI Unit	Unit Name	Base Units
Frequency	Hz	hertz	s^{-1}
Force	N	newton	kg • m • s^{-2}
Pressure	Pa	pascal	kg • m^{-1} • s^{-2}
Stress	Pa	pascal	kg • m^{-1} • s^{-2}
Energy	J	joule	kg • m^2 • s^{-2}
Work	J	joule	kg • m^2 • s^{-2}
Heat	J	joule	kg • m^2 • s^{-2}
Power	W	watt	kg • m^2 • s^{-3}
Electric charge	C	coulomb	A • s
Electric potential (voltage)	V	volt	kg • m^2 • s^{-3} • A^{-1}
Electric resistance	Ω	ohm	kg • m^2 • s^{-3} • A^{-2}
Magnetic flux	Wb	weber	kg^{-1} • m • s^{-2} • A^{-1}
Luminous flux	lm	lumen	cd • sr

referred to simply as *moment*, has the SI units N • m, a force multiplied by a distance. There is no special name for this unit—we simply call it "newton–meter." Another example is the dimension *mass flow rate*. Mass flow rate is the mass of a fluid that flows past a point in a given time. The SI units for mass flow rate are kg • s^{-1}, which we state as "kilograms per second." Note that units that are located in the denominator, that is, those that have a negative sign on their exponent, may also be written using a divisor line. Thus, the units for mass flow rate may be written as kg/s. Caution must be exercised, however, when utilizing this type of notation for some units. For example, the SI units for thermal conductivity, a quantity used in heat transfer, are W • m^{-1} • K^{-1}. How do we write these units with a divisor line? Do we write these units as W/m/K? How about W/m • K? The first choice can cause some confusion. Does a "watt per meter per kelvin" mean that the kelvin unit is inverted twice and therefore goes above the divisor line? One glance at the units written as W • m^{-1} • K^{-1} tells us that the temperature unit belongs "downstairs" because K has a negative exponent. If the kelvin unit were placed above the divisor line, and the thermal conductivity were used in an equation, a dimensional inconsistency would result. The second choice is the preferred method of writing units when more than one unit is below the divisor line. Because the meter and kelvin units are located to the right of the divisor line and they are separated by a dot, both units are interpreted as being in the denominator. Sometimes, parentheses are used to group units above or below the divisor line. Units for thermal conductivity would then be written as W/(m • K). In any case, a dot or a dash should always be placed between adjacent units to separate them regardless of whether the units are above or below the divisor line. Some derived dimensions and their SI units are given in Table 5.

TABLE 5 Derived Dimensions and SI Units.

Quantity	SI Units
Acceleration	$m \cdot s^{-2}$
Angular acceleration	$rad \cdot s^{-2}$
Angular velocity	$rad \cdot s^{-1}$
Area	m^2
Concentration	$mol \cdot m^{-3}$
Density	$kg \cdot m^{-3}$
Electric field strength	$V \cdot m^{-1}$
Energy	$N \cdot m$
Entropy	$J \cdot K^{-1}$
Heat	J
Heat transfer	W
Magnetic field strength	$A \cdot m^{-1}$
Mass flow rate	$kg \cdot s^{-1}$
Moment of force	$N \cdot m$
Radiant intensity	$W \cdot sr^{-1}$
Specific energy	$J \cdot kg^{-1}$
Surface tension	$N \cdot m^{-1}$
Thermal conductivity	$W \cdot m^{-1} \cdot K^{-1}$
Velocity	$m \cdot s^{-1}$
Viscosity, dynamic	$Pa \cdot s$
Viscosity, kinematic	$m^2 \cdot s^{-1}$
Volume	m^3
Volume flow rate	$m^3 \cdot s^{-1}$
Wavelength	m
Weight	N

When a physical quantity has a numerical value that is very large or very small, it is cumbersome to write the number in standard decimal form. The general practice in engineering is to express numerical values between 0.1 and 1000 in standard decimal form. If a value cannot be expressed within this range, a *prefix* should be used. Because the SI unit system is based on powers of 10, it is more convenient to express such numbers by using prefixes. A prefix is a letter in front of a number that denotes multiples of powers of 10. For example, if the internal force in an I-beam is three million seven hundred and fifty thousand newtons, it would be awkward to write this number as 3,750,000 N. It is preferred to write the force as 3.75 MN, which is stated as "3.75 mega-newtons." The prefix "M" denotes a multiple of a million. Hence, 3.75 MN equals 3.75×10^6 N. Electrical current is a good example of a quantity represented by a small number. Suppose the current flowing in a wire is 0.0082 A. This quantity would be expressed as 8.2 mA, which is stated as "8.2 milliamperes." The prefix "m" denotes a multiple of one-thousandth, or 1×10^{-3}. A term we often hear in connection with personal computers is the storage capacity of hard disks. When personal computers first appeared in the early 1980s, most hard disks could hold around 10 or 20 MB (megabytes) of information. Nowadays, hard disks typically can hold around one thousand times that amount. Perhaps, a few years from now, the typical storage capacity of a personal computer's hard disk will be on the order of TB (terabytes). The standard prefixes for SI units are given in Table 6.

TABLE 6 Standard Prefixes for SI Units

Multiple	Exponential Form	Prefix	Prefix Symbol
1,000,000,000,000	10^{12}	tera	T
1,000,000,000	10^{9}	giga	G
1,000,000	10^{6}	mega	M
1000	10^{3}	kilo	k
0.01	10^{-2}	centi	c
0.001	10^{-3}	milli	m
0.000 001	10^{-6}	micro	μ
0.000 000 001	10^{-9}	nano	n
0.000 000 000 001	10^{-12}	pico	p

As indicated in Table 6, the most widely used SI prefixes for science and engineering quantities come in multiples of one thousand. For example, stress and pressure, which are generally large quantities for most structures and pressure vessels, are normally expressed in units of kPa, MPa, or GPa. Frequencies of electromagnetic waves such as radio, television, and telecommunications are also large numbers. Hence, they are generally expressed in units of kHz, MHz, or GHz. Electrical currents, on the other hand, are often small quantities, so they are usually expressed in units of μA or mA. Because frequencies of most electromagnetic waves are large quantities, the wavelengths of these waves are small. For example, the wavelength range of the visible light region of the electromagnetic spectrum is approximately 0.4 μm to 0.75 μm. It should be noted that the SI mass unit, kilogram (kg), is the only base unit that has a prefix.

Here are some rules on how to use SI units properly that every beginning engineering student should know:

1. A unit symbol is never written as a plural with an "s." If a unit is pluralized, the "s" may be confused with the unit second (s).
2. A period is never used after a unit symbol, unless the symbol is at the end of a sentence.
3. Do not use invented unit symbols. For example, the unit symbol for "second" is (s), not (sec), and the unit symbol for "ampere" is (A), not (amp).
4. A unit symbol is always written by using lowercase letters, with two exceptions. The first exception applies to units named after people, such as the newton (N), joule (J), and watt (W). The second exception applies to units with the prefixes M, G, and T. (See Table 6.)
5. A quantity consisting of several units must be separated by dots or dashes to avoid confusion with prefixes. For example, if a dot is not used to express the units of "meter-second" (m • s), the units could be interpreted as "millisecond" (ms).
6. An exponential power for a unit with a prefix refers to both the prefix and the unit; for example, $\text{ms}^2 = (\text{ms})^2 = \text{ms} \cdot \text{ms}$.
7. Do not use compound prefixes. For example, a "kilo MegaPascal" (kMPa) should be written as GPa, because the product of "kilo" (10^3) and "mega" (10^6) equals "giga" (10^9).
8. Put a space between the numerical value and the unit symbol.
9. Do not put a space between a prefix and a unit symbol.
10. Do not use prefixes in the denominator of composite units. For example, the units N/mm should be written as kN/m.

Table 7 provides some additional examples of these rules.

TABLE 7 Correct and Incorrect Ways of Using SI Units.

Correct	Incorrect	Rules
12.6 kg	12.6 kgs	1
450 N	450 Ns	1
36 kPa	36 kPa.	2
1.75 A	1.75 amps	1, 3
10.2 s	10.2 sec	3
20 kg	20 Kg	4
150 W	150 w.	2, 4
4.50 kg/m • s	4.50 kg/ms	5
750 GN	750 MkN	7
6 ms	6 kμs	7
800 Pa • s	800Pa • s	8
1.2 MΩ	1.2 M Ω	9
200 MPa	200 M Pa	9
150 μA	150 μ A	9
6 MN/m	6 N/μm	10

APPLICATION: DERIVING FORMULAS FROM UNIT CONSIDERATIONS

To the beginning engineering student, it can seem as if there is an infinite number of formulas to learn. Formulas contain physical quantities that have numerical values plus units. Because formulas are written as equalities, formulas must be numerically and dimensionally equivalent across the equal sign. Can this feature be used to help us derive formulas that we do not know or have forgotten? Suppose that we want to know the mass of gasoline in an automobile's gas tank. The tank has a volume of 70 L, and a handbook of fluid properties states that the density of gasoline is 736 kg/m^3. Thus, we write

$$\rho = 736 \text{ kg/m}^3 \quad V = 70 \text{ L} = 0.070 \text{ m}^3$$

If the tank is completely filled with gasoline, what is the mass of the gasoline? Suppose that we have forgotten that density is defined as mass per volume, $\rho = m/V$. Because our answer will be a mass, the unit of our answer must be kilogram (kg). Looking at the units of the input quantities, we see that if we multiply density, ρ, by volume, V, the volume unit (m^3) divides out, leaving mass (kg). Hence, the formula for mass in terms of ρ and V is

$$m = \rho V$$

so the mass of gasoline is

$$m = (736 \text{ kg/m}^3)(0.070 \text{ m}^3) = 51.5 \text{ kg}$$

PROFESSIONAL SUCCESS: USING SI UNITS IN EVERYDAY LIFE

The SI unit system is used commercially to a limited extent in the United States, so the average person does not know the highway speed limit in kilometers per hour, his or her weight in newtons, atmospheric pressure in kilopascals, or the outdoor air temperature in kelvin or degrees Celsius. It is ironic that the leading industrialized nation on earth has yet to embrace this international standard. Admittedly, American beverage containers routinely show the volume of the liquid product in liters (L) or milliliters (mL), gasoline pumps often show liters of gasoline delivered, speedometers may indicate speed in kilometers per hour (km/h), and automobile tires indicate the proper inflation pressure in kilopascals (kPa) on the sidewall. On each of these products, and many others like them, a corresponding English unit is written along side the SI unit. The beverage container shows pints or quarts, the gasoline pump shows gallons, speedometers show miles per hour, and tires show pounds per square inch. Dual labeling of SI and English units on U.S. products are supposed to help people learn the SI system, "weaning" them from the antiquated English system in anticipation of the time when a full conversion to SI units occurs. This transition is analogous to the process of incrementally quitting smoking. Rather than quitting "cold turkey," we employ nicotine patches, gums, and other substitutes until our habit is broken. So, you may ask, "Why don't we make the total conversion now? Is it as painful as quitting smoking suddenly?" It probably is. As you might guess, the problem is largely an economic one. A complete conversion to SI units may not occur until we are willing to pay the price in actual dollars. People could learn the SI unit system fairly quickly if the conversion were done suddenly, but an enormous financial commitment would have to be made.

As long as dual product labeling of units is employed in the United States, most people will tend to ignore the SI unit and look only at the English unit, the unit with which they are most familiar. In U.S. engineering schools, SI units are emphasized. Therefore, the engineering student is not the average person on the street who does not know, or know how to calculate, his or her weight in newtons. So, what can engineering students in the United States do to accelerate the conversion process? A good place to start is with yourself. Start using SI units in your everyday life. When you make a purchase at the grocery store, look only at the SI unit on the label. Learn by inspection how many milliliters of liquid product are packaged in your favorite sized container. Abandon the use of inches, feet, yards, and miles as much as possible. How many kilometers lie between your home and school? What is 65 miles per hour in kilometers per hour? What is the mass of your automobile in kilograms? Determine your height in meters, your mass in kilograms, and your weight in newtons. How long is your arm in centimeters? What is your waist size in centimeters? What is the current outdoor air temperature in degrees Celsius? Most fast-food restaurants offer a "quarter pounder" on their menu. It turns out that 1 N = 0.2248 lb, almost a quarter pound. On the next visit to your favorite fast-food place, order a "newton burger" and fries. (See Figure 8.)

Figure 8. An engineering student orders lunch (art by Kathryn Hagen).

PRACTICE!

1. A structural engineer states that an I-beam in a truss has a design stress of "five million, six hundred thousand pascals." Write this stress, using the appropriate SI unit prefix.

   Answer: 5.6 MPa
2. The power cord on an electric string trimmer carries a current of 5.2A. How many milliamperes is this? How many microamperes?

   Answer: 5.2×10^3 mA, 5.2×10^6 μA
3. Write the pressure 13.8 GPa in scientific notation.

   Answer: 13.8×10^9 Pa
4. Write the voltage 0.00255 V, using the appropriate SI unit prefix.

   Answer: 2.55 mV
5. In the following list, various quantities are written using SI units incorrectly. Write the quantities, using the correct form of SI units.
   a. 4.5 mw
   b. 8.75 M pa
   c. 200 Joules/sec
   d. 20 W/m^2 K
   e. 3 Amps

   Answer:
   a. 4.5 mW
   b. 8.75 MPa
   c. 200 J/s
   d. 20 W/m$^2\cdot$K
   e. 3 A

5 ENGLISH UNITS

The English unit system is known by various names. Sometimes it is referred to as the United States Customary System (USCS), the British System or the Foot-Pound-Second (FPS) system. The English unit system is still used extensively in the United States even though the rest of the industrialized world, including Great Britain, has adopted the SI unit system. English units have a long and colorful history. In ancient times, measures of length were based on human dimensions. The foot started out as the actual length of a man's foot. Because not all men were the same size, the foot varied in length by as much as three or four inches. Once the ancients started using feet and arms for measuring distance, it was only a matter of time before they began using hands and fingers. The unit of length that we refer to today as the inch was originally the width of a man's thumb. The inch was also once defined as the distance between the tip to the first joint of the forefinger. Twelve times that distance made one foot. Three times the length of a foot was the distance from the tip of a man's nose to the end of his outstretched arm. This distance closely approximates what we refer to today as the yard. Two yards equaled a fathom, which was defined as the distance across a man's outstretched arms. Half a yard was the 18-inch cubit, which was called a span. Half a span was referred to as a hand.

The pound, which uses the symbol *lb*, is named after the ancient Roman unit of weight called the libra. The British Empire retained this symbol into modern times. Today, there are actually two kinds of pound units, one for mass and one for weight and force. The first unit is called pound-mass (lb_m), and the second is called pound-force (lb_f). Because mass and weight are not the same quantity, the units lb_f and lb_m are different.

As discussed previously, the seven base dimensions are length, mass, time, temperature, electric current, amount of substance, and luminous intensity. These base dimensions, along with their corresponding English units, are given in Table 8. As with SI units, English units are not capitalized. The slug, which has no abbreviated symbol, is the mass unit in the English system, but the pound-mass (lb_m) is frequently used. Electric current is based on SI units of meter and newton, and luminous intensity is based on SI units of watt. Hence, these two base dimensions do not have English units per se, and these quantities are rarely used in combination with other English units.

TABLE 8 Base Dimensions and Their English Units.

Quantity	Unit	Symbol
Length	foot	ft
Mass	slug(1)	slug
Time	second	s
Temperature	rankine	°R
Electric current	ampere(2)	A
Amount of substance	mole	mol
Luminous intensity	candela(2)	cd

(1) The unit pound-mass (lb_m) is also used. 1 slug = 32.174 lb_m.
(2) There are no English units for electrical current and luminous intensity. The SI units are given here for completeness only.

Recall that derived dimensions consist of a combination of base and supplementary dimensions. Table 9 summarizes some common derived dimensions expressed in English units. Note that Table 9 is the English counterpart of the SI version given by Table 5. The most notable English unit with a special name is the British thermal unit (Btu), a unit of energy. One Btu is defined as the energy required to change the temperature of 1 lb_m of water at a temperature of 68°F by 1°F. One Btu is approximately the energy released by the complete burning of a single kitchen match. The magnitudes of the kilojoule and Btu are almost equal (1 Btu = 1.055 kJ). Unlike the kelvin (K), the temperature unit in the SI system, the rankine (°R) employs a degree symbol as do the Celsius (°C) and Fahrenheit (°F) units. The same rules for writing SI units apply for English units with one major exception: *Prefixes are generally not used with English units.* Thus, units such as kft (kilo-foot), Mslug (megaslug), and GBtu (gigaBtu) should not be used. Prefixes are reserved for SI units. Two exceptions are the units ksi, which refers to a stress of 1000 psi (pounds per square inch), and kip, which is a special name for a force of 1000 lb_f (pound-force).

There are some non-SI units that are routinely used in the United States and elsewhere. Table 10 summarizes some of these units and provides an equivalent value in the SI system. The inch is a common length unit, being found on virtually every student's ruler and carpenter's tape measure in the United States. There are exactly 2.54 centimeters per inch. Inches are still used as the primary length unit in many engineering companies. The yard is commonly used for measuring cloth, carpets, and loads of concrete (cubic yards), as well as ball advancement on the American football field. The ton is used in numerous industries, including shipping, construction, and transportation. Time subdivisions on clocks are measured in hours, minutes, and seconds. Radians and degrees are the most commonly used units for plane angles, whereas minutes and seconds are primarily used in navigational applications when referring to latitude and longitude on the earth's surface. The liter has made a lot of headway into the American culture, being found on beverage and food containers and many gasoline pumps. Virtually every American has seen the liter unit on a product, and many know that there are about four liters in a gallon (actually, 1 gal = 3.7854 L), but fewer people know that 1000 L = 1 m^3.

TABLE 9 Derived Dimensions and English Units.

Quantity	English Units
Acceleration	$ft \cdot s^{-2}$
Angular acceleration	$rad \cdot s^{-2}$
Angular velocity	$rad \cdot s^{-1}$
Area	ft^2
Concentration	$mol \cdot ft^{-3}$
Density	$slug \cdot ft^{-3}$
Electric field strength	$V \cdot ft^{-1}$
Energy	Btu
Entropy	$Btu \cdot slug^{-1} \cdot °R^{-1}$
Force	lb_f
Heat	Btu
Heat transfer	$Btu \cdot s^{-1}$
Magnetic field strength	$A \cdot ft^{-1}$
ass flow rate	$slug \cdot s^{-1}$
Moment of force	$lb_f \cdot ft$
Radiant intensity	$Btu \cdot s^{-1} \cdot sr^{-1}$
Specific energy	$Btu \cdot slug^{-1}$
Surface tension	$lb_f \cdot ft^{-1}$
Thermal conductivity	$Btu \cdot s^{-1} \cdot ft^{-1} \cdot °R$
Velocity	$ft \cdot s^{-1}$
Viscosity, dynamic	$slug \cdot ft^{-1} \cdot s^{-1}$
Viscosity, kinematic	$ft^2 \cdot s^{-1}$
Volume	ft^3
Volume flow rate	$ft^3 \cdot s^{-1}$
Wavelength	ft

TABLE 10 Non-SI Units Commonly Used in the United States.

Quantity	Unit Name	Symbol	SI Equivalent
Length	inch	in	0.0254 m[1]
	yard	yd	0.9144 m (36 in)
Mass	metric ton	t	1000 kg
	short ton	t	907.18 kg (2000 lb_m)
Time	minute	min	60 s
	hour	h	3600 s
	day	d	86,400 s
Plane angle	degree	°	$\pi/180$ rad
	minute	'	$\pi/10{,}800$ rad
	second	"	$\pi/648{,}000$ rad
Volume	liter	L	10^{-3} m^3
Land area	hectare	ha	10^4 m^2
Energy	electron-volt	eV	1.602177×10^{-19} J

[1]Exact conversion

6 MASS AND WEIGHT

The concepts of *mass* and *weight* are fundamental to the proper use of dimensions and units in engineering analysis. Mass is one of the seven base dimensions used in science and engineering. Mass is a base dimension because it cannot be broken down into more fundamental dimensions. **Mass** is defined as a *quantity of matter*. This simple definition of mass may be expanded by exploring its basic properties. All matter possesses mass. The magnitude of a given mass is a measure of its resistance to a change in velocity. This property of matter is called *inertia*. A large mass offers more resistance to a change in velocity than a small mass, so a large mass has a greater inertia than a small mass. Mass may be considered in another way. Because all matter has mass, all matter exerts a gravitational attraction on other matter. Shortly after formulating his three laws of motion, Sir Isaac Newton postulated a law governing the gravitational attraction between two masses. Newton's law of universal gravitation is stated mathematically as

$$F = G\frac{m_1 m_2}{r^2} \tag{1}$$

where

F = gravitational force between masses (N)
G = universal gravitational constant = $6.673 \times 10^{-11}\ \text{m}^3/\text{kg} \cdot \text{s}^2$
m_1 = mass of body 1 (kg)
m_2 = mass of body 2 (kg)
r = distance between the centers of the two masses (m)

According to Equation (1), between any two masses there exists an attractive gravitational force whose magnitude varies inversely as the square of the distance between the masses. Because Newton's law of universal gravitation applies to *any* two masses, let's apply Equation (1) to a body resting on the surface of the earth. Accordingly, we let $m_1 = m_e$, the mass of the earth and $m_2 = m$, the mass of the body. The distance, r, between the body and the earth may be taken as the mean radius of the earth, r_e. The quantities m_e and r_e have the approximate values

$$m_e = 5.979 \times 10^{24}\ \text{kg} \qquad r_e = 6.378 \times 10^6\ \text{m}$$

Thus, we have

$$\begin{aligned} F &= G\frac{m_e m}{r_e^2} \\ &= \frac{(6.673 \times 10^{-11}\ \text{m}^3/\text{kg} \cdot \text{s}^2)(5.979 \times 10^{24}\ \text{kg})}{(6.378 \times 10^6\ \text{m})^2} m \\ &= (9.808\ \text{m/s}^2)\ m \end{aligned}$$

We can see that upon substituting values, the term Gm_e/r_e^2 yields a number of approximately 9.81 m/s^2, the standard acceleration of gravity on the earth's surface. Redefining this term as g, and letting $F = W$, we express the law of universal gravitation in a special form as

$$W = mg \tag{2}$$

where

W = weight of body (N)
m = mass of body (kg)
g = standard gravitational acceleration = 9.81 m/s^2

This derivation clearly shows the difference between mass and weight. We may therefore state the definition of **weight** as *a gravitational force exerted on a body by the earth*. Because mass is defined as a quantity of matter, the mass of a body is independent of its location in the universe. A body has the same mass whether it is located on the earth, the moon, Mars, or in outer space. The weight of the body, however, depends on its location. The mass of an 80 kg astronaut is the same whether or not he is on earth or in orbit about the earth. The astronaut weighs approximately 785 N on the earth, but while in orbit he is "weightless." His weight is zero while he orbits the earth, because he is continually "falling" toward earth. A similar weightless or "zero-g" condition is experienced by a skydiver as he free falls prior to opening the parachute.

The greatest source of confusion about mass and weight to the beginning engineering student is not the physical concept, but the units used to express each quantity. To see how units of mass and weight relate to each other, we employ a well-known scientific principle, **Newton's second law** of motion. Newton's second law of motion states that *a body of mass, m, acted upon by an unbalanced force, F, experiences an acceleration, a, that has the same direction of the force and a magnitude that is directly proportional to the force*. Stated mathematically, this law is

$$F = ma \tag{3}$$

where

F = force (N)
m = mass (kg)
a = acceleration (m/s^2)

Note that this relation resembles Equation (2). Weight is a particular type of force, and acceleration due to gravity is a particular type of acceleration, so Equation (2) is a special case of Newton's second law, given by Equation (3). In the SI unit system, the newton (N) is *defined* as the force that will accelerate a 1-kg mass at a rate of 1 m/s^2. Hence, we may write Newton's second law dimensionally as

$$1\ \text{N} = 1\ \text{kg} \cdot \text{m/s}^2$$

In the English unit system, the pound-force (lb_f) is *defined* as the force that will accelerate a 1-slug mass at a rate of 1 ft/s^2. Hence, we may write Newton's second law dimensionally as

$$1\ \text{lb}_\text{f} = 1\ \text{slug} \cdot \text{ft/s}^2$$

See Figure 9 for an illustration of Newton's second law. Confusion arises from the careless interchange of the English mass unit, pound-mass (lb_m), with the English force unit, pound-force (lb_f). These units are not the same thing! In accordance with our definitions of mass and weight, pound-mass refers to a quantity of matter, whereas pound-force refers to a force or weight. In order to write Newton's second law in terms of pound-mass instead of slug, we rewrite Equation (3) as

$$F = \frac{ma}{g_c} \tag{4}$$

where g_c is a constant that is required to make Newton's second law dimensionally consistent when mass, m, is expressed in lb_m, rather than slug. As stated previously, the English unit for force is lb_f, the English unit for acceleration is ft/s^2, and, as indicated in

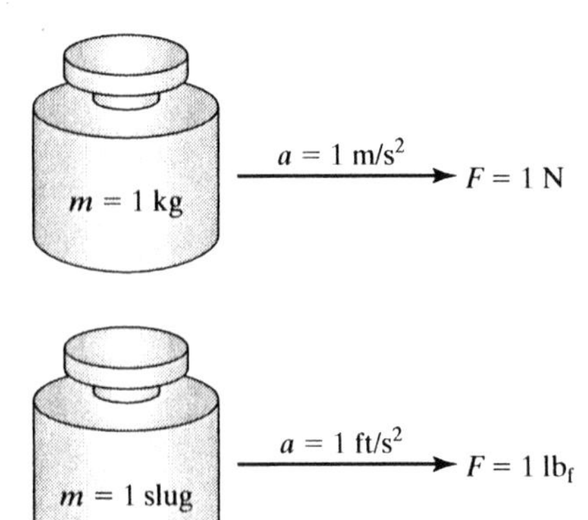

Figure 9. Definitions of the force units newton (N) and pound-force (lb_f).

Table 8, 1 slug = 32.174 lb_m. Thus, the constant g_c is

$$g_c = \frac{ma}{F} = \frac{(32.174\ lb_m)(ft/s^2)}{lb_f} = 32.174 \frac{lb_m \cdot ft}{lb_f \cdot s^2}$$

This value is usually rounded to

$$g_c = 32.2 \frac{lb_m \cdot ft}{lb_f \cdot s^2}$$

Note that g_c has the same numerical value as g, the standard acceleration of gravity on the earth's surface. Newton's second law as expressed by Equation (4) is dimensionally consistent when the English unit of mass, lb_m, is used.

To verify that Equation (4) works, we recall that the pound-force is defined as the force that will accelerate a 1-slug mass at a rate of 1 ft/s². Recognizing that 1 slug = 32.2 lb_m, we have

$$F = \frac{ma}{g_c} = \frac{(32.2\ lb_m)(1\ ft/s^2)}{32.2 \frac{lb_m \cdot ft}{lb_f \cdot s^2}} = 1\ lb_f$$

Note that in this expression, all the units, except lb_f, cancel. Hence, the pound-force (lb_f) is *defined* as the force that will accelerate a 32.2-lb_m mass at a rate of 1 ft/s². Therefore, we may write Newton's second law dimensionally as

$$1\ lb_f = 32.2\ lb_m \cdot ft/s^2$$

To have dimensional consistency when English units are involved, Equation (4) *must* be used when mass, m, is expressed in lb_m. When mass is expressed in slug, however, the use of g_c in Newton's second law is not required for dimensional consistency because 1 lb_f is already defined as the force that will accelerate a 1-slug mass at a rate of 1 ft/s^2. Furthermore, because 1 N is already defined as the force that will accelerate a 1-kg mass at a rate of 1 m/s^2, the use of g_c is not required for dimensional consistency in the SI unit system. *Thus, Equation (3) suffices for all calculations, except for those in which mass is expressed in lb$_m$; in that case, Equation (4) must be used.* However, Equation (4) may be universally used when recognizing that the numerical value and units for g_c can be defined such that any consistent unit system will work. For example, substituting $F = 1$ N, $m = 1$ kg, and $a = 1$ m/s^2 into Equation (4) and solving for g_c we obtain

$$g_c = \frac{1\ \text{kg} \cdot \text{m}}{\text{N} \cdot \text{s}^2}$$

Since the numerical value of g_c is 1, we can successfully use Equation (3) as long as we recognize that 1 N is the force that will accelerate a 1-kg mass at a rate of 1 m/s^2.

Sometimes, the units pound-mass (lb$_m$) and pound-force (lb$_f$) are casually interchanged because a body with a mass of 1 lb$_m$ has a weight of 1 lb$_f$ (i.e., the mass and weight are *numerically equivalent*). Let's see how this works: By definition, a body with a mass of 32.2 lb$_m$ (1 slug) when accelerated at a rate of 1 ft/s^2 has a weight of 1 lb$_f$. Therefore, using Newton's second law in the form, $W = mg$, we can also state that a body with a mass of 1 lb$_m$, when accelerated at a rate of 32.2 ft/s^2 (the standard value of g), has a weight of 1 lb$_f$. Our rationale for making such a statement is that we maintained the same numerical value on the right side of Newton's second law by assigning the mass, m, a value of 1 lb$_m$ and the gravitational acceleration, g, the standard value of 32.2 ft/s^2. The numerical values of the mass and weight are equal even though a pound-mass and a pound-force are conceptually different quantities. It must be emphasized, however, that mass in pound-mass and weight in pound-force are numerically equivalent only when the standard value, $g = 32.2$ ft/s^2, is used. See Figure 10 for an illustration. The next example illustrates the use of g_c.

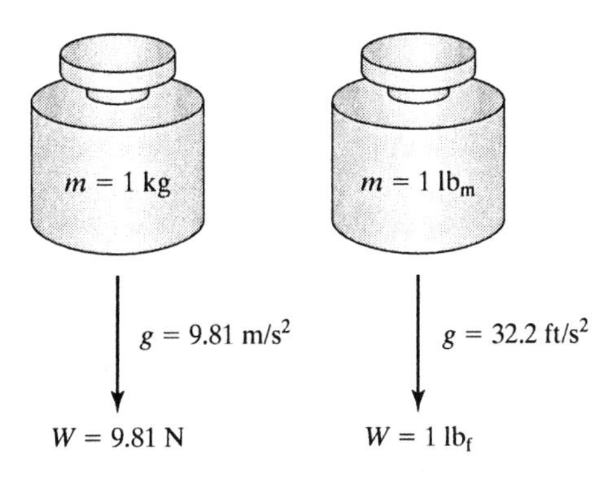

Figure 10. Definitions of weight for the standard value of gravitational acceleration.

EXAMPLE 4

Find the weight of some objects with the following masses:

(a) 50 slug
(b) 50 lb$_m$
(c) 75 kg

SOLUTION

To find weight, we use Newton's second law, where the acceleration, a, is the standard acceleration of gravity, $g = 9.81 \text{ m/s}^2 = 32.2 \text{ ft/s}^2$.

(a) The mass unit, slug, is the standard unit for mass in the English unit system. The weight is

$$\begin{aligned} W &= mg \\ &= (50 \text{ slug})(32.2 \text{ ft/s}^2) = 1{,}610 \text{ lb}_f \end{aligned}$$

(b) When mass is expressed in terms of lb_m, we must use Equation (4):

$$W = \frac{mg}{g_c} = \frac{(50 \text{ lb}_m)(32.2 \text{ ft/s}^2)}{32.2 \dfrac{\text{lb}_m \cdot \text{ft}}{\text{lb}_f \cdot \text{s}^2}} = 50 \text{ lb}_f$$

Note that the mass and weight are numerically equivalent. This is true only in cases where the standard value of g is used, which means that an object with a mass of x lb_m will always have a weight of x lb_f on the earth's surface.

(c) The mass unit, kg, is the standard unit for mass in the SI unit system. The weight is

$$\begin{aligned} W &= mg \\ &= (75 \text{ kg})(9.81 \text{ m/s}^2) = 736 \text{ N} \end{aligned}$$

Alternatively, we can find weight by using Equation (4):

$$W = \frac{mg}{g_c} = \frac{(75 \text{ kg})(9.81 \text{ m/s}^2)}{1 \dfrac{\text{kg} \cdot \text{m}}{\text{N} \cdot \text{s}^2}} = 736 \text{ N}$$

■

Now that we understand the difference between mass and weight and know how to use mass and weight units in the SI and English systems, let's revisit the astronaut we discussed earlier. (See Figure 11.) The mass of the astronaut is 80 kg, which equals about 5.48 slug. His mass does not change, regardless of where he ventures. Prior to departing

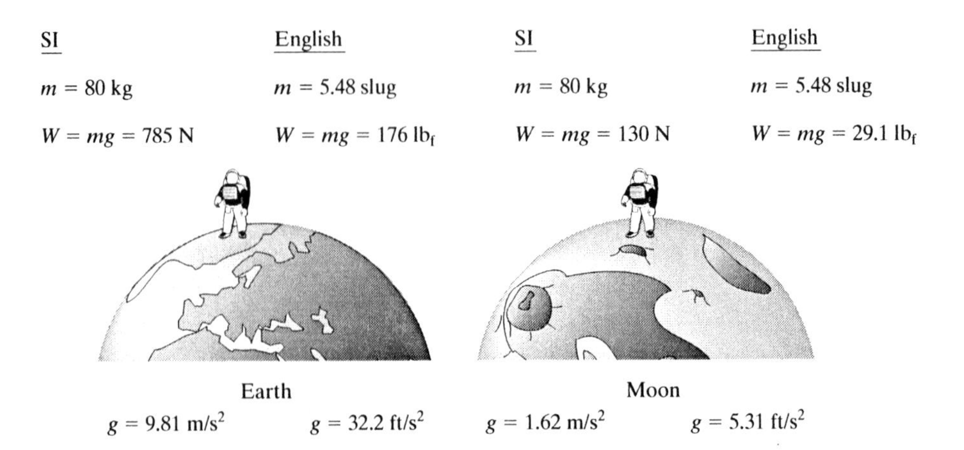

Figure 11. An astronaut's mass and weight on the earth and moon.

on a trip to the moon, he weighs in at 785 N (176 lb_f). What is the mass of the astronaut in pound-mass? Three days later, his vehicle lands on the moon, and he begins constructing a permanent base for future planetary missions. The mass of the moon is about one-sixth that of the earth, so the value of the gravitational acceleration on the moon is only 1.62 m/s^2(5.31 ft/s^2). The astronaut's mass is still 80 kg, but his weight is only 130 N (29.1 lb_f) due to the smaller value of g. Is the mass and weight of the astronaut in pound-mass and pound-force numerically equivalent? No, because the standard value of g is not used.

EXAMPLE 5

Special hoists are used in automotive repair shops to lift engines. As illustrated in Figure 12, a 200-kg engine is suspended in a fixed position by a chain attached to the cross member of an engine hoist. Neglecting the weight of the chain itself, what is the tension in portion AD of the chain?

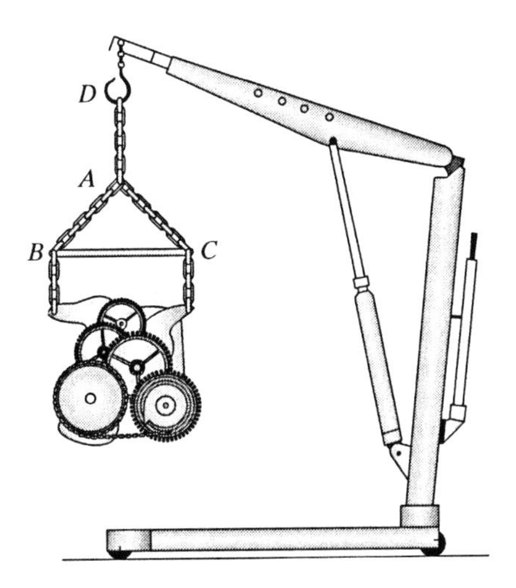

Figure 12. Engine hoist for Example 5.

SOLUTION

This example is a simple problem in engineering statics. Statics is the branch of engineering mechanics that deals with forces acting on bodies at rest. The engine is held by the chain in a fixed position, so clearly the engine is at rest; that is, it is not in motion. This problem can be solved by recognizing that the entire weight of the engine is supported by portion AD of the chain. (The tension in portions AB and AC could also be calculated, but a thorough equilibrium analysis would be required.) Hence, the tension, which is a force that tends to elongate the chain, is equivalent to the weight of the engine. Using Equation (2), we have

$$F = mg$$
$$= (200 \text{ kg})(9.81 \text{ m/s}^2) = 1962 \text{ N}$$

Therefore, the tension in portion AD of the chain is 1962 N, the weight of the engine.

PRACTICE!

1. It has been said that you do not fully understand a basic technical concept, unless you can explain it in terms simple enough that a second grader can understand it. Write an explanation of the difference between mass and weight for a second grader.
2. Which is larger, a slug or a pound-mass?

   Answer: slug
3. Consider a professional linebacker who weighs 310 lb_f. What is his mass in slugs?

   Answer: 9.63 slug
4. A rock (ρ = 2300 kg/m^3) is suspended by a single rope. Assuming the rock to be spherical, with a radius of 15 cm, what is the tension in the rope?

   Answer: 319 N

7 UNIT CONVERSIONS

Although the SI unit system is the international standard, English units are in widespread use in the United States. Americans as a whole are much more familiar with English units than SI units. Students of science and engineering in U.S. schools primarily use SI units in their course work because most textbooks and the professors who teach out of them, stress SI units. Unfortunately, when students of these disciplines go about their day-to-day activities outside of the academic environment, they tend to slip back into the English unit mode along with everyone else. It seems as if students have a "unit switch" in their brains. When they are in the classroom or laboratory, the switch is turned to the "SI position." When they are at home, in the grocery store, or driving their car, the switch is turned to the "English position." Ideally, there should be no unit switch at all, but as long as science and engineering programs at colleges and universities stress SI units and American culture stresses English units, our cerebral unit switch toggles. In this section, a systematic method for converting units between the SI and English systems is given.

A **unit conversion** enables us to convert from one unit system to the other by using **conversion factors**. A conversion factor is an equivalency ratio that has a *unit value* of 1. Stated another way, a conversion factor simply relates the same physical quantity in two different unit systems. For example, 0.0254 m and 1 in are equivalent length quantities because 0.0254 m = 1 in. The ratio of these two quantities has a unit value of 1 because they are physically the same quantity. Obviously, the numerical value of the ratio is not 1, but depends on the numerical value of each individual quantity. Thus, when we multiply a given quantity by one or more conversion factors, we alter only the numerical value of the result and not its dimension. Table 11 summarizes some common conversion factors used in engineering analysis. A more extensive listing of unit conversions is given in Appendix B.

A systematic procedure for converting a quantity from one unit system to the other is as follows:

Unit Conversion Procedure

1. Write the given quantity in terms of its numerical value and units. Use a horizontal line to divide units in the numerator (upstairs) from those in the denominator (downstairs).
2. Determine the units *to* which you want to make the conversion.

TABLE 11 Some Common SI-to-English Unit Conversions

Quantity	Unit Conversion
Acceleration	$1\ m/s^2 = 3.2808\ ft/s^2$
Area	$1\ m^2 = 10.7636\ ft^2 = 1550\ in^2$
Density	$1\ kg/m^3 = 0.06243\ lb_m/ft^3$
Energy, work, heat	$1055.06\ J = 1\ Btu = 252\ cal$
Force	$1\ N = 0.22481\ lb_f$
Length	$1\ m = 3.2808\ ft = 39.370\ in$
	$0.0254\ m = 1\ in^{(1)}$
Mass	$1\ kg = 2.20462\ lb_m = 0.06852\ slug$
Power	$1\ W = 3.4121\ Btu/h$
	$745.7\ W = 1\ hp$
Pressure	$1\ kPa = 20.8855\ lb_f/ft^2 = 0.14504\ lb_f/in^2$
Specific heat	$1\ kJ/kg \cdot °C = 0.2388\ Btu/lb_m \cdot °F$
Temperature	$T(K) = T(°C) + 273.16 = T(°R)/1.8 = [T(°F) + 459.67]/1.8$
Velocity	$1\ m/s = 2.2369\ mi/h$

(1) Exact conversion

3. Multiply the given quantity by one or more conversion factors that, upon cancellation of units, leads to the desired units. Use a horizontal line to divide the units in the numerator and denominator of each conversion factor.
4. Draw a line through all canceled units.
5. Perform the numerical computations on a calculator, retaining infinite decimal place accuracy until the end of the computations.
6. Write the numerical value of the converted quantity by using the desired number of significant figures (three significant figures is standard practice for engineering) with the desired units.

Examples 6, 7, and 8 illustrate the unit conversion procedure.

EXAMPLE 6

An engineering student is late for an early morning class, so she runs across campus at a speed of 9 mi/h. Determine her speed in units of m/s.

SOLUTION

The given quantity, expressed in English units, is 9 mi/h, but we want our answer to be in SI units of m/s. Thus, we need a conversion factor between mi and m and a conversion factor between h and s. To better illustrate the unit conversion procedure, we will use two length conversion factors rather than one. Following the procedure outlined, we have

$$\underbrace{9\frac{\cancel{mi}}{\cancel{h}}}_{\text{given quantity}} \times \underbrace{\frac{5280\ \cancel{ft}}{1\ \cancel{mi}} \times \frac{1\ m}{3.2808\ \cancel{ft}} \times \frac{1\ \cancel{h}}{3600\ s}}_{\text{conversion factors}} = \underbrace{4.02\frac{m}{s}}_{\text{answer}}$$

The key aspect of the unit conversion process is that the conversion factors must be written such that the appropriate units in the conversion factors cancel those in the given quantity. If we had inverted the conversion factor between ft and mi, writing it instead as 1 mi/5280 ft, the mi unit would not cancel and our unit conversion exercise would not work, because we would end up with units of mi^2 in the numerator. Similarly, the conversion factor between m and ft was written such that the ft unit canceled the ft unit in the first conversion factor. Also, the conversion factor between h and s was written such that the h unit canceled with the h unit in the given quantity. Writing conversion factors with the units in the proper locations, "upstairs" or "downstairs," requires some practice, but after doing several conversion problems, the correct placement of units will become second nature to you. Note that our answer is expressed in three significant figures.

EXAMPLE 7

Lead has one of the highest densities of all the pure metals. The density of lead is 11,340 kg/m^3. What is the density of lead in units of lb$_m$/in^3?

SOLUTION

A direct conversion factor from kg/m^3 to lbm/in^3 may be available, but to illustrate an important aspect of converting units with exponents, we will use a series of conversion factors for each length and mass unit. Thus, we write our unit conversion as

$$11{,}340 \frac{\text{kg}}{\text{m}^3} \times \frac{(1\ \text{m})^3}{(3.2808\ \text{ft})^3} \times \frac{(1\ \text{ft})^3}{(12\ \text{in})^3} \times \frac{2.20462\ \text{lb}_\text{m}}{1\ \text{kg}} = 0.410\ \text{lb}_\text{m}/\text{in}^3$$

We used two length conversion factors, one factor between m and ft and the other between ft and in. But the given quantity is a density than has a volume unit. When performing unit conversions involving exponents, *both* the numerical value and the unit must be raised to the exponent. A common error that students make is to raise the unit to the exponent, which properly cancels units, but to forget to raise the numerical value also. Failure to raise the numerical value to the exponent will lead to the wrong numerical answer even though the units in the answer will be correct. Using the direct conversion factor, we obtain the same result:

$$11{,}340\ \text{kg/m}^3 \times \frac{(3.6127 \times 10^{-5}\ \text{lb}_\text{m}/\text{in}^3)}{1\ \text{kg/m}^3} = 0.410\ \text{lb}_\text{m}/\text{in}^3$$

EXAMPLE 8

Specific heat is defined as the energy required to raise the temperature of a unit mass of a substance by one degree. Pure aluminum has a specific heat of approximately 900 J/kg · °C. Convert this value to units of Btu/lb$_m$ · °F.

SOLUTION

By following the unit conversion procedure, we write the given quantity and then multiply it by the appropriate conversion factors, which can be found in Appendix B:

$$\frac{900\ \text{J}}{\text{kg} \cdot {}^\circ\text{C}} \times \frac{1\ \text{Btu}}{1055.06\ \text{J}} \times \frac{1\ \text{kg}}{2.20462\ \text{lb}_\text{m}} \times \frac{1^\circ\text{C}}{1.8^\circ\text{F}} = 0.215\ \text{Btu/lb}_\text{m} \cdot {}^\circ\text{F}$$

The temperature unit, °C, in the original quantity has a unique interpretation. Because specific heat is the energy required to raise a unit mass of a substance by one degree, the temperature unit in this quantity denotes a temperature *change*, not an absolute temperature value. A temperature change of 1°C is equivalent to a temperature change of 1.8°F. Stated another way, a change of one degree on the Fahrenheit scale is 1.8 times a change of one degree on the Celsius scale, as given by the temperature difference conversion factor, $\Delta T(^\circ\text{C}) = \Delta T(^\circ\text{F})/1.8$. Other thermal properties, such as thermal conductivity, involve the same temperature change interpretation. See problem 39, at the end of this chapter, for reference.

This example can also be done by applying a single conversion factor 1 kJ/kg · °C = 0.2388 Btu/lb$_m$ · °F, which yields the same result.

PROFESSIONAL SUCCESS: UNIT CONVERSIONS AND CALCULATORS

Scientific pocket calculators have evolved from simple electronic versions of adding machines to complex portable computers. Today's high-end scientific calculators have numerous capabilities, including programming, graphing, numerical methods, and symbolic mathematics. Most scientific calculators also have an extensive compilation of conversion factors either burned into a chip within the calculator itself or available as a plug-in application module. Why, then, should students learn to do unit conversions by hand when calculators will do the work? This question lies at the root of a more fundamental question: Why should students learn to do *any* computational task by hand when calculators or computers will do the work? Is it because "in the old days" students and practicing engineers did not have the luxury of highly sophisticated computational tools, so professors, who perhaps lived in the "old days," force their students to do things the old fashioned way? Not really.

Students will always need to learn engineering by *thinking* and *reasoning* their way through a problem, regardless of whether that problem is a unit conversion or a stress calculation in a machine component. Computers, and the software that runs on them, do not replace the thinking process. The calculator, like the computer, should never become a "black box" to the student. A black box is a mysterious device whose inner workings are largely unknown, but that, nonetheless, provides output for every input supplied. By the time you graduate with an engineering degree, or certainly by the time you have a few years of professional engineering practice under your belt, you will come to realize that a calculator program or computer software package exists for solving almost any conceivable type of engineering problem. This does not mean that you need to learn every one of these programs and software packages. It means that you should become proficient in the use of those computational tools that pertain to your particular engineering field *after* learning the underlying basis for each. By all means, use a calculator to perform unit conversions, but *first* know how to do them by hand, so you gain confidence in your own computational skills and have a way of verifying the results of your calculator.

PRACTICE!

1. A microswitch is an electrical switch that requires only a small force to operate it. If a microswitch is activated by a 0.25-oz force, what is the force in units of N that will activate it?
   Answer: 0.0695 N
2. At room temperature, water has a density of about 62.4 lb_m/ft^3. Convert this value to units of $slug/in^3$ and kg/m^3.
   Answer: 1.12×10^{-3} $slug/in^3$, 999.5 kg/m^3
3. At launch, the Saturn V rocket that carried astronauts to the moon developed five million pounds of thrust. What is the thrust in units of MN?
   Answer: 22.2 MN
4. Standard incandescent light bulbs produce more heat than light. Assuming that a typical house has twenty 60-W bulbs that are continuously on, how much heat in units of Btu/h is supplied to the house from light bulbs if 90 percent of the energy produced by the bulbs is in the form of heat?
   Answer: 3685 Btu/h
5. Certain properties of animal (including human) tissue can be approximated by using those of water. Using the density of water at room temperature, $\rho = 62.4$ lb_m/ft^3, calculate the weight of a human male by approximating him as a cylinder with a length and diameter of 6 ft and 1 ft, respectively.
   Answer: 294 lb_f
6. The standard frequency for electrical power in the United States is 60 Hz. For an electrical device that operates on this power, how many times does the current alternate during a year?
   Answer: 1.89×10^9

KEY TERMS

base dimension
conversion factors
derived dimension
dimension
dimensionally consistent
English unit system
mass
Newton's second law
physical standards
SI unit system
unit
unit conversion
weight

REFERENCES

Cardarelli, F., *Encyclopaedia of Scientific Units, Weights and Measures: Their SI Equivalences and Origins*, 3d ed., NY: Springer-Verlag, 2003.
Lewis, R., *Engineering Quantities and Systems of Units*, NY: Halsted Press, 1972.
Lide, D.R., Editor, *CRC Handbook of Chemistry and Physics*, 84th ed. Boca Raton, FL: CRC Press, 2003.

Problems

1. For the following dimensional equations, find the base dimensions of the parameter K:

   a. $[M][L][t]^{-2} = k[M][L]^{-1}[t]^{-2}$
   b. $[M][L][t]^{-2}[L]^{-1} = k[L][t]^{-3}$
   c. $[L]^{2}[t]^{-2} = k[M]^{4}[T]^{2}$
   d. $[M][L]^{2}[t]^{-3} = k[L][T]$
   e. $[N][L][L]^{3}k = [T]^{2}[M]^{-2}[L]$
   f. $[M][I]^{2}k = [N][T][M]^{-3}[L]^{-1}$
   g. $[I][L]^{2}[t] = k^{2}[M]^{4}[t]^{2}$
   h. $k^{3}[T]^{6}[M]^{3}[L]^{-5} = [T]^{-3}[t]^{-6}[L]$
   i. $[T]^{-1/2}[L]^{-1}[I]^{2} = k^{-1/2}[t]^{4}[T]^{-5/2}[L]^{-3}$
   j. $[M][L][t]^{-2} = [M][L][t]^{-2}\sin(k[L]^{-2}[M]^{-1})$
   k. $[T]^{2}[N] = [T]^{2}[N]\ln(k[N][T]^{-1})$

2. Is the following dimensional equation dimensionally consistent? Explain.

$$[M][L] = [M][L]\cos([L][t])$$

3. Is the following dimensional equation dimensionally consistent? Explain.

$$[t]^{2}[L][T] = [t][L][T]\log([t][t]^{-1})$$

4. Is the following dimensional equation dimensionally consistent? Explain.

$$[T][N][T] = [T][N][T]\exp([M][M]^{-1})$$

5. In the following list, various quantities are written using SI units incorrectly: Write the quantities, using the correct form of SI units.

   a. 10.6 secs
   b. 4.75 amp
   c. 120 M hz

d. 2.5 kw
e. 0.00846 kg/μs
f. 90 W/m^2 K
g. 650 mGPa
h. 25 MN.
i. 950 Joules
j. 1.5 m/s/s

6. The dimension *moment*, sometimes referred to as *torque*, is defined as a force multiplied by a distance and is expressed in SI units of newton-meter (N • m). In addition to moment, what other physical quantities are expressed in SI units of N • m? What is the special name given to this combination of units?

7. Consider a 60-W light bulb. A watt (W) is defined as a joule per second (J/s). Write the quantity 60 W in terms of the units newton (N), meter (m), and second (s).

8. A commonly used formula in electrical circuit analysis is $P = IV$, power (W) equals current (A) multiplied by voltage (V). Using Ohm's law, write a formula for power in terms of current $[I]$ and resistance $[R]$.

9. A particle undergoes an average acceleration of 5 m/s^2 as it travels between two points during a time interval of 2 s. Using unit considerations, derive a formula for the average velocity of a particle in terms of average acceleration and time interval. Calculate the average velocity of the particle for the numerical values given.

10. A crane hoists a large pallet of materials from the ground to the top of a building. In hoisting this load, the crane does 100 kJ of work during a time interval of 5 s. Using unit considerations, derive the formula for power in terms of work and time interval. Calculate the power expended by the crane in lifting the load.

11. A spherical tank with a radius of 0.25 m is filled with water ($\rho = 1000$ kg/m^3). Calculate the mass and the weight of the water in SI units.

12. A large indoor sports arena is roughly cylindrical in shape. The height and diameter of the cylinder are 120 m and 180 m, respectively. Calculate the mass and weight of air contained in the sports arena in SI units if the density of air is $\rho = 1.20$ kg/m^3.

13. A 90-kg astronaut biologist searches for microbial life on Mars where the gravitational acceleration is $g = 3.71$ m/s^2. What is the weight of the astronaut in units of N and lb_f?

14. A 90-kg astronaut biologist places a 4-lb_m rock sample on two types of scales on Mars in order to measure the rock's weight. The first scale is a beam balance, which operates by comparing masses. The second scale operates by the compression of a spring. Calculate the weight of the rock sample in units of lb_f using (a) the beam balance and (b) the spring scale.

15. A stainless steel plate measuring 1.2 m × 0.8 m × 3 mm has a density of $\rho = 8000$ kg/m^3. Find the mass and weight of the plate in SI units.

16. A circular tube of polyethylene plastic ($\rho = 930$ kg/m^3) has an inside radius of 1.2 cm and an outside radius of 4.6 cm. If the cylinder is 40 cm long, what is the mass and weight of the cylinder in SI units?

17. The density of porcelain is $\rho = 144$ lb_m/ft^3. Approximating a porcelain dinner plate as a flat disk with a diameter and thickness of 9 in and 0.2 in, respectively,

find the mass of the plate in units of slug and lb_m. What is the weight of the plate in units of lb_f?

18. In an effort to reduce the mass of an aluminum bulkhead for a spacecraft, a machinist drills an array of holes in the bulkhead. The bulkhead is a triangular-shaped plate with a base and height of 2.5 m and 1.6 m, respectively, and a thickness of 8 mm. How many 5-cm diameter holes must be drilled clear through the bulkhead to reduce its mass by 8 kg? For the density of aluminum, use $\rho = 2800\ kg/m^3$.

19. A world-class sprinter can run 100 m in a time of 10 s, an average speed of 10 m/s. Convert this speed to mi/h.

20. A world-class mile runner can run 1 mi in a time of 4 min. What is the runner's average speed in units of mi/h and m/s?

21. The typical home is heated by a forced-air furnace that burns natural gas or fuel oil. If the heat output of the furnace is 120,000 Btu/h, what is the heat output in units of kW?

22. Calculate the temperature at which the Celsius (°C) and Fahrenheit (°F) scales coincide.

23. A large shipping container of ball bearings is suspended by a cable in a manufacturing plant. The combined mass of the container and ball bearings is 2500 lb_m. Find the tension in the cable in units of N.

24. A typical human adult loses about 65 $Btu/h \cdot ft^2$ of heat while engaged in brisk walking. Approximating the human adult body as a cylinder with a height and diameter of 5.8 ft and 1.1 ft, respectively, find the total amount of heat lost in units of J if the brisk walking is maintained for a period of 2 h. Include the two ends of the cylinder in the surface area calculation.

25. A symmetric I-beam of structural steel ($\rho = 7860\ kg/m^3$) has the cross section shown in Figure 25. Calculate the weight per unit length of the I-beam in units of N/m and lb_f/ft.

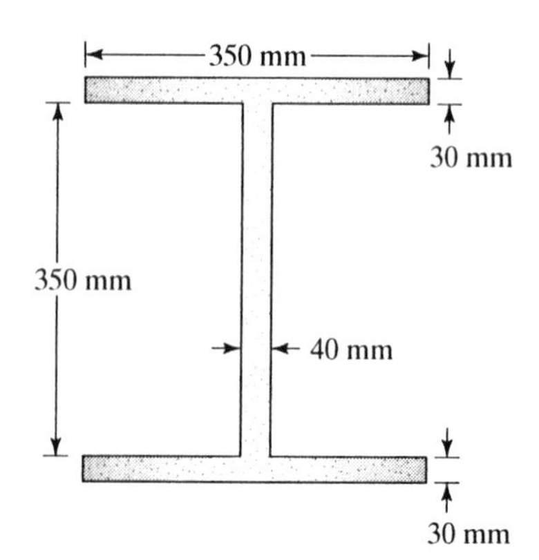

Figure 25.

26. A sewer pipe carries waste away from a commercial building at a mass flow rate of 5 kg/s. What is this flow rate in units of lb_m/s and slug/h?

27. The rate at which solar radiation is intercepted by a unit area is called solar heat flux. Just outside the earth's atmosphere, the solar heat flux is approximately 1350 W/m^2. Determine the value of this solar heat flux in units of $Btu/h \cdot ft^2$.

28. During a typical summer day in the arid southwest regions of the United States, the outdoor air temperature may range from 115°F during the late afternoon to 50°F several hours after sundown. What is this temperature range in units of °C, K, and °R?

29. An old saying is "an ounce of prevention is worth a pound of cure." Restate this maxim in terms of the SI unit newton.

30. How many seconds are there in a leap year?

31. What is your approximate age in seconds?

32. A highway sign is supported by two posts as shown in Figure 32. The sign is constructed of a high-density pressboard material (ρ = 900 kg/m^3) and its thickness is 2 cm. Assuming that each post carries half the weight of the sign, calculate the compressive force in the posts in units of N and lb_f.

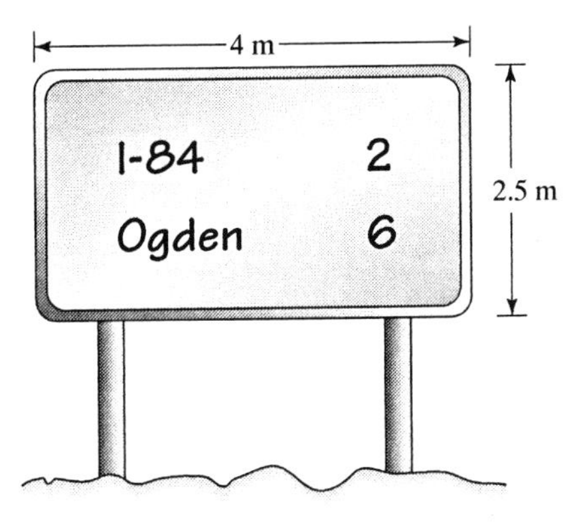

Figure 32.

33. A boiler is a vessel containing water or other fluid at a high temperature and pressure. Consider a boiler containing water at a temperature and pressure of 250°C and 5 MPa, respectively. What is the temperature and pressure in units of K and psi, respectively?

34. A pressure gauge designed to measure small pressure differences in air ducts has an operating range of 0 to 16 inch H_2O. What is this pressure range in units of Pa and psi?

35. Resistors are electrical devices that retard the flow of current. These devices are rated by the maximum power they are capable of dissipating as heat to the surrounding area. How much heat does a 25-W resistor dissipate in units of Btu/h if the resistor operates at maximum capacity? Using the formula $P = I^2R$, what is the current flow, I, in the resistor if is has a resistance, R, of 100 Ω?

36. Chemical reactions can generate heat. This type of heat generation is often referred to as volume heat generation because the heat is produced internally by every small parcel of chemical. Consider a chemical reaction that generates heat at the rate of 50 MW/m^3. Convert this volume heat generation to units of Btu/h · ft^3.

37. A sport-utility vehicle has an engine that delivers 250 hp. How much power does the engine produce in units of kW and Btu/h?

38. An underground pipe carries culinary water to a home at a volume flow rate of 5 gal/min. Determine the flow rate in units of m^3/s and ft^3/h.

39. Thermal conductivity is a property that denotes the ability of a material to conduct heat. A material with a high thermal conductivity readily transports heat, whereas a material with a low thermal conductivity tends to retard heat flow. Fiberglass insulation and silver have thermal conductivities of 0.046 W/m · °C and 429 W/m · °C, respectively. Convert these values to units of Btu/h · ft · °F.

40. A standard incandescent 75-W light bulb has an average life of 1000 h. What is the total amount of energy that this light bulb produces during its lifetime? Express the answer in units of J, Btu, and cal.

41. A steam power plant produces 400 MW of power. How much energy does the power plant produce in a year? Express your answer in units of J and Btu.

42. It is estimated that about 50 million Americans go on a new diet each year. If each of these people cuts 300 cal from their diets each day, how many 100-W light bulbs could be powered by this energy?

43. The standard acceleration of gravity at the earth's surface is $g = 9.81\ m/s^2$. Convert this acceleration to units of ft/h^2 and mi/s^2.

44. At room temperature, air has a specific heat of 1.007 kJ/kg · °C. Convert this value to units of J/kg · K and $Btu/lb_m \cdot °F$.

45. The yield stress for structural steel is approximately 250 MPa. Convert this value to units of psi.

4

Analysis Methodology

1 INTRODUCTION

One of the most important things an engineering student learns during his or her program of study is how to approach an engineering problem in a systematic and logical fashion. In this respect, the study of engineering is somewhat similar to the study of science in that a science student learns how to think like a scientist by employing the scientific method. The scientific method is a process by which hypotheses about the physical world are stated, theories formulated, data collected and evaluated, and mathematical models constructed. The **engineering method** may be thought of as a problem-solving process by which the needs of society are met through design and manufacturing of devices and systems. Engineering analysis is a major part of this problem-solving process. Admittedly, engineering and science are not the same, because they each play a different role in our technical society. Science seeks to explain how nature works through fundamental investigations of matter and energy. The objective of engineering is more pragmatic. Engineering, using science and mathematics as tools, seeks to design and build products and processes that enhance our standard of living. Generally, the scientific principles underlying the function of any engineering device were derived and established *before* the device was designed. For example, Newton's laws of motion and Kepler's orbital laws were well established scientific principles long before spacecraft orbited the earth or the other planets. Despite their contrasting objectives, both engineering and science employ tried-and-true methodologies that enable people working in each field to solve a variety of problems. To do science, the scientist must know how to employ the scientific method. To do engineering, the engineer must know how to employ the "engineering method."

SECTIONS

OBJECTIVES

After reading this chapter, you will have learned

- How to make order-of-magnitude calculations
- The proper use of significant figures
- How to perform an analysis systematically
- The proper method of analysis presentation
- Advantages and disadvantages of using computers for analysis

Engineering analysis is the solution of an engineering problem by using mathematics and principles of science. Because of the close association between analysis and design, analysis is one of the key steps in the design process. Analysis also plays a major role in the study of engineering failures. The engineering method for conducting an analysis is a logical, systematic procedure characterized by a well-defined format. This procedure, when consistently and correctly applied, leads to the successful solution of any analytical engineering problem. Practicing engineers have been using this analysis procedure successfully for decades, and engineering graduates are expected to know how to apply it upon entering the technical workforce. Therefore, it behooves the engineering student to learn the analysis methodology as thoroughly as possible. The best way to do so is to practice solving analytical problems. As you advance in your engineering course work, you will have ample opportunities to apply the analysis methodology outlined in this chapter. Courses such as statics, dynamics, strength of materials, thermodynamics, fluid mechanics, heat and mass transfer, electrical circuits, and engineering economics are analysis intensive. These courses, and others like them, focus almost exclusively on solving engineering problems that are analytical in nature. That is the character of these engineering subjects. The analysis methodology presented here is a *general* procedure that can be used to solve problems in any analytical subject. Clearly, engineering analysis heavily involves the use of numerical calculations.

2 NUMERICAL CALCULATIONS

As a college student, you are well aware of the rich diversity of academic programs and courses offered at institutions of higher learning. Because you are an engineering major, you are perhaps more familiar with the genre of engineering, science, and mathematics courses than liberal arts courses such as sociology, philosophy, psychology, music, and languages. The tenor of liberal arts is vastly different than that of engineering. Suppose for a moment that you are enrolled in a literature class, studying Herman Melville's great book, *Moby Dick*. While discussing the relationship between the whale and Captain Ahab, your literature professor asks the class, "What is your impression of Captain Ahab's attitude toward the whale?" As an engineering major, you are struck by the apparent looseness of this question. You are accustomed to answering questions that require a quantitative answer, not an "impression." What would engineering be like if our answers were "impressions"? Imagine an engineering professor asking a thermodynamics class, "What is your impression of the superheated steam temperature at the inlet of the turbine?" A more appropriate question would be, "What *is* the superheated steam temperature at the inlet of the turbine?" Obviously, literature and the other liberal arts disciplines operate in a completely different mode than engineering. By its very nature, engineering is based on specific, quantitative information. An answer of "hot" to the second thermodynamics question would be quantitative, but not specific, and therefore insufficient. The temperature of the superheated steam at the inlet of the turbine could be calculated by conducting a thermodynamic analysis of the turbine, thereby providing a *specific* value for the temperature; 400°C, for example. The analysis by which the temperature was obtained may consist of several numerical calculations involving different thermodynamic quantities. Numerical calculations are mathematical operations on numbers that represent physical quantities such as temperature, stress, voltage, mass, flow rate, etc. In this section, you will learn the proper numerical calculation techniques for engineering analysis.

2.1 Approximations

It is often useful, particularly during the early stages of design, to calculate an approximate answer to a given problem when the given information is uncertain or when little information is available. An approximation can be used to establish the cursory aspects of a design and to determine whether a more precise calculation is required. Approximations are usually based on assumptions, which must be modified or eliminated during the latter stages of the design. Engineering approximations are sometimes referred to as "guesstimates," "ballpark calculations," or "back-of-the-envelope calculations." A more appropriate name for them is **order-of-magnitude** calculations. The term order of magnitude means a *power of* 10. Thus, an order-of-magnitude calculation refers to a calculation involving quantities whose numerical values are estimated to within a factor of 10. For example, if the estimate of a stress in a structure changes from about 1 kPa to about 1 MPa, we say that the stress has changed by three orders of magnitude, because 1 MPa is one thousand (10^3) times 1 kPa. Engineers frequently conduct order-of-magnitude calculations to ascertain whether their initial design concepts are feasible. Order-of-magnitude calculations are therefore a useful decision-making tool in the design process. Order-of-magnitude calculations do not require the use of a calculator because all the quantities have simple power-of-10 values, so the arithmetic operations can be done by hand with pencil and paper or even in your head. The example that follows illustrates an order-of-magnitude calculation.

EXAMPLE 1

A warehouse with the approximate dimensions 200 ft × 150 ft × 20 ft is ventilated with 12 large industrial blowers. In order to maintain acceptable air quality in the warehouse, the blowers must provide two air changes per hour, meaning that the entire volume of air within the warehouse must be replenished with fresh outdoor air two times per hour. Using an order-of-magnitude analysis, find the required volume flow rate that each blower must deliver, assuming the blowers equally share the total flow rate.

SOLUTION

To begin, we estimate the volume of the warehouse. The length, width, and height of the warehouse is 200 ft, 150 ft, and 20 ft, respectively. These lengths have order-of-magnitude values of 10^2, 10^2, and 10^1, respectively. Two air changes per hour are required. Thus, the total volume flow rate of air for the warehouse, including the factor of two air changes per hour, is

$$Q_t \approx (10^2 \text{ ft})(10^2 \text{ ft})(10^1 \text{ ft})(2 \text{ air changes/h}) = 2 \times 10^5 \text{ ft}^3/\text{h}$$

(Note that "air changes" is not a unit, so it does not appear in the answer.) The number of blowers (12) has an order-of-magnitude value of 10^1. Based on the assumption that each blower delivers the same flow rate, the flow rate per blower is the total volume flow rate divided by the number of blowers:

$$Q = Q_t/N = (2 \times 10^5 \text{ ft}^3/\text{h})(10^1 \text{ blowers}) = 2 \times 10^4 \text{ ft}^3/\text{h} \cdot \text{blower}$$

Our order-of-magnitude calculation shows that each blower must supply 2×10^4 ft^3/h of outdoor air to the warehouse.

How does our order-of-magnitude answer compare with the exact answer? The exact answer is

$$Q = (200 \text{ ft})(150 \text{ ft})(20 \text{ ft})(2 \text{ air changes/h})/(12 \text{ blowers}) = 1 \times 10^5 \text{ ft}^3/\text{h} \cdot \text{blower}$$

By dividing the exact answer by the approximate answer, we see that the approximate answer differs from the exact answer by a factor of five, which is within an order of magnitude.

2.2 Significant Figures

After order-of-magnitude calculations have been made, engineers conduct more precise calculations to refine their design or to more fully characterize a particular failure mode. Accurate calculations demand more of the engineer than simply keeping track of powers of 10. Final design parameters must be determined with as much accuracy as possible to achieve the optimum design. Engineers must determine how many digits in their calculations are significant. A **significant figure** or *significant digit* in a number is defined as *a digit that is considered reliable as a result of a measurement or calculation*. The number of significant figures in the answer of a calculation indicates the number of digits that can be used with confidence, thereby providing a way of telling the engineer how accurate the answer is. No physical quantity can be specified with infinite precision because no physical quantity is *known* with infinite precision. Even the constants of nature such as the speed of light in a vacuum, c, and the gravitational constant, G, are known only to the precision with which they can be measured in a laboratory. Similarly, engineering material properties such as density, modulus of elasticity, and specific heat are known only to the precision with which these properties can be measured. A common mistake is to use more significant figures in an answer than are justified, giving the impression that the answer is more accurate than it really is. No answer can be more accurate than the numbers used to generate that answer.

How do we determine how many significant figures (colloquially referred to as "sig figs") a number has? A set of rules has been established for counting the number of significant figures in a number. (All significant figures are underlined in the examples given for each rule.)

Rules for Significant Figures

1. All digits *other than zero* are significant. Examples: 8.936, 456, 0.257.
2. All zeroes *between* significant figures are significant. Examples: 14.06, 5.0072.
3. For nondecimal numbers greater than one, all zeroes placed *after* the significant figures are *not* significant. Examples: 2500, 8,640,000. These numbers can be written in scientific notation as 2.5×10^3 and 8.64×10^6, respectively.
4. If a decimal point is used *after* a nondecimal number larger than one, the zeroes are significant. The decimal point establishes the precision of the number. Examples: 3200., 550,000.
5. Zeroes placed *after* a decimal point that are *not necessary* to set the decimal point are significant. The additional zeroes establish the precision of the number. Examples: 359.00, 1000.00.
6. For numbers smaller than one, all zeroes placed *before* the significant figures are *not* significant. These zeroes only serve to establish the location of the decimal point. Examples: 0.0254, 0.000609

Do not confuse the number of significant figures with the number of decimal places in a number. The number of significant figures in a quantity is established by the precision with which a measurement of that quantity can be made. The primary exception to this are numbers such as π and the Naperian base, e, that are derived from mathematical relations. These numbers are accurate to an infinite number of significant figures.

Let's see how the rules for significant figures are used in calculations.

EXAMPLE 2

We wish to calculate the weight of a 25-kg object. Using Newtòns second law, $W = mg$, find the weight of the object in units of N. Express the answer, by using the appropriate number of significant figures.

SOLUTION

We have $m = 25$ kg and $g = 9.81$ m/s^2. Suppose that our calculator is set to display six places to the right of the decimal point. We then multiply the numbers 25 and 9.81. In the display of the calculator, we see the number 245.250000. How many digits in this answer are we justified in writing? The number in the calculator's display implies that the answer is accurate to six decimal places (i.e., to within one-millionth of a newton). Obviously, this kind of accuracy is not justified. The rule for significant figures for *multiplication* and *division* is that *the product or quotient should contain the number of significant figures that are contained in the number with the fewest significant figures.*

Another way to state this rule is to say that the quantity with the fewest number of significant figures *governs* the number of significant figures in the answer. The mass, m, contains two significant figures, and the acceleration of gravity, g, contains three. Therefore, we are only justified in writing the weight by using two significant figures, which is the fewest number of significant figures in our given values. Our answer can be written in two ways. First, we can write the weight as 250 N. According to rule 3, the zero is not significant, so our answer contains two significant figures, the "2" and the "5." Second, we can write the weight by using scientific notation as 2.5×10^2 N. In this form, we can immediately see that two significant figures are used without referring to the rules. Note that in both cases we *rounded* the answer *up* to the nearest tens place, because the value of the first digit dropped is 5 or greater. If our answer had been lower than 245 N, we would have rounded *down* to 240 N. If our answer had been precisely 250 N, the rules of rounding suggest rounding up, so our answer would again be 250 N.

The preceding example shows how significant figures are used for multiplication or division, but how are significant figures used for *addition* and *subtraction*?

EXAMPLE 3

Two collinear forces (forces that act in the same direction) of 875.4 N and 9.386 N act on a body. Add these two forces, expressing the result in the appropriate number of significant figures.

SOLUTION

The best way to show how significant figures are used in addition or subtraction is to do the problem by hand. We have

$$\begin{array}{r} 875.4\ \ \ \ \text{N} \\ +\ \ 9.356\ \text{N} \\ \hline 884.786\ \text{N} \end{array}$$

Both forces have four significant figures, but the first force reports one place past the decimal point, whereas the second force reports three places past the decimal point. The answer is written with six significant figures. Are six significant figures justified? Because addition and subtraction are arithmetic operations that require decimal point alignment, the rule for significant figures for *addition* and *subtraction* is different than for multiplication and division. For addition and subtraction, the answer should show *significant figures only as far to the right as is seen in the least precise number in the calculation*. The least precise number in the calculation is the 875.4-N force, because it reports accuracy to the first decimal place, whereas the second force, 9.386 N, reports accuracy to the third decimal place. We are not justified in writing the answer as 884.786 N. We may only write the answer by using the same number of places past the decimal point as seen in the least precise force. Hence, our answer, reported to the appropriate number of significant figures, is 884.8 N. Once again, we rounded the answer up because the value of the first digit dropped is 5 or greater.

In *combined* operations where multiplication and division are performed in the same operation as addition and subtraction, the multiplications and divisions should be performed first, establishing the proper number of significant figures in the intermediate answers, perform the additions and subtractions, and then round the answer to the proper number of significant figures. This procedure, while applicable to operations performed by hand, should not be used in calculator or computer applications, because intermediate rounding is cumbersome and may lead to a serious error in the answer. Perform the entire calculation, letting the calculator or computer software manage the numerical precision, and then express the final answer in the desired number of significant figures:

> *It is standard engineering practice to express final answers in three (or sometimes four) significant figures, because the given input values for geometry, loads, material properties, and other quantities are typically reported with this precision.*

Calculators and computer software such as spreadsheets and equation solvers keep track of and can display a large number of digits. How many digits will your calculator display? The number of digits displayed by a scientific calculator can be set by fixing the decimal point or specifying the numerical format. For example, by fixing the number of decimal places to one, the number 28.739 is displayed as 28.7. Similarly, the number 1.164 is displayed as 1.2. Because the first digit dropped is greater than 5, the calculator automatically rounds the answer up. Small and large numbers should be expressed in scientific notation. For example, the number 68,400 should be expressed as 6.84×10^4, and the number 0.0000359 should be expressed as 3.59×10^{-5}. Scientific calculators also have an *engineering notation* display setting because SI unit prefixes are primarily defined by multiples of one thousand (10^3). In engineering notation, the number 68,400 may be displayed as 68.4×10^3, and the number 0.0000359 may be displayed as 35.9×10^{-6}. Regardless of how numbers are displayed by calculators or computers, the engineering student who uses these computational tools must understand that significant figures have a physical meaning based on our ability to measure engineering and scientific quantities. The casual or sloppy handling of significant figures in engineering analysis may lead to solutions that are inaccurate at best and completely wrong at worst.

APPLICATION: CALCULATING VISCOSITY BY USING THE FALLING-SPHERE METHOD

You know by experience that some fluids are thicker or more "gooey" than others. For example, pancake syrup and motor oil are thicker than water and alcohol. The technical term we use to describe the magnitude of a fluid's thickness is *viscosity*. Viscosity is a fluid property that characterizes the fluid's resistance to flow. Water and alcohol flow more readily than pancake syrup and motor oil under the same conditions. Hence, pancake syrup and motor oil are more viscous than water and alcohol. Gases have viscosities, too, but their viscosities are much smaller than those of liquids.

One of the classical techniques for measuring viscosities of liquids is called the *falling-sphere method*. In the falling-sphere method, the viscosity of a liquid is calculated by measuring the time it takes for a small sphere to fall a prescribed distance in a large container of the liquid, as illustrated in Figure 1. As the sphere falls in the liquid under the influence of gravity, it accelerates

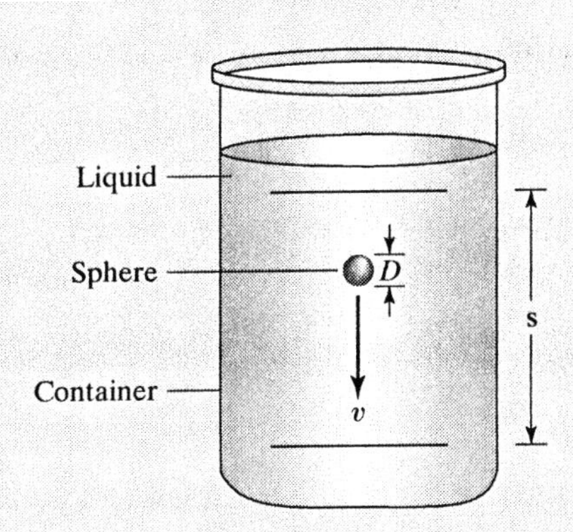

Figure 1. Experimental setup of the falling-sphere method for measuring viscosity.

until the downward force (the sphere's weight) is exactly balanced by the buoyancy force and drag force that act upward. From this time forward, the sphere falls with a constant velocity, referred to as terminal velocity. The buoyancy force, which is equal to the weight of the liquid displaced by the sphere, is usually small compared with the drag force, which is caused directly by viscosity. The terminal velocity of the sphere is inversely proportional to viscosity, since the sphere takes longer to fall a given distance in a very viscous liquid, such as motor oil, than in a less viscous liquid, such as water. By employing a force balance on the sphere and invoking some simple relations from fluid mechanics, we obtain the formula

$$\mu = \frac{(\gamma_s - \gamma_f)D^2}{18v}$$

where

μ = dynamic viscosity of liquid (Pa • s)
γ_s = specific weight of sphere (N/m^3)
γ_f = specific weight of liquid (N/m^3)
D = sphere diameter (m)
v = terminal velocity of sphere (m/s)

Note that the quantity *specific weight* is similar to *density*, except that it is a weight per volume, rather than a mass per volume. The word *dynamic* is used to avoid confusion with another type of viscosity known as *kinematic* viscosity.

Using the falling-sphere method, let's calculate the viscosity of glycerine, a very viscous liquid used to make a variety of chemicals. We set up a large glass cylinder and place two marks, spaced 200 mm apart, on the outside surface. The marks are placed low enough on the cylinder to assure that the sphere will achieve terminal velocity before reaching the top mark. For the sphere, we use a steel (γ_s = 76,800 N/m^3) ball bearing with a diameter of 2.381 mm (measured with a micrometer). From a previous measurement, the specific weight of the glycerin is γ_f = 12,400 N/m^3. Now, we hold the steel sphere above the surface of the glycerin at the center of the cylinder and release the sphere. As accurately as we can determine with our eye, we start a handheld stopwatch when the sphere reaches the top mark. Similarly, we stop the watch when the sphere reaches the bottom mark. Our stopwatch is capable of displaying hundredths of a second, and it reads 11.32 s. Even though the stopwatch is capable of measuring time to the second decimal place, our crude visual timing method does not justify using a time interval with this precision. Sources of uncertainty such as human reaction time and thumb response do not justify the second decimal place. Thus, our time interval is reported as 11.3 s, which has three significant figures. We know that terminal velocity is distance divided by time:

$$v = \frac{s}{t} = \frac{0.200\ \text{m}}{11.3\ \text{s}} = 0.0177\ \text{m/s}$$

The distance was measured to the nearest millimeter, so the quantity, s, has three significant figures. Thus, terminal velocity may be written in three significant figures. (Remember that the zero, according to rule 6, is not significant.) Values of the given quantities for our calculation are summarized as follows:

$$\gamma_s = 76,800\ \text{N/m}^3 = 7.68 \times 10^4\ \text{N/m}^3$$
$$\gamma_f = 12,400\ \text{N/m}^3 = 1.24 \times 10^4\ \text{N/m}^3$$
$$v = 0.0177\ \text{m/s} = 1.77 \times 10^{-2}\ \text{m/s}$$
$$D = 2.381\ \text{mm} = 2.381 \times 10^{-3}\ \text{m}$$

Each quantity, with the exception of D, which has four significant figures, has three significant figures. Upon substituting values into the equation for dynamic viscosity, we obtain

$$\mu = \frac{(\gamma_s - \gamma_f)D^2}{18v}$$
$$= \frac{(76,800 - 12,400)\text{N/m}^3\,(2.381 \times 10^{-3}\ \text{m})}{18(0.0177\ \text{m/s})}$$
$$= 1.1459\ \text{Pa} \cdot \text{s}$$

(Where did the pressure unit, Pa, come from?) According to the rules of significant figures for multiplication and division, our answer should contain the same number of significant figures as the number with the fewest significant figures. Our answer should therefore have three significant figures, so the dynamic viscosity of glycerin, expressed in the proper number of significant figures, is reported as

$$\mu = 1.15 \text{ Pa} \cdot \text{s}$$

Note that, because the value of the first digit dropped is 5, we rounded our answer up.

PROFESSIONAL SUCCESS: LEARN HOW TO USE YOUR CALCULATOR

As an engineering student, your best friend is your scientific calculator. If you do not yet own a quality scientific calculator, purchase one as soon as you can and begin learning how to use it. You cannot succeed in school without one. Do not scrimp on cost. You will probably only need one calculator for your entire academic career, so purchase one that offers the greatest number of functions and features. Professors and fellow students may offer advice on which calculator to buy. Your particular engineering department or college may even require that you use a particular calculator because they have heavily integrated calculator usage into the curriculum, and it would be too cumbersome to accommodate several types of calculators. Your college bookstore or local office supply store carry two or three name brands that have served engineering students and professionals for many years. Today's scientific calculators are remarkable engineering tools. A high-end scientific calculator has hundreds of built-in functions a large storage capacity graphics capabilities, and communication links to other calculators or personal computers.

Regardless of which scientific calculator you own or plan to purchase, *learn how to use it*. Begin with the basic arithmetic operations and the standard mathematical and statistical functions. Learn how to set the number of decimal places in the display and how to display numbers in scientific and engineering notation. After you are confident with performing unit conversions by hand, learn how to do them with your calculator. Learn how to write simple programs on your calculator. This skill will come in handy numerous times throughout your course work. Learn how to use the equation solving functions, matrix operations and calculus routines. By the time you learn most of the calculator's operations, you will probably have devoted a few hundred hours. The time spent mastering your calculator is perhaps as valuable as the time spent attending lectures, conducting experiments in a laboratory, doing homework problems, or studying for exams. Knowing your calculator thoroughly will help you succeed in your engineering program. Your engineering courses will be challenging enough. Do not make them an even bigger challenge by failing to adequately learn how to use your principal computational asset, your calculator.

PRACTICE!

1. Using an order-of-magnitude analysis, estimate the surface area of your body in units of m^2.
2. Using an order-of-magnitude analysis, estimate the number of hairs on your head.
3. Use an order-of-magnitude analysis to estimate the number of telephones in use in the United States.
4. Use an order-of-magnitude analysis to estimate the electrical energy in kWh used by your city in one month.
5. Underline the significant figures in the following numbers (the first number is done for you):
   a. $0.00\underline{254}$
   b. 29.8
   c. 2001
   d. 407.2

e. 0.0303
f. 2.006

Answer: b. 29.8 c. 2001 d. 407.2 e. 0.0303 f. 2.006

6. Perform the following calculations, reporting the answers with the correct number of significant figures:
   a. 5.64/1.9
   b. 500./0.0025
   c. (45.8 − 8.1)/1.922
   d. $2\pi/2.50$
   e. $(5.25 \times 10^4)/(100 + 10.5)$
   f. $0.0008/(1.2 \times 10^{-5})$

   Answer: a. 3.0 b. 2.0×10^5 c. 19.6 d. 3 e. 473 f. 70
7. A ball bearing is reported to have a radius of 3.256 mm. Using the correct number of significant figures, what is the weight of this bearing in units of N if its density is $\rho = 1675\ \text{kg/m}^3$?

   Answer: 2.38×10^{-3} N
8. The cylinder of an internal combustion engine is reported to have a diameter of 4.000 in. If the stroke (length) of the cylinder is 6.25 in, what is the volume of the cylinder in units of in^3? Write the answer by using the correct number of significant figures.

   Answer: 25.0 in^3

3 GENERAL ANALYSIS PROCEDURE

Engineers are problem solvers. In order to solve an engineering analysis problem thoroughly and accurately, engineers employ a solution method that is systematic, logical, and orderly. This method, when consistently and correctly applied, leads the engineer to a successful solution of the analytical problem at hand. The problem-solving method is an integral part of a good engineer's thought process. To the engineer, the procedure is second nature. When challenged by a new analysis, a good engineer knows precisely how to approach the problem. The problem may be fairly short and simple or extremely long and complex. Regardless of the size or complexity of the problem, the same solution method applies. Because of the *general* nature of the procedure, it applies to analytical problems associated with *any* engineering discipline: chemical, civil, electrical, mechanical, etc. Practicing engineers in all disciplines have been using the **general analysis procedure** in one form or another for a long time, and the history of engineering achievements is a testament to its success. While you are a student, it is vitally important that you learn the steps of the general analysis procedure. After you have learned the steps in the procedure and feel confident that you can use the procedure to solve problems, apply it in your analytical course work. Apply it religiously. Practice the procedure over and over again until it becomes a habit. Establishing good habits while still in school will make it that much easier for you to make a successful transition into professional engineering practice.

General Analysis Procedure

The general analysis procedure consists of the following seven steps:

1. PROBLEM STATEMENT

The problem statement is a written description of the analytical problem to be solved. It should be written clearly, concisely, and logically. The problem statement summarizes the given information, providing all necessary input data to solve the problem. The problem statement also states what is to be determined by performing the analysis.

2. DIAGRAM

The diagram is a sketch, drawing or schematic of the system being analyzed. Typically, it is a simplified pictorial representation of the actual system, showing only those aspects of the system that are necessary to perform the analysis. The diagram should show all given information contained in the problem statement such as geometry, applied forces, energy flows, mass flows, electrical currents, temperatures, or other physical quantities as required.

3. ASSUMPTIONS

Engineering analysis almost always involves some assumptions. Assumptions are special assertions about the physical characteristics of the problem that simplify or refine the analysis. A very complex analytical problem would be difficult or even impossible to solve without making some assumptions.

4. GOVERNING EQUATIONS

All physical systems may be described by mathematical relations. Governing equations are those mathematical relations that specifically pertain to the physical system being analyzed. These equations may represent physical laws, such as Newton's laws of motion, conservation of mass, conservation of energy, and Ohm's law; or they may represent fundamental engineering definitions such as velocity, stress, moment of force, and heat flux. The equations may also be basic mathematical or geometrical formulas involving angles, lines, areas, and volumes.

5. CALCULATIONS

In this step, the solution is generated. First, the solution is developed algebraically as far as possible. Then numerical values of known physical quantities are substituted for the corresponding algebraic variables. All necessary calculations are performed, using a calculator or computer, to produce a numerical result with the correct units and the proper number of significant figures.

6. SOLUTION CHECK

This step is crucial. Immediately after obtaining the result, examine it carefully. Using established knowledge of similar analytical solutions and common sense, try to ascertain whether the result is reasonable. However, whether the result seems reasonable or not, double-check every step of the analysis. Flush out defective diagrams, bad assumptions, erroneously applied equations, incorrect numerical manipulations, and improper use of units.

7. DISCUSSION

After the solution has been thoroughly checked and corrected, discuss the result. The discussion may include an assessment of the assumptions, a summary of the main conclusions, a proposal on how the result may be verified experimentally in a laboratory, or a parametric study, demonstrating the sensitivity of the result to a range of input parameters.

Now that the seven-step procedure has been summarized, further discussion of each step is warranted:

1. Problem statement In your engineering textbook, the problem statement will generally be supplied to you in the form of a problem or question at the end of each chapter. These problem statements are written by the textbook authors, professors or practicing engineers, who have expertise in the subject area. The great majority of end-of-chapter problems in engineering texts are well organized and well written, so you do not have to fret too much about the problem statement. Alternatively, your engineering professor may give you problem statements from sources outside your textbook or from his or her own engineering experience. In either case, the problem statement should be well posed, contain all the necessary input information, and clearly state what is to be determined by the analysis. What is known and what is unknown in the problem should be clearly identified. If the problem statement is flawed in any way, a meaningful analysis is impossible.

2. Diagram The old saying, "One picture is worth a thousand words," is certainly applicable to engineering analysis. A complete diagram of the system being analyzed is critical. A good diagram helps the engineer visualize the physical processes or characteristics of the system. It also helps the engineer identify reasonable assumptions and the appropriate governing equations. A diagram might even reveal flaws in the problem statement or alternative methods of solution. Engineers use a variety of diagrams in their analytical work. One of the most widely used diagrams in engineering is the *free-body diagram*. Free-body diagrams are used to solve engineering mechanics (statics, dynamics, strength of materials) problems. These diagrams are called "free-body" diagrams because they represent a specific body, isolated from all other bodies that are in physical contact with, or that may be in the vicinity of, the body in question. The influences of nearby bodies are represented as external forces acting on the body being analyzed. Hence, a free-body diagram is a sketch of the body in question, showing all external forces applied to the body. A free-body diagram is a pictorial representation of a "force balance" on the body. Diagrams are also used in the analysis of thermal systems. Unlike a free-body diagram, which shows forces applied to the body, a diagram of a thermal system shows all the various forms of energy entering and leaving the system. This type of diagram is a pictorial representation of an "energy balance" on the system. Another type of diagram represents a system that transports mass at known rates. Common examples include pipe and duct systems, conveyors and storage systems. A diagram for these systems shows all the mass entering and leaving the system. This type of diagram is a pictorial representation of a "mass balance" on the system. Still another type of diagram is an electrical circuit schematic. Electrical schematics show how components are connected and the currents, voltages and other electrical quantities in the circuit. Some examples of diagrams used in analysis are given in Figure 2.

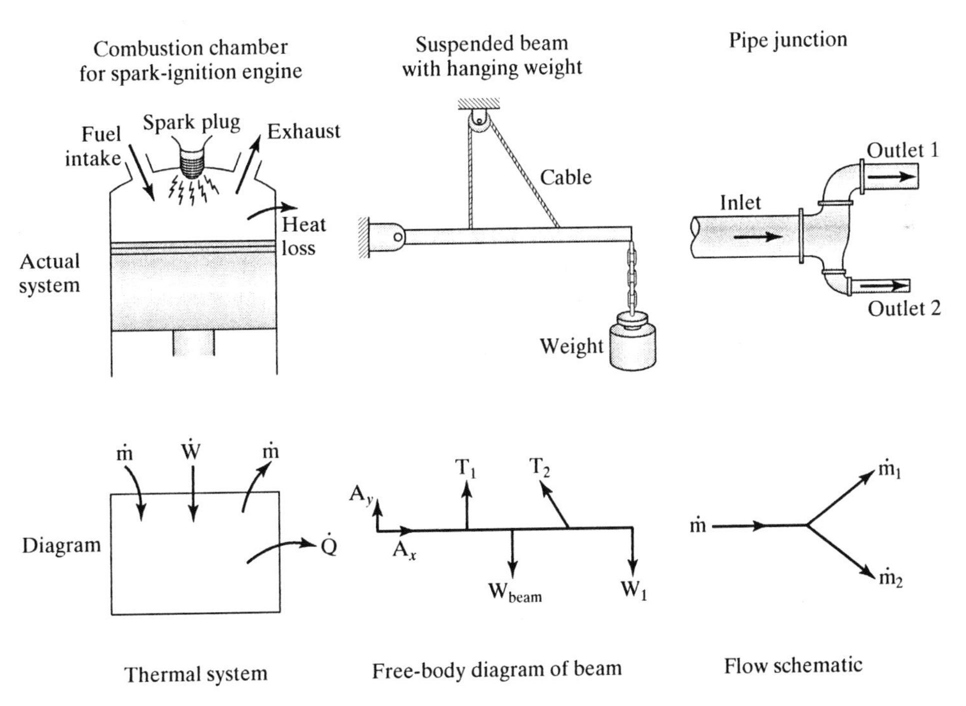

Figure 2. Examples of typical diagrams used in engineering analysis.

3. Assumptions I attended a lecture given by a physicist who referred to himself as an "atmospheric scientist" who studied various processes that occur in the upper atmosphere. He recounted an accomplishment that seemed truly remarkable. After convincing the audience that atmospheric processes are some of the most complex phenomena in physics, he boasted that he had developed, over the space of a few months, an analytical model of the upper atmosphere that contained *no* assumptions. There was only one problem: His model had no solution either. By including every physical mechanism to the minutest detail in the model, his analysis was so mathematically convoluted that it could not generate a solution. Had he made some simplifying assumptions, his atmospheric model could have worked even though the results would have been approximate.

Engineers and scientists routinely employ assumptions to simplify a problem. As my story illustrates, an approximate answer is better than no answer at all. Failure to invoke one or more simplifying assumptions in the analysis, particularly a complex one, can increase the complexity of the problem by an order of magnitude, leading the engineer down a very long road, only to reach a dead end. How do we determine which assumptions to use and whether our assumptions are good or bad? To a large extent, the application of good assumptions is an acquired skill, a skill that comes with engineering experience. However, you can begin to learn this skill in school through repeated application of the general analysis procedure in your engineering courses. As you apply the procedure to a variety of engineering problems, you will gain a basic understanding of how assumptions are used in engineering analysis. Then, after you graduate and accept a position with an engineering firm, you can refine this skill as you apply the analysis procedure to solve problems that are specific to the company. Sometimes, a problem can be overly constrained by assumptions such that the problem is simplified to the point where it becomes grossly inaccurate or even meaningless. The engineer must therefore be able to apply the proper *number* as well as the proper *type* of assumptions in a given analysis. A common assumption made in the stress analysis of a column is shown in Figure 3.

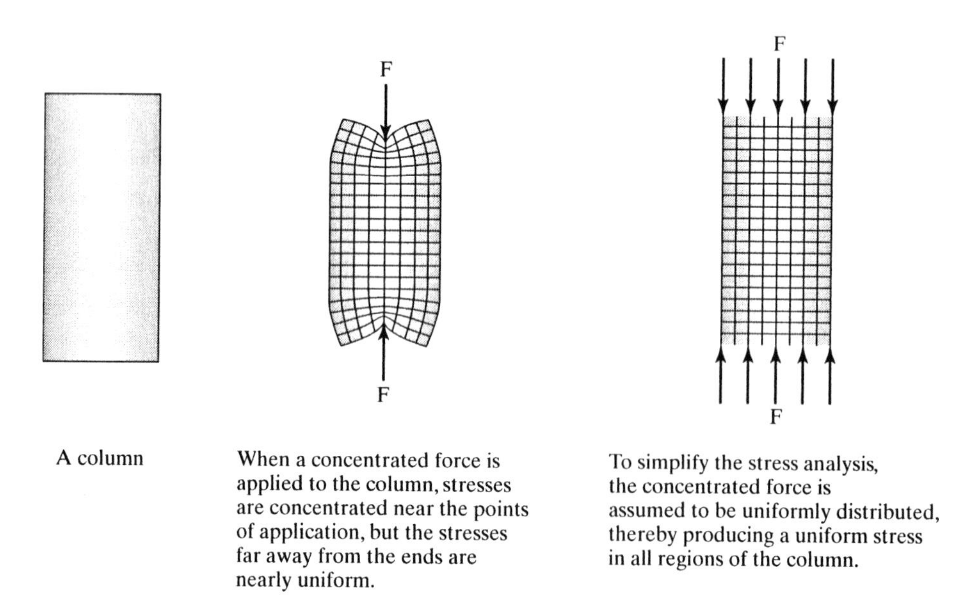

Figure 3. A common assumption made in the stress analysis of a column.

4. Governing equations The governing equations are the "workhorses" of the analysis. To a very limited extent, we may be able to afford some sloppiness in the other steps in the analysis procedure, but not in the governing equations. The governing equations are either right or they are wrong—there is no middle ground. They either describe the physical problem at hand, or they do not. If the wrong governing equations are used, the analysis will most certainly lead to a result that does not reflect the true physical nature of the problem, or the analysis will not be possible at all because the governing equations are not in harmony with the problem statement or assumptions. When using a governing equation to a solve a problem, the engineer must ascertain that the equation being used *actually* applies to the specific problem at hand. As an extreme (and probably absurd) example, imagine an engineer attempting to use Newton's second law, $F = ma$, to calculate the heat loss from a boiler? How about trying to apply Ohm's law, $V = IR$, to find the stress in a concrete column that supports a bridge deck? The problem of matching governing equations to the problem at hand is usually more subtle. In thermodynamics, for example, the engineer must determine whether the thermal system is "closed" or "open" (i.e., whether the system allows mass to cross the system boundary). After the type of thermal system has been identified, the thermodynamic equations which apply to that type of system are chosen, and the analysis proceeds. Governing equations must also be consistent with the assumptions. It is counterproductive to invoke simplifying assumptions if the governing equations do not make allowances for them. Some governing equations, particularly those that are experimentally derived, have built-in restrictions that limit the use of the equations to specific numerical values of key variables. A common mistake made in the application of a governing equation in this situation is failing to recognize the restrictions by forcing the equation to accept numerical values that lie outside the equation's range of applicability.

5. Calculations A common practice, particularly among beginning students, is to substitute numerical values of quantities into equations *too early* in the calculations. It seems that students are more comfortable working with *numbers* than *algebraic variables*, so their first impulse is to substitute numerical values for all parameters at the beginning of the calculation. Avoid this impulse. To the extent that it is practical, develop the solution *analytically* prior to assigning physical quantities their numerical values. Before rushing to "plug" numbers into equations, carefully examine the equations to see if they can be mathematically manipulated to yield simpler expressions. A variable from one equation can often be substituted into another equation to reduce the total number of variables. Perhaps an expression can be simplified by factoring. By developing the solution analytically first, you might uncover certain physical characteristics about the system or even make the problem easier to solve. The analytical skills you learned in your algebra, trigonometry and calculus courses are meant to be used for performing mathematical operations on *symbolic* quantities, not numbers. When doing engineering analysis, do not put your mathematics skills on a shelf to collect dust—*use* them.

The calculations step demands more of an engineer than the ability to simply "crunch numbers" on a calculator or computer. The numbers have to be meaningful, and the equations containing the numbers must be fully understood and properly used. All mathematical relations must be dimensionally consistent, and all physical quantities must have a numerical value plus the correct units. Here is a tip concerning units that will save you time and help you avoid mistakes: *If the quantities given in the problem statement are not expressed in terms of a consistent set of units, convert all quantities to a consistent set of units before performing any calculations.* If some of the input parameters are expressed as a mixture of SI units and English units, convert all parameters to either SI units or English units, and then perform the calculations. Students tend to make more mistakes when they attempt to perform unit conversions *within* the governing equations. If all unit conversions are done prior to substituting numerical values into the equations, unit consistency is assured throughout the remainder of the calculations, because a consistent set of units is established at the onset. Dimensional consistency should still be verified, however, by substituting all quantities along with their units into the governing equations.

6. Solution check This step is perhaps the easiest one to overlook. Even good engineers sometimes neglect to thoroughly check their solution. The solution may "look" good at first glance, but a mere glance is not good enough. Much effort has gone into formulating the problem statement, constructing diagrams of the system, determining the appropriate number and type of assumptions, invoking governing equations and performing a sequence of calculations. All this work may be for naught if the solution is not carefully checked. Checking the solution of an engineering analysis is analogous to checking the operation of an automobile immediately following a major repair. It's always a good idea if the mechanic checks the overhauled transmission to verify that it works before returning the vehicle to its owner.

There are two main aspects of the solution check. First, the result itself should be checked. Ask the question, "Is this result reasonable?" There are several ways to answer this question. The result must be consistent with the information given in the problem statement. For example, suppose you wish to calculate the temperature of a microprocessor chip in a computer. In the problem statement, the ambient air temperature is given as 25°C, but your analysis indicates that the chip temperature is only 20°C. This result is not consistent with the given information because it is physically impossible for a heat-producing component, a microprocessor chip in this case, to have a lower temperature than the surrounding environment. If the answer had been 60°C, it is at least consistent with the problem statement, but it may still be incorrect. Another way to check the result is to compare it with that of similar analyses performed by you or other engineers. If the result of a similar analysis is not available, an alternative analysis that utilizes a different solution approach may have to be conducted. In some cases, a laboratory test may be needed to verify the solution experimentally. Testing is a normal part of engineering design anyway, so a test to verify an analytical result may be customary.

The second aspect of the solution check is a thorough inspection and review of each step of the analysis. Returning to our microprocessor example, if no mathematical or numerical errors are committed, the answer of 60°C may be considered correct insofar as the calculations are concerned, but the answer could still be in error. How? By applying bad assumptions. For example, suppose that the microprocessor chip is air cooled by a small fan, so we assert that forced convection is the dominant mechanism by which heat is transferred from the chip. Accordingly, we assume that conduction and radiation heat transfer are negligible, so we do not include these mechanisms in the analysis. A temperature of 60°C seems a little high, so we revise our assumptions. A second analysis that includes conduction and radiation reveals that the microprocessor chip is much cooler, about 42°C. Knowing whether assumptions are good or bad comes through increased knowledge of physical processes and practical engineering experience.

7. Discussion This step is valuable from the standpoint of communicating to others what the results of the analysis mean. By discussing the analysis, you are in effect writing a "minitechnical report." This report summarizes the major conclusions of the analysis. In the microprocessor example given earlier, the main conclusion may be that 42°C is below the recommended operating temperature for the chip, and therefore, the chip will operate reliably in the computer for a minimum of 10,000 hours before failing. If the chip temperature was actually measured at 45°C shortly after performing the analysis, the discussion might include an examination of why the predicted and measured temperatures differ and particularly why the predicted temperature is lower than the measured temperature. A brief parametric study may be included that shows how the chip temperature varies as a function of ambient air temperature. The discussion may even include an entirely separate analysis that predicts the chip temperature in the event of a fan failure. In the discussion step, the engineer is given one last opportunity to gain additional insights into the problem.

PROFESSIONAL SUCCESS: REAL-WORLD PROBLEM STATEMENTS

Engineering programs strive to give students a sense of what is it like to actually practice engineering in the "real world." But *studying* engineering in school and *practicing* engineering in the real world are not the same thing. One difference is amply illustrated by considering the origins of problem statements for analysis. In school, problem statements are typically found at the end of each chapter of your engineering texts. (The answers to many of these problems are even provided at the back of the book.) Sometimes your professors obtain problem statements from other texts or invent new ones (especially for exams). In any case, problem statements are supplied to you in a nice, neat little package all ready for you to tackle the problem. If textbooks and professors supply problem statements to students in school, who or what supplies problem statements to practicing engineers in industry? Real-world engineering problems are not typically found in textbooks (answers are never found in the back of the book, either), and your engineering professors are not going to follow you around after you graduate. So, where do the real-world problem statements come from? They are *formulated* by the engineer who is going to perform the analysis. As stated before, analysis is an integral part of engineering design. As a design matures, quantitative parameters that characterize the design begin to emerge. When an analysis is called for, these parameters are woven into a problem statement from which an analysis may be conducted. The engineer must be able to formulate a coherent, logical problem statement from the design information available. Because engineering design is an iterative process, the values of some or all of the input parameters may be uncertain. The engineer must therefore be able to write the problem statement in such a way as to allow for these uncertainties. The analysis will have to be repeated several times until the parameters are no longer in a state of flux, at which time the design is complete.

The seven-step procedure for performing an engineering analysis is a time-tested method. In order to effectively communicate an analysis to others, the analysis must be presented in a format that can be readily understood and followed. Engineers are known for their ability to present analyses and other technical information with clarity in a thorough, neat, and careful manner. As an engineering student, you can begin to develop this ability by consistently applying the analysis procedure outlined in this section. Your engineering professors will insist that you follow the procedure, or a procedure similar to it, in your engineering courses. You will probably be graded not only on how well you perform the analysis itself, but how well you *present* the analysis on paper. This grading practice is meant to convince students of the importance of presentation standards in engineering and to assist them in developing good presentation skills. An engineering analysis is of little value to anyone unless it can be read and understood. A good analysis is one that can be easily read by others. If your analysis resembles "hen scratchings" or "alien hieroglyphics" that require an interpreter, the analysis is useless. Apply the presentation guidelines given in this section to the point where they become second nature. Then, after you graduate and begin practicing engineering, you can hone your presentation skills as you gain industrial experience.

The 10 guidelines that follow will help you present an engineering analysis in a clear and complete manner. These guidelines are applicable to analysis work in school as well as industrial engineering practice. It should be noted that the guidelines apply specifically to analyses performed by hand with the use of pencil and paper, as opposed to computer-generated analyses.

Analysis Presentation Guidelines

1. A standard practice of engineers who do analysis is to use a special type of *paper*. This paper is usually referred to as "engineer calculation pad" or "engineer's computation paper." The paper is light green in color, and should be available in your college or university bookstore. The back side of the paper is ruled horizontally and vertically with five squares per inch, with only heading and margin rulings on the front side. The rulings on the back side are faintly visible through the paper to help the engineer maintain the proper position and orientation for lettering, diagrams and graphs. (See Figure 4) All work is to be done on the *front* side of the paper. The back side is not used. The paper usually comes prepunched with a standard three-hole pattern at the left edge for placement in a three-ring binder.

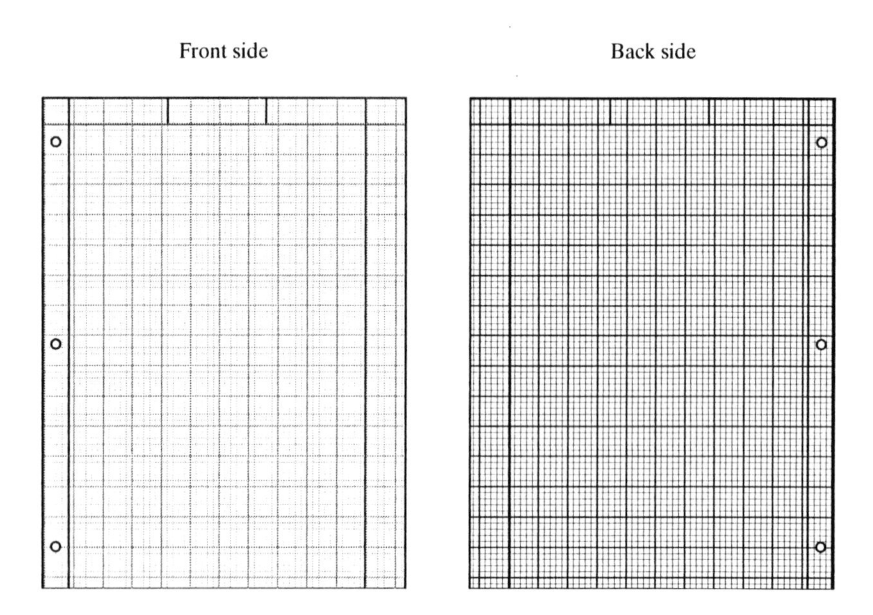

Figure 4. Engineer's computation paper is standard issue for analysis work.

2. No more than *one* problem should be placed on a page. This practice helps maintain clarity by keeping different problems separate. Even if a problem occupies a small fraction of a page, the next problem should be started on a separate page.
3. The *heading* area at the top of the page should indicate your name, date, course number, and assignment number. The upper right corner of the heading area is usually reserved for page numbers. To alert the reader to the total number of pages present, page numbers are often reported, for example, as "1/3", which is read as "page 1 of 3." Page 1 is the current page, and there are a total of three pages. When multiple pages are used, they should be stapled in the upper left corner. Each page should nonetheless be identified with your name, in the unlikely event the pages become separated.
4. The *problem statement* should be written out completely, not summarized or condensed. All figures that accompany the problem statement should be shown. If the problem statement originates from a textbook, it should be

written *verbatim* so the reader does not have to refer back to the textbook for the full version. One way to do this is to photocopy the problem statement, along with any figures given, and then cut and paste it by using rubber cement directly beneath the heading area on the engineer's computation paper. The problem statement could also be electronically scanned and printed directly onto the paper.

5. Work should be done in *pencil*, not ink. Everyone makes mistakes. If the analysis is written in pencil, mistakes can be easily erased and corrected. If the analysis is written in ink, mistakes will have to be crossed out, and the presentation will not have a neat appearance. To avoid smudges, use a pencil lead with the appropriate hardness. All markings should be dark enough to reproduce a legible copy if photocopies are needed. If you still use a standard wooden pencil, throw it out. Mechanical pencils are superior. They do not require sharpening, contain several months worth of lead, have replaceable erasers, produce no waste, and come in a range of lead diameters to suit your own writing needs. Mechanical pencils are also durable. (I have been using the same mechanical pencil since 1977!)
6. Lettering should be *printed*. The lettering style should be consistent throughout.
7. Correct *spelling* and *grammar* must be used. Even if the technical aspects of the presentation are flawless, the engineer will lose some credibility if the writing is poor.
8. There are seven steps in the general analysis procedure. These steps should be sufficiently *spaced* so that the reader can easily follow the analysis from problem statement to discussion. A horizontal line drawn across the page is one way of providing this separation.
9. Good *diagrams* are a must. A straight edge, drawing templates and other manual drafting tools should be used. All pertinent quantitative information such as geometry, forces, energy flows, mass flows, electrical currents, pressures, etc., should be shown on the diagrams.
10. Answers should be *double underlined* or *boxed* for ready identification. To enhance the effect, colored pencils may be used.

These 10 guidelines for analysis presentation are recommended to the engineering student. You may find that your particular engineering department or professors may advocate guidelines that are slightly different. By all means, follow the guidelines given to you. Your professors may have special reasons for teaching their students certain methods of analysis presentation. Methods may vary somewhat from professor to professor, but should still reflect the major points contained in the guidelines given in this section.

The next four examples illustrate the general analysis procedure and the recommended guidelines for analysis presentation. Each example represents a basic analysis taken from the subject areas of statics, electrical circuits, thermodynamics, and fluid mechanics. You probably have not yet taken courses in these subjects, so do not be overly concerned if you do not understand all the technical aspects of the examples. Therefore, do not focus on the theoretical and mathematical details. Focus instead on how the general analysis procedure is used to solve problems from different engineering areas and the systematic manner in which the analyses are presented.

EXAMPLE 4

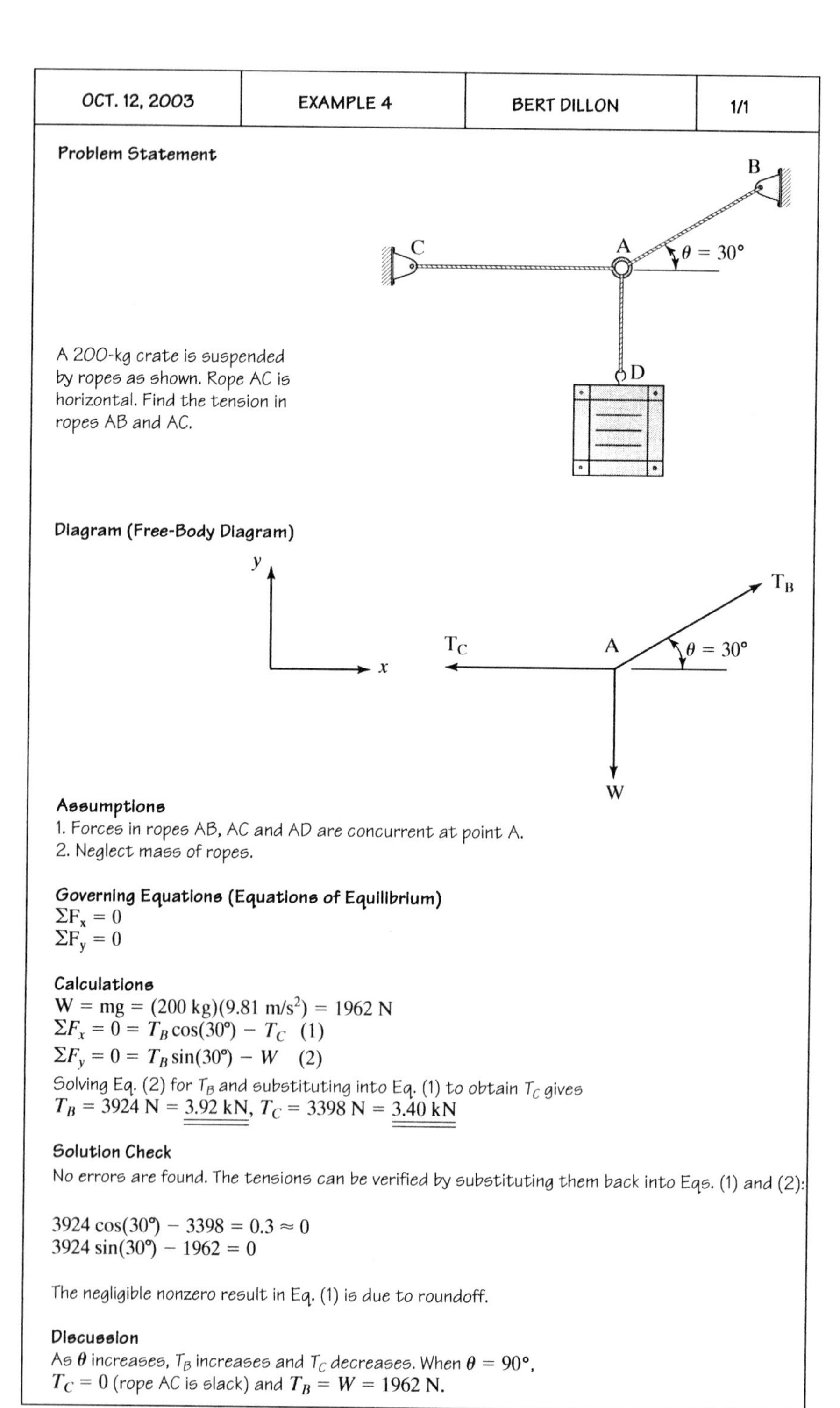

OCT. 12, 2003	EXAMPLE 4	BERT DILLON	1/1

Problem Statement

A 200-kg crate is suspended by ropes as shown. Rope AC is horizontal. Find the tension in ropes AB and AC.

Diagram (Free-Body Diagram)

Assumptions

1. Forces in ropes AB, AC and AD are concurrent at point A.
2. Neglect mass of ropes.

Governing Equations (Equations of Equilibrium)

$\Sigma F_x = 0$

$\Sigma F_y = 0$

Calculations

$W = mg = (200 \text{ kg})(9.81 \text{ m/s}^2) = 1962 \text{ N}$

$\Sigma F_x = 0 = T_B \cos(30°) - T_C \quad (1)$

$\Sigma F_y = 0 = T_B \sin(30°) - W \quad (2)$

Solving Eq. (2) for T_B and substituting into Eq. (1) to obtain T_C gives

$T_B = 3924 \text{ N} = \underline{\underline{3.92 \text{ kN}}}, \; T_C = 3398 \text{ N} = \underline{\underline{3.40 \text{ kN}}}$

Solution Check

No errors are found. The tensions can be verified by substituting them back into Eqs. (1) and (2):

$3924 \cos(30°) - 3398 = 0.3 \approx 0$

$3924 \sin(30°) - 1962 = 0$

The negligible nonzero result in Eq. (1) is due to roundoff.

Discussion

As θ increases, T_B increases and T_C decreases. When $\theta = 90°$, $T_C = 0$ (rope AC is slack) and $T_B = W = 1962$ N.

EXAMPLE 5

JAN. 03, 2004	EXAMPLE 5	MARIE NORTON	1/2

Problem Statement
Two resistors with resistances of 5Ω and 50Ω are connected in parallel across a 10 V battery. Find the current in each resistor.

Diagram (Electrical Schematic)

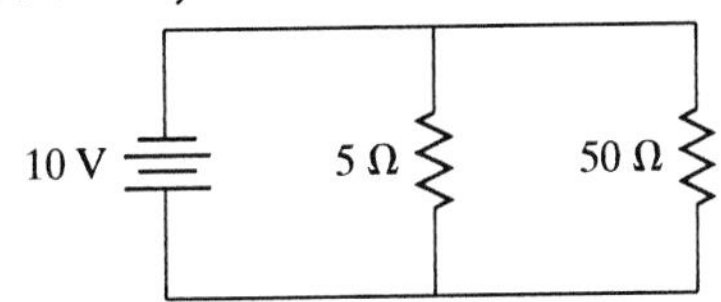

Assumptions
1. Neglect resistance of wires.
2. Battery voltage is a constant 10 V.

Governing Equations (Ohm's law)

$V = IR$ $\quad$ V = Voltage (V)
I = Current (A)
R = Resistance (Ω)

Calculations

Rearranging Ohm's law: $I = \frac{V}{R}$.

Define: $R_1 = 5\ \Omega, R_2 = 50\ \Omega$
Because resistors are connected in parallel with battery,
$V = V_1 = V_2 = 10\ V$.

$$\therefore I_1 = \frac{V_1}{R_1} = \frac{10\ V}{5\ \Omega} = \underline{\underline{2\ \text{A}}}, I_2 = \frac{V_2}{R_2} = \frac{10\ V}{50\ \Omega} = \underline{\underline{0.2\ \text{A}}}$$

Solution Check (no errors found)

JAN. 03, 2004	EXAMPLE 5	MARIE NORTON	2/2

Discussion
Current flow in a resistor is inversely proportional to the resistance.
Total current is split according to the ratio of resistances:

$$\frac{I_1}{I_2} = \frac{R_2}{R_1} = \frac{2\ \text{A}}{0.2\ \text{A}} = \frac{50\ \Omega}{5\ \Omega} = 10$$

Total current:

$$\begin{aligned} I_T &= I_1 + I_2 \\ &= 2\ \text{A} + 0.2\ \text{A} = 2.2\ \text{A} \end{aligned}$$

Total current may also be found by finding total resistance and then using Ohm's law.

Resistors in parallel as follows:

$$R_T = \frac{1}{\frac{1}{R_1} + \frac{1}{R_2}} = \frac{1}{\frac{1}{5} + \frac{1}{50}}$$

$$R_T = 4.5455\ \Omega$$

$$I_T = \frac{V}{R_T} = \frac{10\ V}{4.5455\ \Omega} = 2.2\ \text{A}$$

EXAMPLE 6

MAR. 24, 2004	EXAMPLE 6	CY BRAYTON	1/2

Problem Statement
A classroom occupied by 50 students is to be air conditioned with window-mounted air conditioning units with a 4-kW rating. There are 20 florescent lights in the room, each rated at 60 W. While sitting at their desks, each student dissipates 100 W. If the heat transfer to the classroom through the roof, walls and windows is 5 kW, how many air conditioning units are required to maintain the classroom at a constant temperature of 22°C?

Diagram (Thermodynamic System)

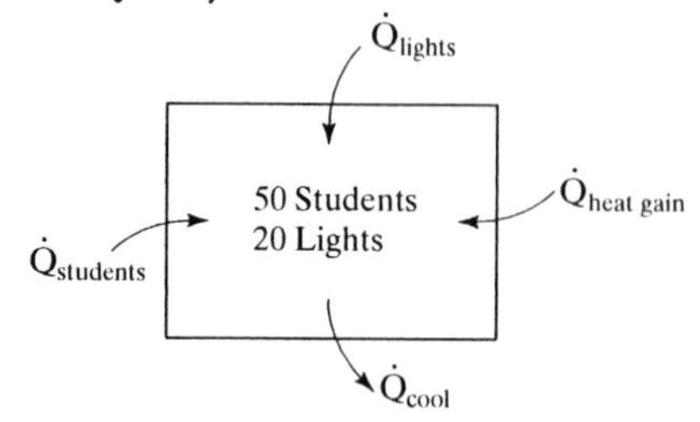

Assumptions
1. Classroom is a closed system, i.e., no mass flows.
2. All heat flows are steady.
3. No other heat sources in classroom such as computers, TVs, etc.

Governing Equations (Conservation of Energy)

$$\dot{E}_{in} - \dot{E}_{out} = \Delta E_{system}$$

Calculations

$$\dot{E}_{in} = \dot{Q}_{students} + \dot{Q}_{lights} + \dot{Q}_{heat\ gain}$$
$$= (50)(100\text{ W}) + (20)(60\text{ W}) + 5000\text{ W} = 11{,}200\text{ W} = 11.2\text{ kW}$$

$\Delta E_{system} = 0$ (Classroom is maintained at constant temperature)

$$\dot{E}_{in} - \dot{E}_{out} = \dot{Q}_{cool}$$

Number of A.C. units required $= \dfrac{\dot{Q}_{cool}}{4\text{ kW}} = \dfrac{11.2\text{ kW}}{4\text{ kW}} = 2.8$

Fractions of A.C. units are impossible, so round up answer to next integer.

MAR. 24, 2004	EXAMPLE 6	CY BRAYTON	2/2

Number of A.C. units required = 3.

Solution check (no errors found)

Discussion
The classroom temperature of 22°C was not used in the calculation because this temperature, as well as the outdoor air temperature, are inferred in the given heat gain by a prior heat transfer analysis.

Suppose that the classroom was a computer lab containing 30 computers each dissipating 250 W. We eliminate assumption 3 by including heat input by the computers.

$$\dot{Q}_{cool} = \dot{Q}_{students} + \dot{Q}_{lights} + \dot{Q}_{heat\ gain} + \dot{Q}_{computers}$$
$$= 11{,}200\text{ W} + 30(250\text{ W}) = 18{,}700\text{ W} = 18.7\text{ kW}$$

Number of A.C. units required $= \dfrac{\dot{Q}_{cool}}{4\text{ kW}} = \dfrac{18.7\text{ kW}}{4\text{ kW}} = 4.7$

Number of A.C. units required = 5.

This example illustrates the effect computers have on air-conditioning requirements.

EXAMPLE 7

MAY 17, 2004	EXAMPLE 7	EDDIE POWERS	1/2

Problem Statement

Water enters a pipe junction at a mass flow rate of 3.6 kg/s. If the mass flow rate in the small branch is 1.4 kg/s, what is the mass flow rate in the large pipe branch? If the inside diameter of the large pipe branch is 5 cm, what is the velocity in the large pipe branch?

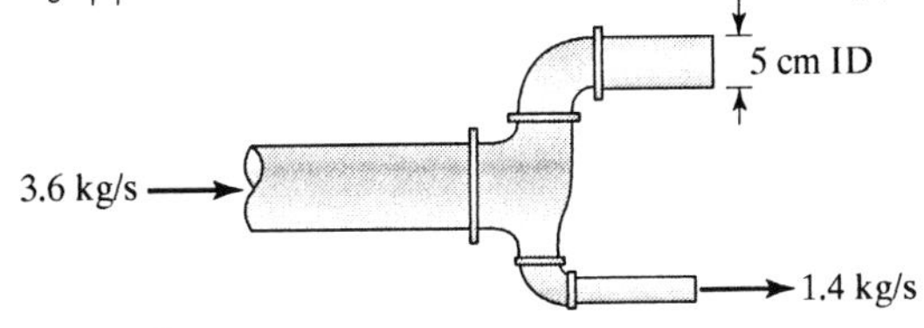

Diagram (Flow Schematic)

$\dot{m}_2$

$\dot{m} = 3.6$ kg/s

$\dot{m}_1 = 1.4$ kg/s

Assumptions

1. Steady, incompressible flow
2. Density of water: $\rho = 1000\ \text{kg/m}^3$

Governing Equations

Conservation of mass: $\dot{m}_{in} = \dot{m}_{out}$

mass flow rate: $\dot{m} = \rho A v$

$\dot{m}$ = mass flow rate (kg/s)
ρ = fluid density (kg/m^3)
A = flow cross-sectional area (m^2)
v = velocity (m/s)

Calculations

$$\dot{m} = \dot{m}_1 + \dot{m}_2$$
$$\dot{m}_2 = \dot{m} - \dot{m}_1 = 3.6\ \text{kg/s} - 1.4\ \text{kg/s} = 2.2\ \text{kg/s}$$

MAY 17, 2004	EXAMPLE 7	EDDIE POWERS	2/2

$$\dot{m}_2 = \rho A_2 v_2 = \rho \frac{\pi D_2^2}{4} v_2$$

$$v_2 = \frac{4\,\dot{m}_2}{\pi \rho D_2^2} = \frac{4\ (2.2\ \text{kg/s})}{\pi (1000\ \text{kg/m}^3)(0.05\ \text{m})^2}$$

$$= \underline{\underline{1.12\ \text{m/s}}}$$

Solution check (no errors found)

Discussion

The velocity calculated is an average value because there is a velocity profile across the pipe. The velocity profile is caused by viscosity. If the flow condition is laminar, the velocity profile is parabolic, as shown in the following sketch.

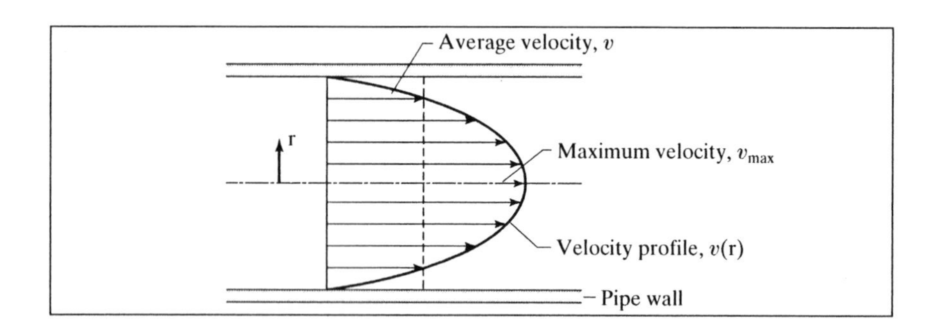

PROFESSIONAL SUCCESS: AVOIDING A "COOKBOOK" LEARNING APPROACH TO ENGINEERING ANALYSIS

A good engineer is a person who solves an engineering analysis problem by reasoning through it, rather than simply following a prepared "recipe" consisting of step-by-step instructions written by someone else. Similarly, a good engineering student is a person who learns engineering analysis by thinking conceptually about each problem, rather than simply memorizing a collection of disjointed solution sequences and mathematical formulas. This "cookbook" learning approach is a detour on the road of engineering education. Furthermore, the cookbook learning style promotes fragmented rather than integrative learning. A student who embraces this type of learning method will soon discover that it will be difficult and take a long time to solve new engineering problems, unless identical or very similar problems have been previously solved by using an established recipe. An analogy may be drawn from the familiar maxim "Give a man a fish, and you have fed him for a day. Teach a man to fish, and you have fed him for a lifetime." A recipe enables a student to solve only one specific type of problem, whereas a more general conceptual-based learning approach enables a student to solve many engineering problems.

PRACTICE!

Use the general analysis procedure to solve the following problems (present the analysis by using the guidelines for analysis presentation covered in this section):

1. Radioactive waste is to be permanently encased in concrete and buried in the ground. The vessel containing the waste measures 30 cm × 30 cm × 80 cm. Federal regulations dictate that there must be a minimum concrete thickness of 50 cm surrounding the vessel on all sides. What is the minimum volume of concrete required to safely encase the radioactive waste?
Answer: 2.97 m^3
2. An elevator in an office building has an operating capacity of 15 passengers with a maximum weight of 180 lb_f each. The elevator is suspended by a special pulley system with four cables, two of which support 20 percent of the total load and two of which support 80 percent of the total load. Find the maximum tension in each elevator cable.
Answer: 270 lb_f, 1080 lb_f
3. A technician measures a voltage drop of 25 V across a 100-Ω resistor by using a digital voltmeter. Ohm's law states that $V = IR$. What is the current flow through the resistor? How much power is consumed by the resistor? (*Hint*: $P = I^2R$.)
Answer: 250 mA, 6.25 W
4. Air flows through a main duct at a mass flow rate of 4 kg/s. The main duct enters a junction that splits into two branch ducts, one with a cross section of

20 cm × 30 cm and one with a cross section of 40 cm × 60 cm. If the mass flow rate in the large branch is 2.8 kg/s, what is the mass flow rate in the small branch? If the density of air is ρ = 1.16 kg/m^3, what is the velocity in each branch?

Answer: 1.2 kg/s, 10.1 m/s, 17.2 m/s

4 THE COMPUTER AS AN ANALYSIS TOOL

Computers are an integral part of the civilized world. They affect virtually every aspect of our everyday lives, including communications, transportation, financial transactions, information processing, food production, and health care, among others. The world is a much different place today than it was prior to the advent of computers. People use computers for accessing and processing information, word processing, electronic mail, entertainment, and on-line shopping. Like everyone else, engineers use computers in their personal lives in the same ways just mentioned, but they also depend heavily on computers in their professional work. To the engineer, the computer is an indispensable tool. Why do engineers need computers? Without the computer, engineers would not be able to do their work accurately or efficiently. The primary advantage of the computer to engineers is its ability to perform various functions extremely rapidly. For example, a complex sequence of calculations that would take days with a slide rule can be carried out in a few seconds by a computer. Furthermore, the numerical precision of the computer enables engineers to make calculations that are much more accurate. Engineers use computers for computer-aided design (CAD), word processing, communications, information access, graphing, process control, simulation, data acquisition, and, of course, analysis.

The computer is one of the most powerful analysis tools available to the engineer, but the computer does not replace the engineer's thinking. When faced with a new analysis, the engineer must reason through the problem by using sound scientific principles, applied mathematics, and engineering judgement. A computer is only a machine, and, as yet, no machine has been developed that can outthink a human being (except at playing chess, perhaps). A computer can only carry out the instructions supplied to it, but it does so with remarkable speed and efficiency. A computer yields wrong answers just as quickly as it yields right ones. The burden is upon the engineer to supply the computer with correct input. An often-used engineering acronym is *GIGO* (Garbage *In*, Garbage *Out*), which refers to a situation in which erroneous input data is supplied to a computer, thereby producing erroneous output. When GIGO is at work, the calculations are numerically correct, but the results of those calculations are meaningless, because the engineer supplied the computer with bad input, or the computer program that the engineer wrote is flawed. The computer is capable of accurately performing enormous numbers of computations in a very short time, but it is incapable of composing a problem statement, constructing a diagram of the engineering system, formulating assumptions, selecting the appropriate governing equations, checking the reasonableness of the solution, or discussing and evaluating the results of the analysis. Thus, the only step in the analysis procedure for which a computer is perfectly suited is step 5: calculations. This is not to say that a computer cannot be used to write problem statements, assumptions and equations, as well as draw diagrams. These steps may also be performed by using the computer, but they must be developed by the engineer, whereas calculations are performed automatically once the equations and numerical inputs are supplied.

Engineers use analysis primarily as a design tool and as a means of predicting or investigating failures. Specifically, how does an engineer use the computer to perform an analysis? Steps 1 through 4 and steps 6 and 7 of the analysis procedure are largely unchanged, whether a computer is employed or not. So, exactly how are the calculations in step 5 carried out on a computer? There are basically five categories of computer tools for doing engineering analysis work:

1. Spreadsheets
2. Equation solvers and mathematics software
3. Programming languages
4. Specialty software
5. Finite element software

4.1 Spreadsheets

The term **spreadsheet** originally referred to a special type of paper, divided into rows and columns, for doing financial calculations. The computer-based spreadsheet is a modern electronic version of the paper spreadsheet and was initially used for business and accounting applications. By virtue of their general structure, spreadsheets are useful not only for doing financial calculations, but can also be used for performing a variety of scientific and engineering calculations. Like the original paper version, the computer-based spreadsheet consists of any array of rows and columns. The intersection of a row with a column is called a *cell*. Cells serve as locations for input and output data such as text, numbers, or formulas. For example, a cell may contain an equation representing Newton's second law of motion, $F = ma$. A nearby cell would contain a number for the mass, m, while another cell would contain a number for the acceleration, a. Immediately after entering these two input values in their respective cells, the spreadsheet automatically evaluates the formula, inserting the numerical value of the force, F, in the cell containing the formula for Newton's second law. If the values of the mass or acceleration are changed, the spreadsheet automatically updates the value of the force. This example is very simple, but spreadsheets are capable of doing calculations that involve hundreds or even thousands of variables. Suppose that our analysis involves 100 variables and that we want to know how changing only *one* of those variables affects the solution. We simply change the variable of interest and the entire spreadsheet automatically updates all calculations to reflect the change. The spreadsheet is an excellent analysis tool for rapidly answering "what if" questions. Numerous design alternatives can be efficiently investigated by performing the analysis on a spreadsheet. In addition to numerical functions, spreadsheets also have graphics capabilities. Excel,[1] Quattro Pro,[2] and Lotus 1-2-3[3] are popular spreadsheet products. Figure 3.5 shows a simple example of calculating force using Newton's second law by using Excel.

4.2 Equation Solvers and Mathematics Software

Equation solvers and **mathematics software** packages are general-purpose scientific and engineering tools for solving equations and performing symbolic mathematical operations. Equation solvers are primarily designed for solving problems that involve *numerical* inputs and outputs, whereas mathematics packages are primarily suited for performing *symbolic* mathematical operations much like you would do in a mathematics course. Equation solvers accept a set of equations that represent the mathematical model of the analytical problem. The equations can be linear or nonlinear. The equations may be written in their original form without prior mathematical manipulation to isolate the unknown quantities on one side of the equals sign. For example, Newton's second law would be written in its original form as $F = ma$ even if the unknown quantity was the acceleration a. Solving this problem by hand, however, we would have to write the equation as $a = F/m$ because we are solving for the acceleration. This is not necessary when we use equation solvers.

---

[1]Excel is a registered trademark of Microsoft® Corporation.

[2]Quattro® Pro is a registered trademark of Corel® Corporation.

[3]Lotus 1-2-3 is a registered trademark of Lotus® Development Corporation part of IBM®.

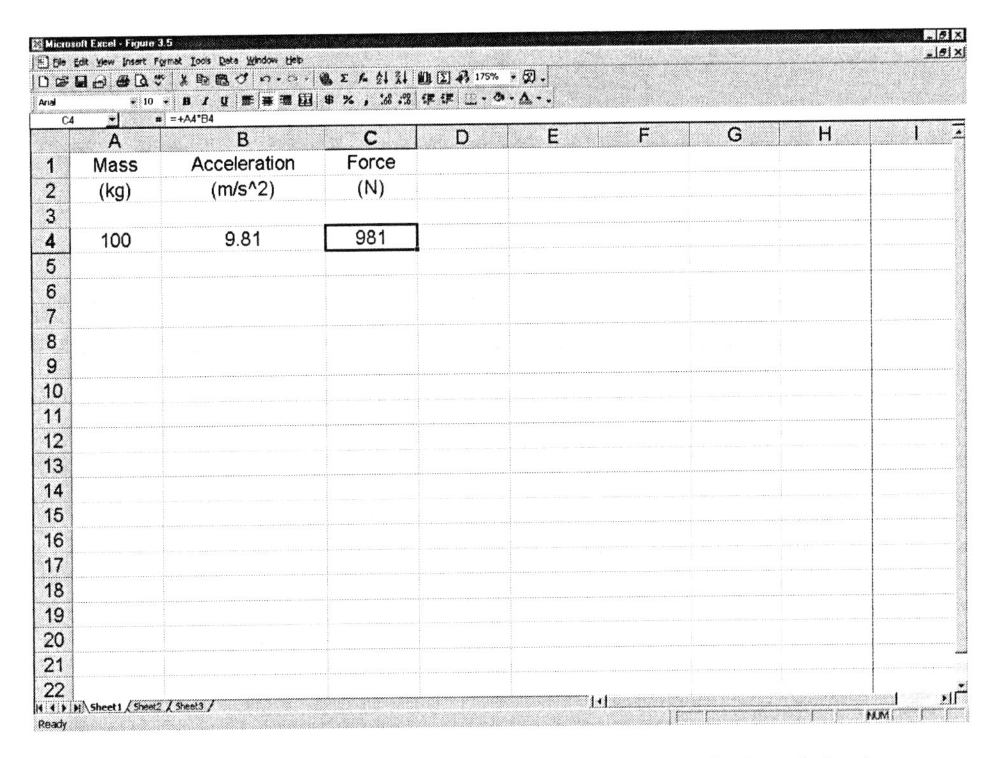

Figure 5. A calculation of Newton's second law using Excel. Note the formula for the force, + A4*B4, entered in cell C4.

After we supply the numerical values for the known quantities, equation solvers solve for the remaining unknown values. Equation solvers have a large built-in library of functions for use in trigonometry, linear algebra, statistics, and calculus. Equation solvers can perform a variety of mathematical operations, including differentiation, integration, and matrix operations. In addition to these mathematical features, equation solvers also do unit conversions. Equation solvers also have the capability of displaying results in graphical form. Programming can also be done within equation solvers. Although all equation solvers have some symbolic capabilities, some have the capacity for data acquisition, image analysis, and signal processing. Popular equation solvers are TK Solver,[4] Mathcad,[5] and Matlab.[6]

The strength of mathematics packages is their ability to perform symbolic mathematical operations. A symbolic mathematical operation is one that involves the manipulation of symbols (variables), using mathematical operators such as the vector product, differentiation, integration, and transforms. These packages are capable of performing very complex and sophisticated mathematical procedures. They also have extensive graphical capabilities. Even though mathematics packages are primarily designed for symbolic operations, they can also perform numerical computations. Mathematica[7] and Maple[8] are popular mathematics software products.

4.3 Programming Languages

Spreadsheets, equation solvers, and mathematics software packages may not always meet the computational demands of every engineering analysis. In such cases, engineers may

---

[4] TK Solver is a registered trademark of Universal Technical Systems, Incorporated.

[5] Mathcad® is a registered trademark of Mathsoft™, Incorporated.

[6] MATLAB® is a registered trademark of The MathWorks, Incorporated.

[7] MATHEMATICA® is a registered trademark of Wolfram Research, Incorporated.

[8] Maple™ is a registered trademark of Maplesoft™, a division of Waterloo Maple, Incorporated.

choose to write their own computer programs with the use of a programming language. **Programming languages** refer to sequential instructions supplied to a computer for carrying out specific calculations. Computer languages are generally categorized according to their level. *Machine language* is a low-level language, based on a binary system of "zeroes" and "ones." Machine language is the most primitive language, because computers are digital devices whose rudimentary logic functions are carried out by using solid state switches in the "on" or "off" positions. *Assembly language* is also a low-level language, but its instructions are written in English-like statements rather than binary. Assembly language does not have many commands, and it must be written specifically for the computer hardware. Computer programs written in low-level languages run very fast because these languages are tied closely to the hardware, but writing the programs is very tedious.

Due to the tediousness of writing programs in low-level languages, engineers usually write programs in high-level languages that consist of straightforward, English-like commands. The most commonly used high-level languages by engineers are Fortran, C, C++, Pascal, Ada, and BASIC. Fortran is the patriarch of all scientific programming languages. The first version of Fortran (FORmula TRANslation) was developed by IBM between 1954 and 1957. Since its inception, Fortran has been the workhorse of scientific and engineering programming languages. It has undergone several updates and improvements and is still in widespread use today. The C language evolved from two languages, BCPL and B, which were developed during the late 1960s. In 1972, the first C program was compiled. The C++ language grew out of C and was developed during the early 1980s. Both C and C++ are popular programming languages for engineering applications because they use powerful commands and data structures. Pascal was developed during the early 1970s and is a popular programming language for beginning computer science students who are learning programming for the first time. The U.S. Department of Defense prompted the development of Ada during the 1970s in order to have a high-level language suitable for embedded computer systems. BASIC (Beginner's All-purpose Symbolic Instruction Code) was developed during the mid-1960s as a simple learning tool for secondary school students as well as college students. BASIC is often included as part of the operating software for personal computers.

Writing programs in high-level languages is easier than writing programs in low-level languages, but the high-level languages utilize a larger number of commands. Furthermore, high-level languages must be written with specific grammatical rules, referred to as *syntax*. Rules of syntax govern how punctuation, arithmetic operators, parentheses, and other characters are used in writing commands. To illustrate the syntactical differences between programming languages, equation solvers and mathematics packages, Table 1 shows how a simple equation is written. Note the similarities and differences in the equals sign, the constant π, and the operator for exponentiation.

TABLE 1 Comparison of Computer Statements for the Equation, $V = 4/3\pi R^3$, the Volume of a Sphere

Computer Tool	Statement
Mathcad	V:=4/3*π*R^3
TK Solver	V = 4/3*pi()*R^3
MATLAB	V = 4/3*pi*R^3;
MATHEMATICA	V = 4/3*Pi*R^3
maple	V: = 4/3*pi*R^3;
Fortran	V = 4/3*3.141593*R**3
C, C++	V = 4/3*3.141593*pow(R,3);
Pascal	V: = 4/3*3.141593*R*R*R;
Ada	V: = 4/3*3.141593*R**3;
BASIC	V = 4/3*3.141593*R^3

4.4 Specialty Software

Considered as a whole, engineering is a broad field that covers a variety of disciplines and careers. Some of the main engineering disciplines are chemical engineering, civil engineering, electrical and computer engineering, environmental engineering, and mechanical engineering. Primary engineering career fields include research, development, design, analysis, manufacturing, and testing. Given the variety of specific problems that engineers who work in these fields encounter, it comes as no surprise that numerous *specialty software* packages are available to help the engineer analyze specific problems relating to a particular engineering system. For example, specialty software packages are available to electrical engineers for analyzing and simulating electrical circuits. Mechanical and chemical engineers can take advantage of software packages designed specifically for calculating flow parameters in pipe networks. Special software is available to civil and structural engineers for calculating forces and stresses in trusses and other structures. Other specialty software packages are available for performing analyses of heat exchangers, machinery, pressure vessels, propulsion systems, turbines, pneumatic and hydraulic systems, manufacturing processes, mechanical fasteners, and many others too numerous to list. After you graduate and begin working for a company that produces a specific product or process, you will probably become familiar with one or more of these specialty software packages.

4.5 Finite Element Software

Some engineering analysis problems are far too complex to solve using any of the aforementioned computer tools. *Finite element* software packages enable the engineer to analyze systems that have irregular configurations, variable material properties, complex conditions at the boundaries, and nonlinear behavior. The finite element method originated in the aerospace industry during the early 1950s when it was used for stress analysis of aircraft. Later, as the method matured, it found application in other analysis areas such as fluid flow, heat transfer, vibrations, impacts, acoustics, and electromagnetics. The basic concept behind the finite-element method is to subdivide a continuous region (i.e., the system to be analyzed is divided into a set of simple geometric shapes called "finite elements"). The elements are interconnected at common points called "nodes." Material properties, conditions at the system boundaries, and other pertinent inputs are supplied. With the use of an advanced mathematical procedure, the finite element software calculates the value of parameters such as stress, temperature, flow rate, or vibration frequency at each node in the region. Hence, the engineer is provided with a set of output parameters at discrete points that approximates a continuous distribution of those parameters for the entire region. The finite element method is an advanced analysis method and is normally introduced in colleges and universities at the senior level or the first-year graduate level.

PROFESSIONAL SUCCESS: PITFALLS OF USING COMPUTERS

The vital role that computers play in engineering analysis cannot be overstated. Given the tremendous advantages of using computers for engineering analysis, however, it may be difficult to accept the fact that there are also pitfalls. A common hazard that entangles some engineers is the tendency to treat the computer as a "black box," a wondrous electronic device whose inner workings are largely unknown, but that nonetheless provides output for every input supplied. Engineers who treat the computer as a black box are not effectively employing the general analysis procedure and in so doing are in danger of losing their ability to systematically reason their way through a problem. The computer is a remarkable computational machine, but it does not replace the engineer's thinking, reasoning, and judgement. Computers, and the software that runs on them, produce output that *precisely* reflects the input supplied to them. If the input is good, the output will be good. If the input is bad, the output will be bad. Computers are not smart enough to compensate for an engineer's inability to make good assumptions or employ the correct governing equations. Engineers must have a thorough understanding of the physical aspects of the problem at hand and the underlying mathematical principles *before* implementing the solution on the computer. A good engineer understands *what* the computer does when it "crunches the numbers" in the analysis. A good engineer is confident that the input data will result in reasonable output because a lot of sound thinking and reasoning has gone into the formulation of that input.

Can the computer be used too much? In a sense, it can. The tendency of some engineers is to use the computer to analyze problems that may not require a computer at all. Upon beginning a new problem, their first impulse is to set up the problem on the computer without even checking to see whether the problem can be solved by hand. For example, a problem in engineering statics may be represented by the quadratic equation, $x^2 + 4x - 12 = 0$.

This problem can be solved analytically by factoring, $(x + 6)(x - 2) = 0$, which yields the two roots, $x = -6$ and $x = 2$. To use the computer in a situation like this is to rely on the computer as a "crutch" to compensate for weak analytical skills. Continued reliance on the computer to solve problems that do not require a computer will gradually dull your ability to solve problems with pencil and paper. Do not permit this to happen. Examine the equations carefully to see whether a computer solution is justified. If it is, use one of the computer tools discussed earlier. If not, solve the problem by hand. Then, if you have time and wish to check your solution with the use of the computer, by all means do so.

APPLICATION: COMPUTERS FOR NUMERICAL ANALYSIS

Most of the equations that you will encounter in school can be solved analytically; that is, they can be solved by employing standard algebraic operations to isolate the desired variable on one side of the equation. Some equations, however, cannot be solved analytically with standard algebraic operations. These equations are referred to as *transcendental* equations because they contain one or more transcendental functions such as a logarithm or trigonometric function. Transcendental equations occur often in engineering analysis work, and techniques for solving them are known as *numerical methods*. For example, consider the transcendental equation

$$e^x - 3x = 0$$

This equation looks straightforward enough, but try solving it by hand. If we add $3x$ to both sides and take the natural logarithm of both sides to undo the exponential function, we obtain

$$x = \ln(3x) \qquad \text{(a)}$$

which, unfortunately, does not isolate the variable, x, because we still have the term $\ln(3x)$ on the right side of the equation. If we add $3x$ to both sides and then divide both sides by 3, we obtain

$$\frac{e^x}{3} = x \qquad \text{(b)}$$

The variable, x, is still not isolated without leaving a transcendental function in the equation. Clearly, this equation cannot be solved analytically, so it must be solved numerically. To solve it numerically, we utilize a method called *iteration*, a process by which we repeat the calculation until an answer is obtained.

Before solving this problem by using the computer, we will work it manually to illustrate how iteration works. To begin, we rewrite Equation (a) in the iterative form

$$x_{i+1} = \ln(3x_i)$$

The "i" and the "$i + 1$" subscripts refer to "old" and "new" values of x, respectively. The iteration process requires that we begin the calculation by immediately substituting a number into the iteration formula. This first number constitutes an estimate for the root (or roots) of the variable, x, that satisfy the formula. To keep track of the iterations, we use an iteration table, illustrated in Table 3.2. To start the iterations, we estimate a value of x by letting $x_i = 1$. We now substitute this number into the right side of the formula, yielding a new value of $x_{i+1} = 1.098612$. We then assign this new value of x to the old variable, x_i, and substitute it into the right side of the formula, yielding the second new value, $x = 1.192660$. Substituting this number into the right side of the formula, we obtain the third new value,

TABLE 2 Iteration Table for Finding One Root of the Equation $e^x - 3x = 0$

Iteration	x_i	x_{i+1}
1	1	1.098612
2	1.098612	1.192660
3	1.192660	1.274798
4	1.274798	1.341400
5	1.341400	1.392326
.		
.		1.512134
41	1.512134	1.512135

$x_{i+1} = 1.274798$. This process is repeated until the value of x stops changing by the desired amount. At this point, we say that the calculation has *converged* to an answer. Table 2 shows the first five iterations and indicates that 41 iterations are required for the calculation to converge to an answer that is accurate to the sixth decimal place. Upon substituting $x = 1.512135$ into the original equation, we see that the equation is satisfied. As this example illustrates, numerous iterations may be required to obtain an accurate solution. The accuracy of the answer depends on how many iterations are taken. Some equations converge to a precise answer in a few iterations, but others, like this one, require several iterations. It is important to note that 1.512135 is not the only root of this equation. The equation has a second root at $x = 0.619061$. If we attempt to find this root by using Equation (a), we discover that our calculation either converges again to 1.512135 or does not converge at all by leading us to an illegal operation; that is, taking the logarithm of a negative number. To find the second root, we iterate on Equation (b), writing it in the iterative form

$$x_{i+1} = \frac{e^{x_i}}{3}$$

With numerical methods, there are often no guarantees that a certain iteration formula will converge rapidly or even converge at all. The success of the iteration formula may also depend on the initial estimate chosen to start the iterations. If our initial estimate for Equation (a) is less than $\frac{1}{3}$, the new value of x immediately goes negative, leading to an illegal operation. If our initial estimate for Equation (b) is too large, the new value of x grows large very rapidly, leading to an exponential overflow. These and other kinds of numerical difficulties can occur whether the iterations are performed by hand or by using a computer.

As Table 2 suggests, performing iterations by hand can be a long and tedious task. The computer is tailor-made for performing repetitive calculations. The roots of our transcendental equation can readily be found by using one of the computer tools discussed earlier. Figure 6 shows a computer program, written in the BASIC language, for finding the first root, $x = 1.512135$. In the first line the user inputs an initial estimate, which is assigned the variable name XOLD. The program then executes what is referred to as a DO loop that performs the iterations. Each time through the loop, a new value of x is calculated from the old value and an absolute value of the difference between the old and new values is calculated. This value is called DIFF. While DIFF is larger than a preselected convergence tolerance of 0.0000001, the new value of x, XNEW, is reset to the old value, XOLD, and looping continues. When DIFF is less than, or equal to, the convergence tolerance, convergence has been achieved, and looping is halted. The root is then printed. The same program, with the third line replaced with XNEW = EXP(XOLD)/3, could be used to find the second root. There are more sophisticated numerical methods for finding roots than the simple iteration technique illustrated here, and you will study them in your engineering or mathematics courses.

```
INPUT "ESTIMATE = ", XOLD
DO
      XNEW = LOG (3*XOLD)
      DIFF = ABS (XNEW - XOLD)
      XOLD = XNEW
LOOP WHILE DIFF > 0.0000001
PRINT XNEW
END
```

Figure 6. BASIC computer program for finding one root of the equation $e^x - 3x = 0$.

PRACTICE!

Using one of the computer tools discussed in this section, work the following problems:
(Note: These problems are identical to those in Section 3.)

1. Radioactive waste is to be permanently encased in concrete and buried in the ground. The vessel containing the waste measures 30 cm × 30 cm × 80 cm.

Federal regulations dictate that there must be a minimum concrete thickness of 50 cm surrounding the vessel on all sides. What is the minimum volume of concrete required to safely encase the radioactive waste?
Answer: 2.97 m^3

2. An elevator in an office building has an operating capacity of 15 passengers with a maximum weight of 180 lb$_f$ each. The elevator is suspended by a special pulley system with four cables, two of which support 20 percent of the total load and two of which support 80 percent of the total load. Find the maximum tension in each elevator cable.
Answer: 270 lb$_f$, 1080 lb$_f$
3. A technician measures a voltage drop of 25 V across a 100-Ω resistor by using a digital voltmeter. Using Ohm's law, we find that $V = IR$. What is the current flow through the resistor? How much power is consumed by the resistor? (*Hint*: $P = I^2R$.)
Answer: 250 mA, 6.25 W
4. Air flows through a main duct at a mass flow rate of 4 kg/s. The main duct enters a junction that splits into two branch ducts, one with a cross section of 20 cm $\times$ 30 cm and one with a cross section of 40 cm $\times$ 60 cm. If the mass flow rate in the large branch is 2.8 kg/s, what is the mass flow rate in the small branch? If the density of air is $\rho = 1.16$ kg/m^3, what is the velocity in each branch?
Answer: 1.2 kg/s, 10.1 m/s, 17.2 m/s

KEY TERMS

engineering method
equation solver
general analysis procedure
mathematics software
order of magnitude
programming language
significant figure
spreadsheet

REFERENCES

Bahder, T.B., *Mathematica for Scientists and Engineers*, NY: Addison-Wesley, 1995.
Dubin, D., *Numerical and Analytical Methods for Scientists and Engineers Using Mathematica*, NY: John Wiley & Sons, 2003.
Etter, D.M. *Introduction to* C++, Upper Saddle River, NJ: Prentice Hall, 1999.
Etter, D.M. and Kuncicky, D.C. *Introduction to Matlab 6*, Upper Saddle River, NJ: Prentice Hall, 2004.
Ferguson, R.J., *TK Solver for Engineers*, NY: Addison-Wesley, 1996.
Kuncicky, D.C., *Introduction to Excel* 2002, Upper Saddle River, NJ: Prentice Hall, 2003.
Larsen, R.W., *Introduction to Mathcad* 11, Upper Saddle River, NJ: Prentice Hall, 2004.
Nyhoff, L. and S. Leestma, *Introduction to FORTRAN 90*, 2d ed., Upper Saddle River, NJ: Prentice Hall, 1999.
Schwartz, D.I., *Introduction to Maple* 8, Upper Saddle River, NJ: Prentice Hall, 2003.

Problems

1. Using an order-of-magnitude analysis, estimate the number of gallons of gasoline used by all automobiles in the United States each year.

2. Using an order-of-magnitude analysis, estimate the number of 4 ft $\times$ 8 ft plywood sheets required for the floor, roof, and exterior sheathing of a 3000-ft^2 house.

3. Using an order-of-magnitude analysis, estimate the number of basketballs (fully inflated) that would fit in your engineering classroom.

4. Using an order-of-magnitude analysis, estimate the number of spam e-mail messages received by residents of the United States each year.

5. Using an order-of-magnitude analysis, estimate the number of breaths you will take during your lifetime.

6. Use an order-of-magnitude analysis to estimate the number of short tons of human waste produced worldwide each year.

7. The earth has a mean radius of about 6.37×10^6 m. Assuming the earth is made of granite ($\rho = 2770\ \mathrm{kg/m^3}$), estimate the mass of the earth, using an order-of-magnitude analysis.

8. The solar radiation flux just outside the earth's atmosphere is about 1350 $\mathrm{W/m^2}$. Using an order-of-magnitude analysis, estimate the amount of solar energy that is intercepted by the United States each year.

9. Using an order-of-magnitude analysis, estimate the total textbook expenditure incurred by all engineering majors at your school per year.

10. Underline the significant figures in the following numbers (the first number is done for you):

    a. 3450
    b. 9.807
    c. 0.00216
    d. 5000
    e. 7000.
    f. 12.00
    g. 2066
    h. 106.07
    i. 0.02880
    j. 523.91
    k. 1.207×10^{-3}

11. Perform the following calculations, reporting the answers with the correct number of significant figures:

    a. (8.14)(260)
    b. 456/4.9
    c. (6.74)(41.07)/8.72
    d. (10.78 − 4.5)/300
    e. (10.78 − 4.50)/300.0
    f. (65.2 − 13.9)/240.0
    g. $(1.2 \times 10^6)/(4.52 \times 10^3 + 988)$
    h. $(1.764 - 0.0391)/(8.455 \times 10^4)$
    i. $1000/(1.003 \times 10^9)$

j. $(8.4 \times 10^{-3})/5000$
k. $(8.40 \times 10^{3})/5000.0$
l. 8π
m. $(2\pi - 5)/10$

12. A 250-kg mass hangs by a cable from the ceiling. Using the standard value of gravitational acceleration, $g = 9.81$ m/s^2, what is the tension in the cable? Express your answer with the correct number of significant figures.

13. A 9-slug mass hangs by a rope from the ceiling. Using the standard value of gravitational acceleration, $g = 32.2$ ft/s^2, what is the tension in the rope? Express your answer with the correct number of significant figures. Redo the problem, using a mass of 9.00 slug. Is the answer different? Why?

14. A 175 mA current flows through a 62-Ω resistor. Using Ohm's law, $V = IR$, what is the voltage across the resistor? Express your answer with the correct number of significant figures.

15. A rectangular building lot is reported to have the dimensions 200 ft × 300 ft. Using the correct number of significant figures, what is the area of this lot in units of acre?

For problems 16 through 31, use the general analysis procedure of (1) problem statement, (2) diagram, (3) assumptions, (4) governing equations, (5) calculations, (6) solution check, and (7) discussion.

16. An excavation crew digs a hole in the ground measuring 20 yd × 30 yd × 6 yd to facilitate a basement for a small office building. Five dump trucks, each with a capacity of 20 yd^3, are used to haul the material away. How many trips must each truck make to remove all the material?

17. Find the current in each resistor and the total current for the circuit shown in Figure P17.

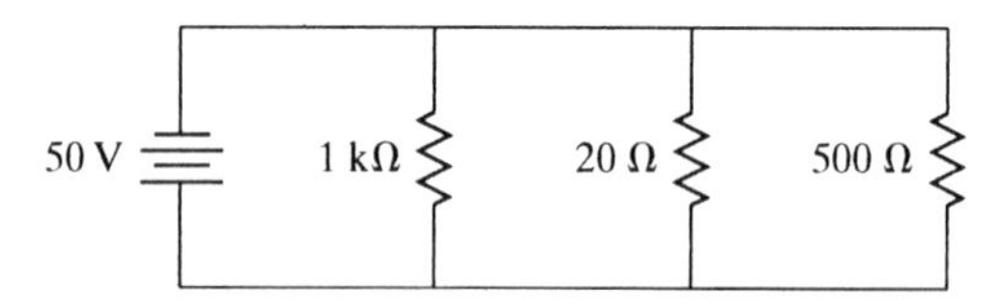

Figure P17.

18. For easy handling, long sheets of steel for manufacturing automobile body panels are tightly rolled up into a cylinder-shaped package. Consider a roll of steel with an inside and outside diameter of 45 cm and 1.6 m, respectively, that is suspended by a single cable. If the length of the roll is 2.25 m and the density of steel is $\rho = 7850$ kg/m^3, what is the tension in the cable?

19. In a chemical processing plant, glycerin flows toward a pipe junction at a mass flow rate of 30 kg/s as shown in Figure P3.19. If the mass flow rate in the small pipe branch is 8 kg/s, find the velocity in both branches. The density of glycerin is $\rho = 1260$ kg/m^3.

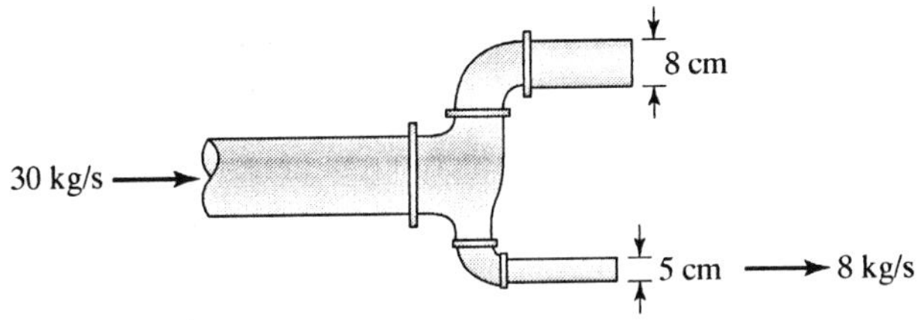

Figure P19.

20. A portable classroom is heated with small propane heating units with a capacity of 3 kW each. The portable classroom is occupied by 24 students, each dissipating 120 W, and is lighted by 10 light fixtures that dissipate 100 W each. If the heat loss from the portable classroom is 15 kW, how many heating units are required to maintain the classroom at a temperature of 20°C?

21. A man pushes on a barrel with a force of $P = 80\ \mathrm{lb}_f$ as shown. Assuming that the barrel does not move, what is the friction force between the barrel and the floor? (*Hint:* The friction force acts parallel to the floor toward the man. See Figure P21.)

Figure P21.

22. The total resistance for resistors connected in series is the arithmetic sum of the resistances. Find the total resistance for the series circuit shown in Figure P22. Because the resistors are connected in series, the current is the same in each resistor. Using Ohm's law, find this current. Also, find the voltage drop across each resistor.

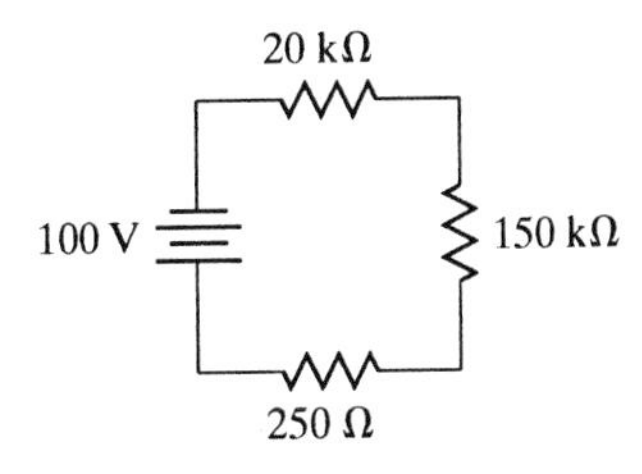

Figure P22.

23. The pressure exerted by a static liquid on a vertical submerged surface is calculated from the relation

$$P = \rho g h$$

where

P = pressure (Pa)
ρ = density of the liquid (kg/m^3)
g = gravitational acceleration = 9.81 m/s^2
h = height of vertical surface that is submerged (m)

Consider the dam shown in Figure P23. What is the pressure exerted on the dam's surface at depths of 2 m, 6 m, and 20 m? For the density of water, use $\rho = 1000\ kg/m^3$.

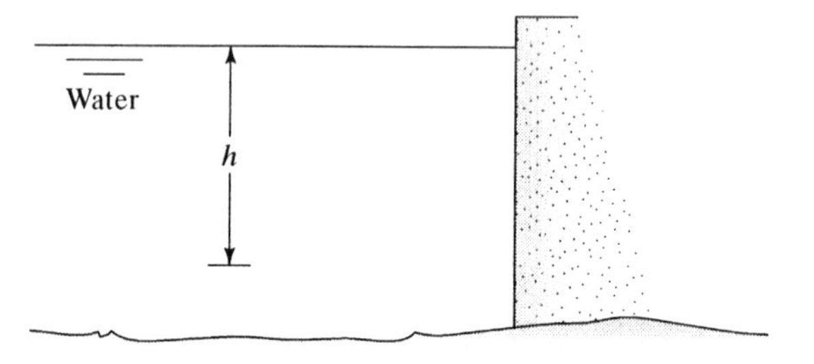

Figure P23.

24. Work Problem 16, using one of the computer tools discussed in this chapter.

25. Work Problem 17, using one of the computer tools discussed in this chapter.

26. Work Problem 18, using one of the computer tools discussed in this chapter.

27. Work Problem 19, using one of the computer tools discussed in this chapter.

28. Work Problem 20, using one of the computer tools discussed in this chapter.

29. Work Problem 21, using one of the computer tools discussed in this chapter.

30. Work Problem 22, using one of the computer tools discussed in this chapter.

31. Work Problem 23, using one of the computer tools discussed in this chapter.

5

Graphing with Excel

SECTIONS

OBJECTIVES

After reading this chapter, you will know

- How to import data for graphing
- How to create an XY Scatter plot
- How to modify plot formatting
- How to add trend lines to graphs
- How to add error bars to graphs

1 INTRODUCTION

An Excel spreadsheet is a convenient place to generate graphs. The process is quick and easy, and Excel gives you a lot of control over the appearance of the graph. Once a graph is created, you can then begin analyzing your data by adding a trendline to a graphed data set with just a few mouse clicks. The majority of Excel's trendlines are regression lines, and the equation of the best-fit curve through your data set is immediately available. Excel graphs are great tools for visualizing and analyzing data.

2 GETTING READY TO GRAPH

You must have some data in the spreadsheet before creating a graph, and those data can come from a variety of sources. Creating a graph from values that were calculated within the spreadsheet is probably the most common, but data can also be imported from data files, copied from other programs (such as getting data from the Internet by using a browser), or perhaps even read directly from an experiment that uses automated data acquisition. Once the data, from whatever source, are in your spreadsheet, there are some things you can do to make graphing quicker and easier. That is the subject of this section on getting ready to create a graph.

Excel provides a *Chart Wizard* to speed the process of creating a graph. The wizard will try to analyze your data and automatically fill in a number of required fields to help create the graph. You can assist the process by laying out your data in a standard form. A typical set of data for plotting might look like this:

	A	B	C
1	**Temperature vs. Time Data**		
2			
3	Time (sec.)	Temp. (°C)	
4	0	54.23	
5	1	45.75	
6	2	28.41	
7	3	28.30	
8	4	26.45	
9	5	17.36	
10	6	17.64	
11	7	9.51	
12	8	5.76	
13	9	8.55	
14	10	6.58	
15	11	4.62	
16	12	2.73	
17	13	2.91	
18	14	0.32	
19	15	1.68	
20			

Excel is fairly flexible, but the typical data layout for an *X–Y* graph, such as the preceding, includes the following elements:

- The data to be plotted on the *x*-axis (Time) are stored in a single column.
    - No blank rows exist between the first *x* value and the last *x* value.
- The data to be plotted on the *y*-axis (Temp.) are stored in a single column to the right of the column of *x* values.
    - No blank rows exist between the first *y* value and the last *y* value.
    - The series name may be included in the cell directly above the first *y* value. If the top cell in the *y* values column contains text rather than a number, Excel will use that text as the name of the series and will include that name in the graph's legend.

Keeping data in columns is the most common practice, but rows will also work. The same data set shown above would look as follows if it were stored in rows. (Only the first seven values of each row have been shown.)

	A	B	C	D	E	F	G	H
1	**Temperature vs. Time Data**							
2								
3	Time (sec.)	0	1	2	3	4	5	6
4	Temp. (°C)	54.23	45.75	28.41	28.30	26.45	17.36	17.64
5								

By putting your data into a standard form, you make it possible for the Chart Wizard to assist in the creation of graphs, so creating graphs in Excel becomes even easier.

3 CREATING AN XY SCATTER PLOT

Once you have a block of data in the spreadsheet, it can be plotted by following these steps:

1. Select the Data Range
2. Start the Chart Wizard
3. Select the Chart Type
4. Check the Data Series
5. Format Basic Graph Features
6. Select the Location for the Graph

Select the Data Range

The majority of graphs used by engineers are XY Scatter plots, so preparing this type of graph is covered here. Other types of graphs available in Excel are described in Section 7.

For an XY Scatter plot, select the two columns (or rows) of data to be graphed and call up Excel's Chart Wizard to assist you with this task. Excel assumes that the first column (or row) of data contains the x values and that the second column (or row) contains the y values.

To select the data to be plotted, simply click on the cell containing the first x value and hold the left mouse button down as you move the mouse pointer to the cell containing the last y value. In the temperature-versus-time data shown here, cells A4 through B19 have been selected for graphing.

	A	B	C
1	Temperature vs. Time Data		
2			
3	Time (sec.)	Temp. (°C)	
4	0	54.23	
5	1	45.75	
6	2	28.41	
7	3	28.30	
8	4	26.45	
9	5	17.36	
10	6	17.64	
11	7	9.51	
12	8	5.76	
13	9	8.55	
14	10	6.58	
15	11	4.62	
16	12	2.73	
17	13	2.91	
18	14	0.32	
19	15	1.68	
20			

Including Series Names

Excel will interpret any text in the top row of the column of y values as the name of the series and will automatically use this name in the legend that is created for the graph. If you want to use this feature, then include the column headings in the selected range (A3:B19 in this example).

	A	B	C
1	**Temperature vs. Time Data**		
2			
3	Time (sec.)	Temp. (°C)	
4	0	54.23	
5	1	45.75	
6	2	28.41	
7	3	28.30	
8	4	26.45	
9	5	17.36	
10	6	17.64	
11	7	9.51	
12	8	5.76	
13	9	8.55	
14	10	6.58	
15	11	4.62	
16	12	2.73	
17	13	2.91	
18	14	0.32	
19	15	1.68	
20			

Note: The degree symbol may be entered in several ways:

1. *From the numeric keypad (not the numbers at the top of the keyboard), press [Alt-0176]; that is, hold down the [Alt] key while pressing 0176 on the numeric keypad.*
2. *Use Insert/Symbol, and select the degree symbol from the list of available symbols.*

Start the Chart Wizard

Click on the Chart Wizard button on the standard toolbar or select Insert/Chart....

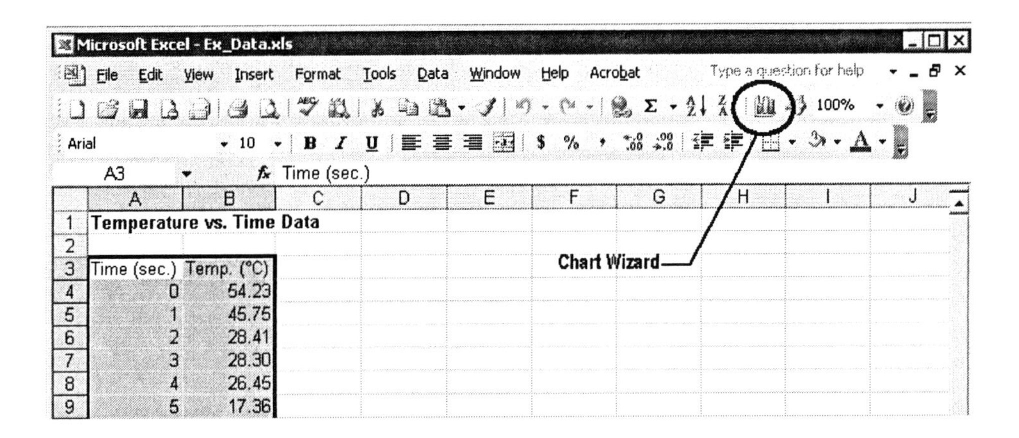

Select a Chart Type

The Chart Wizard will first ask you to select a graph type. The most common graph type for scientific work is the XY (Scatter) graph, which has been highlighted in the menu illustrated next. You can also choose how you want the points connected. In the following figure, *smooth curves with data-point markers* has been selected:

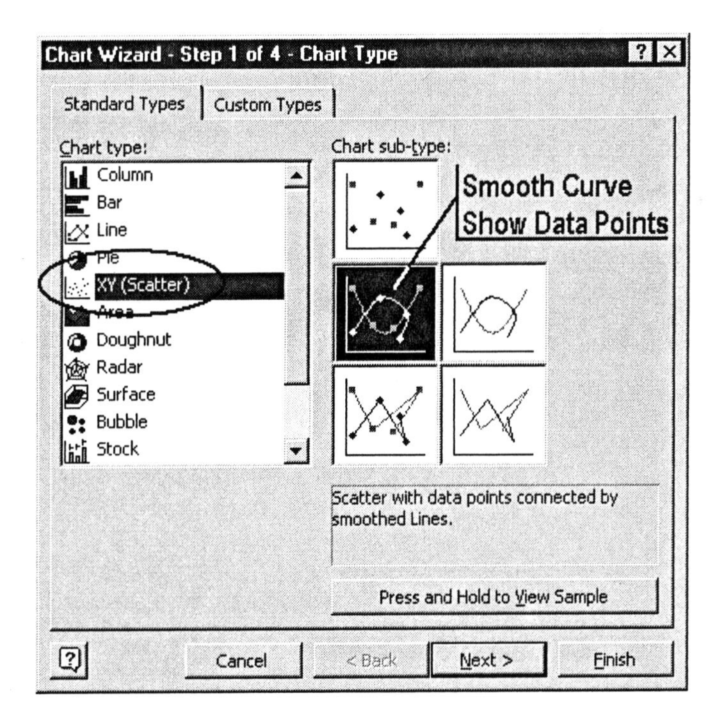

Click Next > to continue.

Check the Data Series

The Chart Wizard indicates the range of cells containing the data and shows a preview of what your graph will look like, using all the default parameters. On this screen, click on the Series tab:

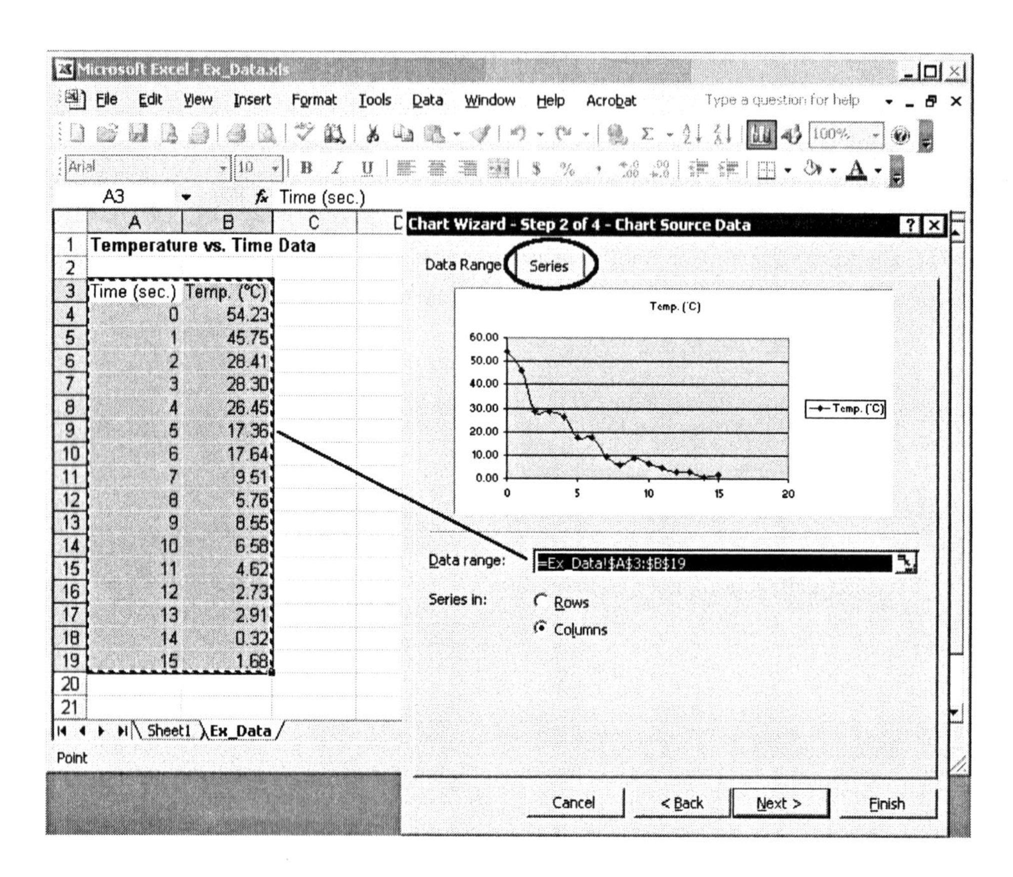

On the Series panel, notice that the contents of cell B3 are being used as the name of the series. This is because we included the y-column heading in the range selected for graphing. The series name is also used, by default, in the legend and as the graph title. If you want to use a different name for the series (and in the legend), enter the new name in the Name field. The graph title may be changed in the next step of the Chart Wizard.

Press Next > to continue.

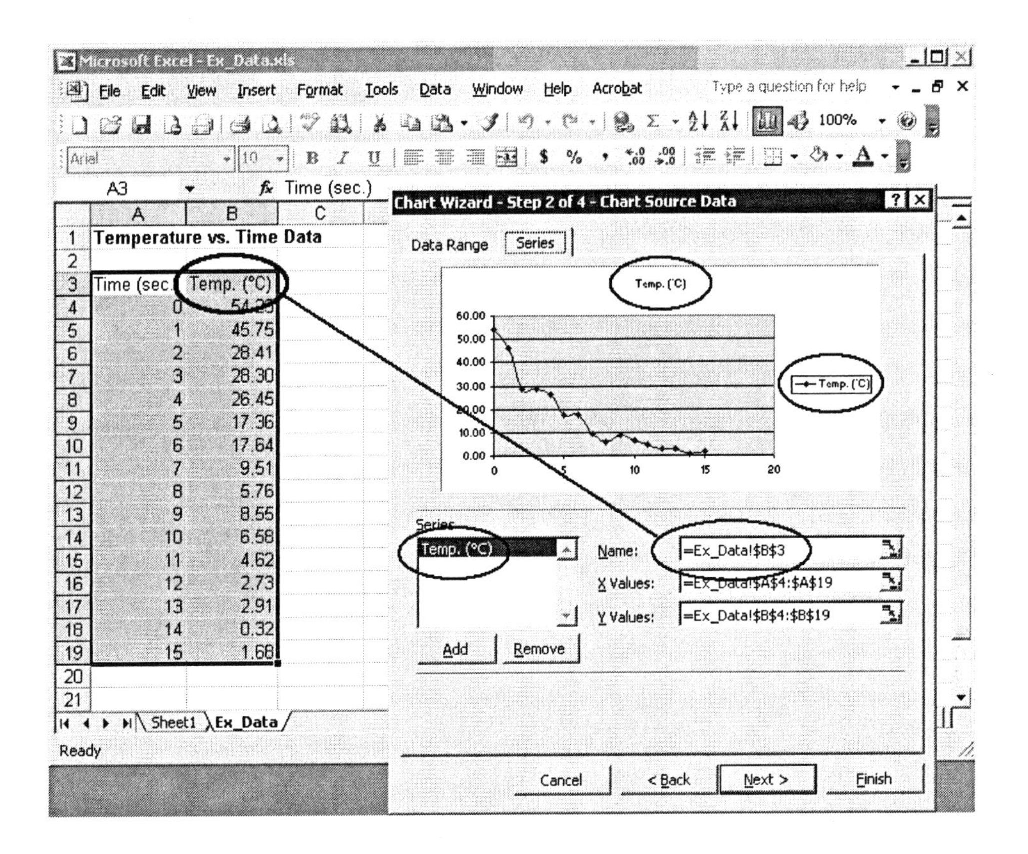

Formatting the Graph

We can now enter titles for the graph:

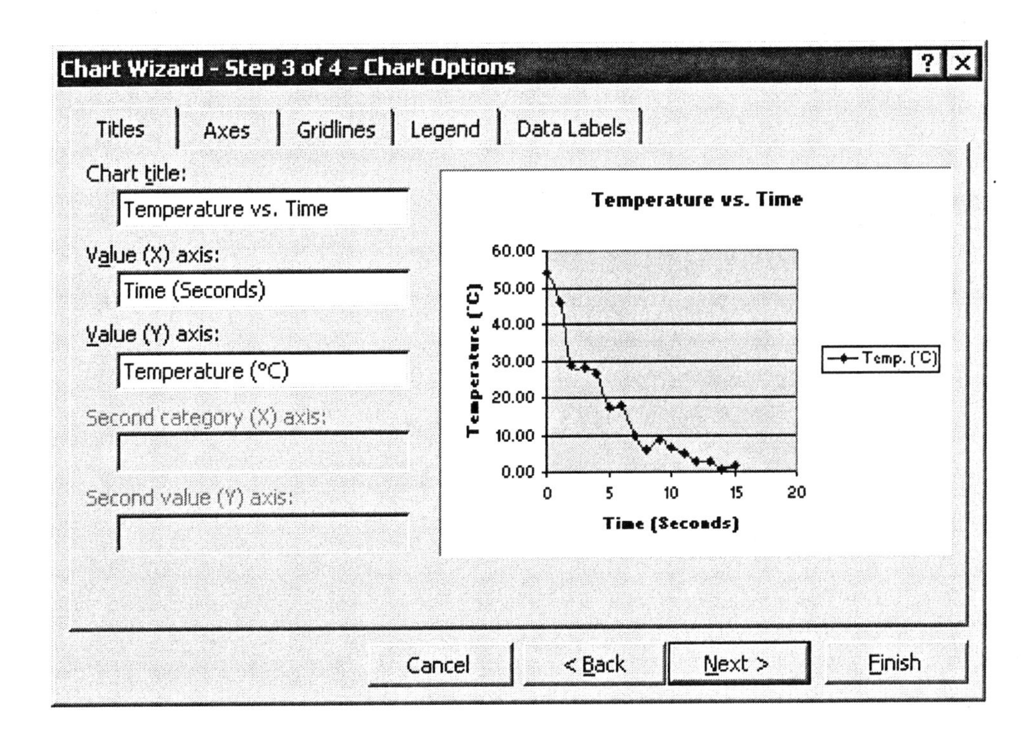

Note: The degree symbol must be entered from the numeric keypad as [Alt-0176], since Insert/Symbol is not available.

You can also use this screen to change a variety of other chart features. For example, the *legend* is taking up a lot of space, so let's move it to the bottom of the chart. To do this, click on the Legend tab, and select "Bottom."

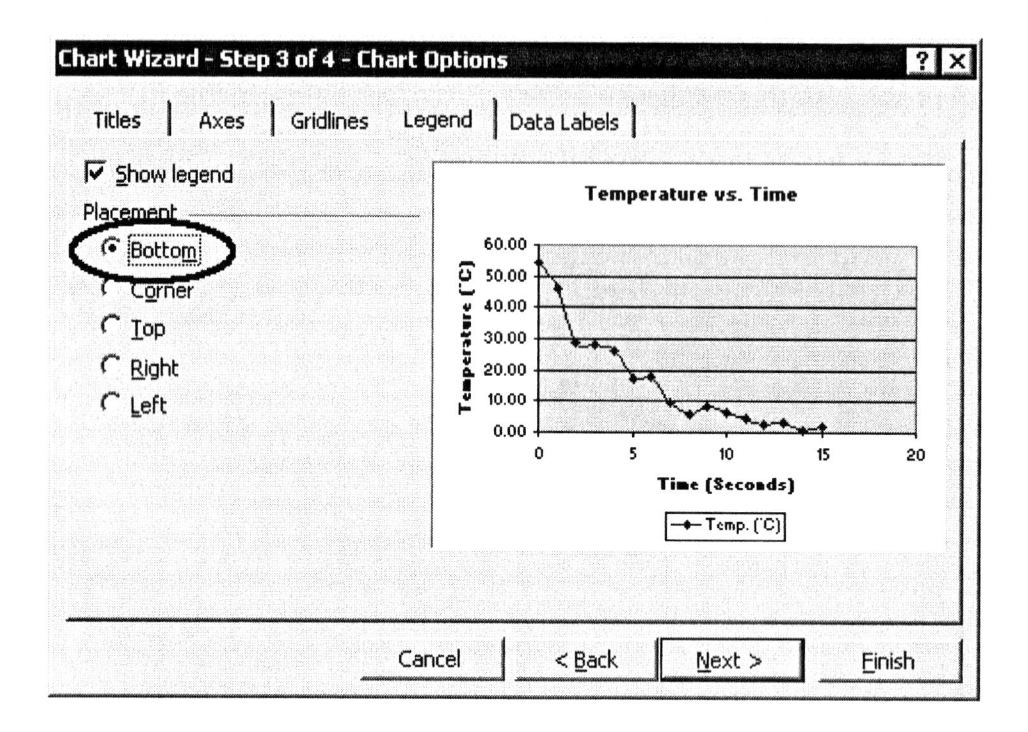

If you did not want a legend, you would clear the check box in front of the "Show legend" label.

When you are done changing chart options, press Next > to continue.

Placing the Graph on the Worksheet

The final Chart Wizard screen asks where you want to put your graph. The default is to place the graph on the current spreadsheet, called Ex_Data in this example. Click "Finish" to accept the default:

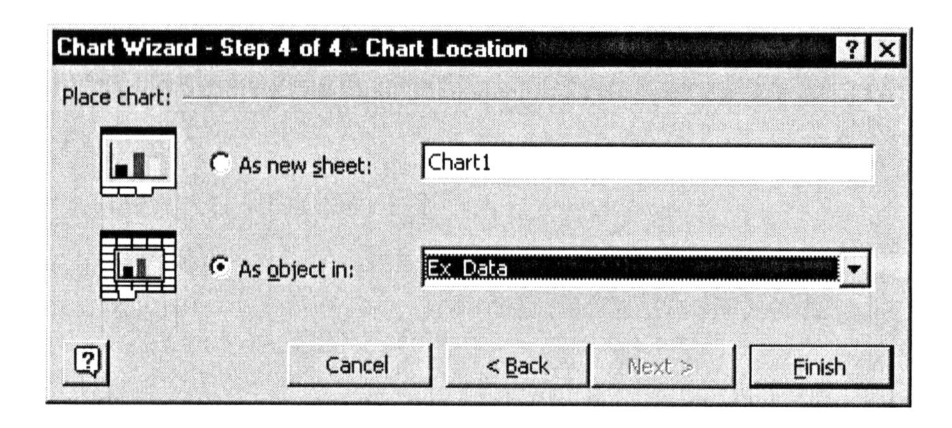

At this point, the Chart Wizard places your graph on the spreadsheet:

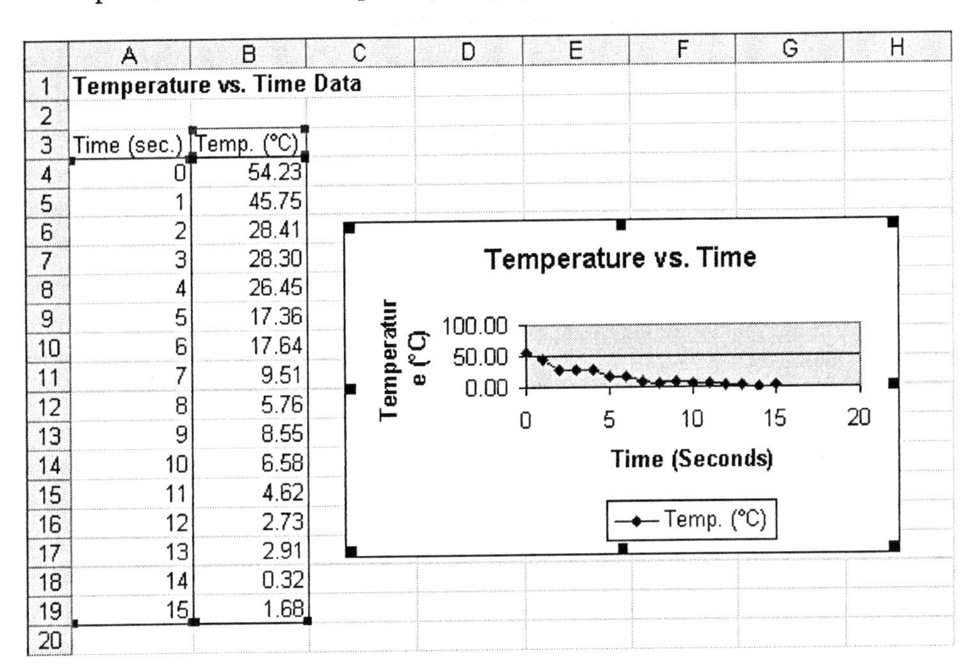

The size and location are set by default and can look unappealing, but they can be changed. Also, you can continue to edit the graph after it has been placed on the spreadsheet.

4 EDITING AN EXISTING GRAPH

4.1 Modifying Graph Features

You can still change the appearance of the graph. Click anywhere on the graph to enter edit mode. A graph in edit mode is indicated by squares (called *handles*) located around the border. Click and drag on any white space inside the graph to move the graph

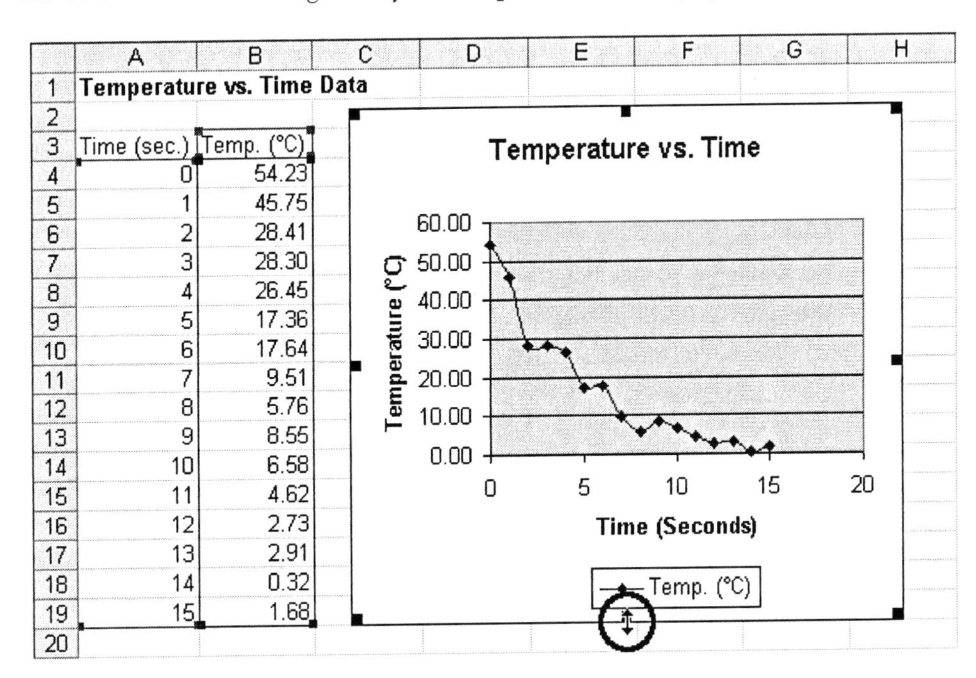

around on the spreadsheet. Or grab a handle with the mouse and drag it to change the size of the graph as follows:

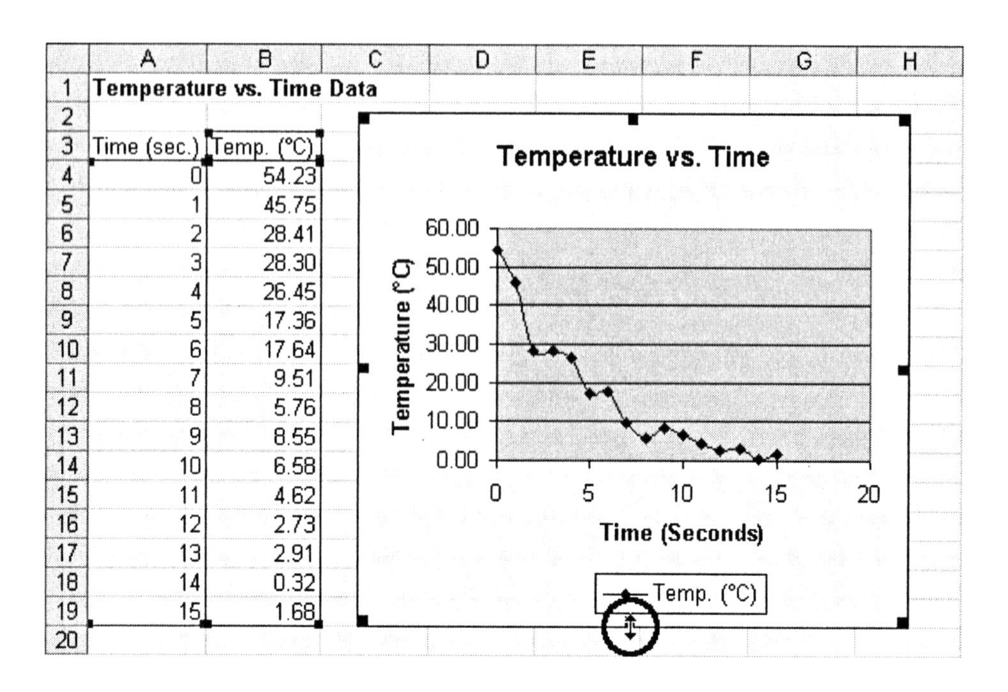

There are three ways to change an existing graph (after entering edit mode):

1. Right click on the graph to bring up a menu of options.
2. Double click on a particular feature of the graph (e.g., an axis, a curve, or the legend) to bring up a dialog box for that feature. For example, double clicking the graph's background brings up the following dialog box:

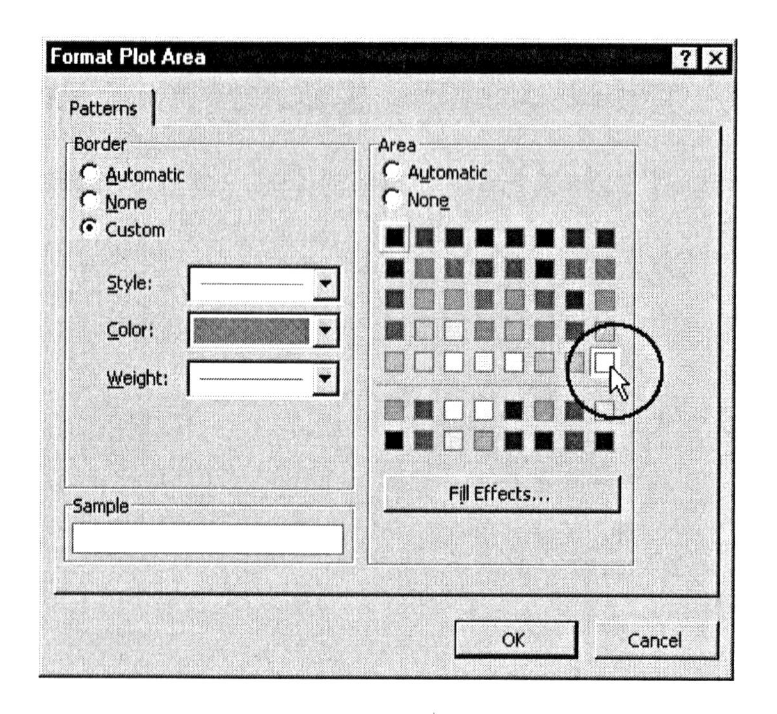

To get rid of the shaded background, change the properties of the *plot area*. Click on the white color sample to change the background color to white.

3. Select a feature from the Chart toolbar. To activate the Chart toolbar, select View/Toolbars/Chart. The Chart toolbar is displayed only when a graph is in edit mode:

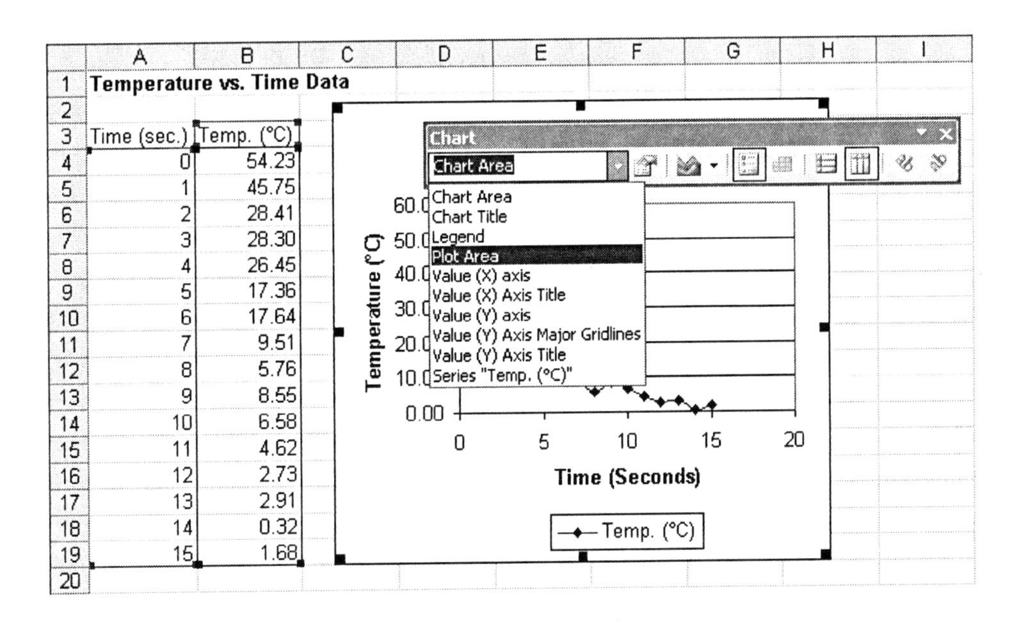

There are many properties of the chart, axes, and curves that may be set. As a typical illustration, consider changing the scaling on the x-axis from automatic (the default) to manual with a maximum value of 15. To change the scaling on the x-axis, double click it. The Format Axis dialog box will appear:

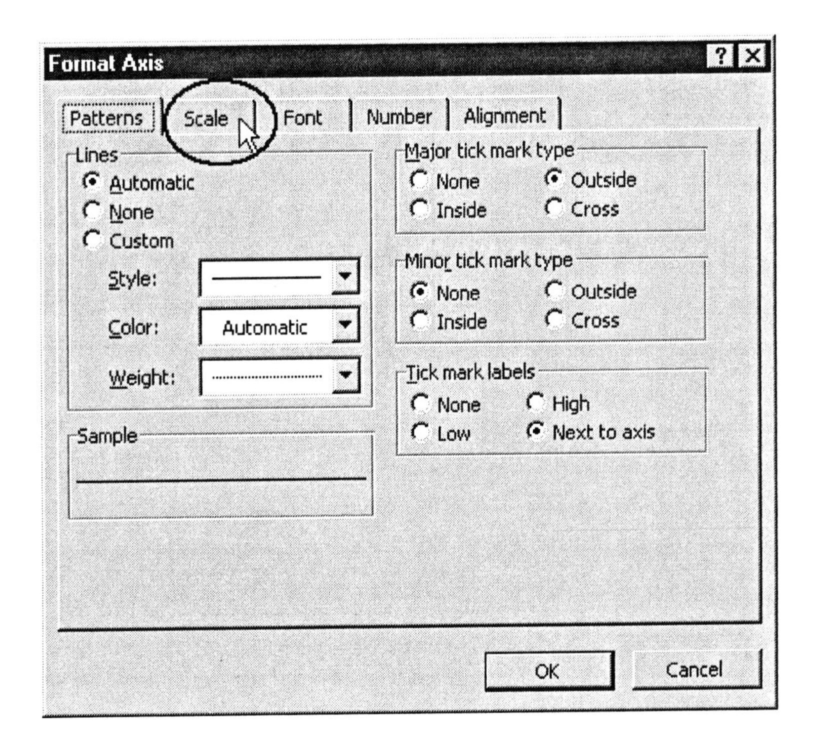

The Format Axis dialog box has a number of panels. In the Scale section, the maximum value displayed on the x-axis was changed from 20 to 15. When you enter a value for an axis limit, the Auto (*automatic scaling*) check box for that limit is automatically cleared:

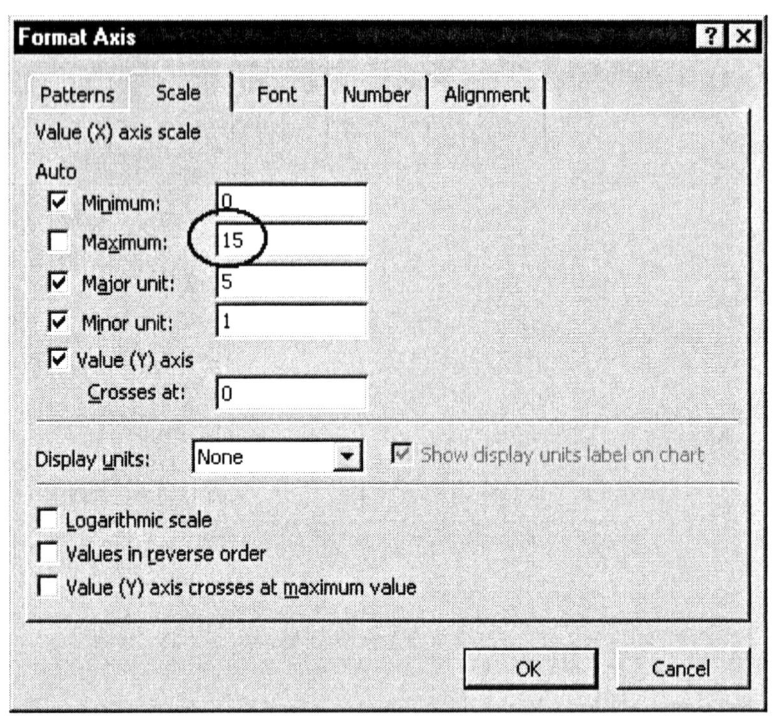

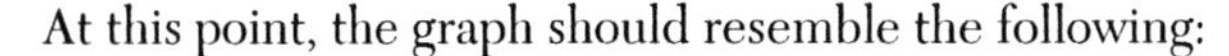

Note that this is also the dialog box that is used to change the axis to log-scale if that is desired.

At this point, the graph should resemble the following:

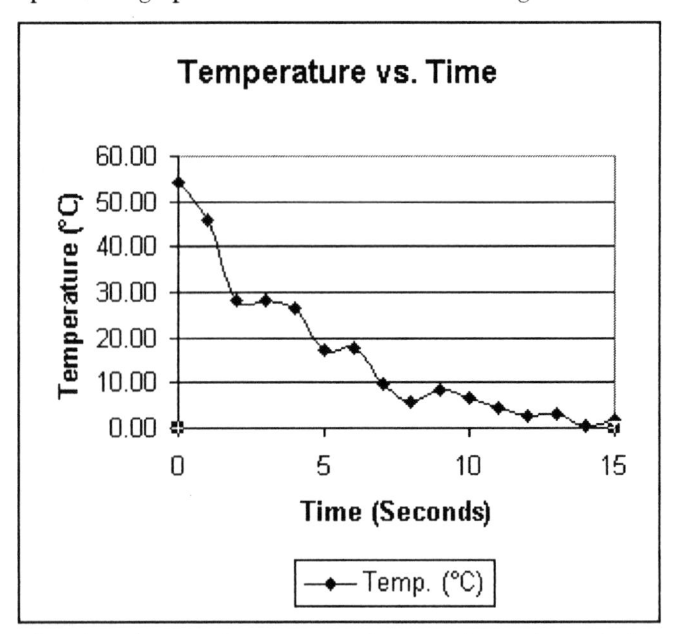

Notice that the values on the y-axis are shown with two decimal places. The y values in column B were formatted to show two decimal places, and Excel carried that formatting into the label values displayed on the y-axis. To change the number of displayed decimal places on axis labels, click on the axis to select it, and then use the Increase Decimal or Decrease Decimal button on the Format Toolbar.

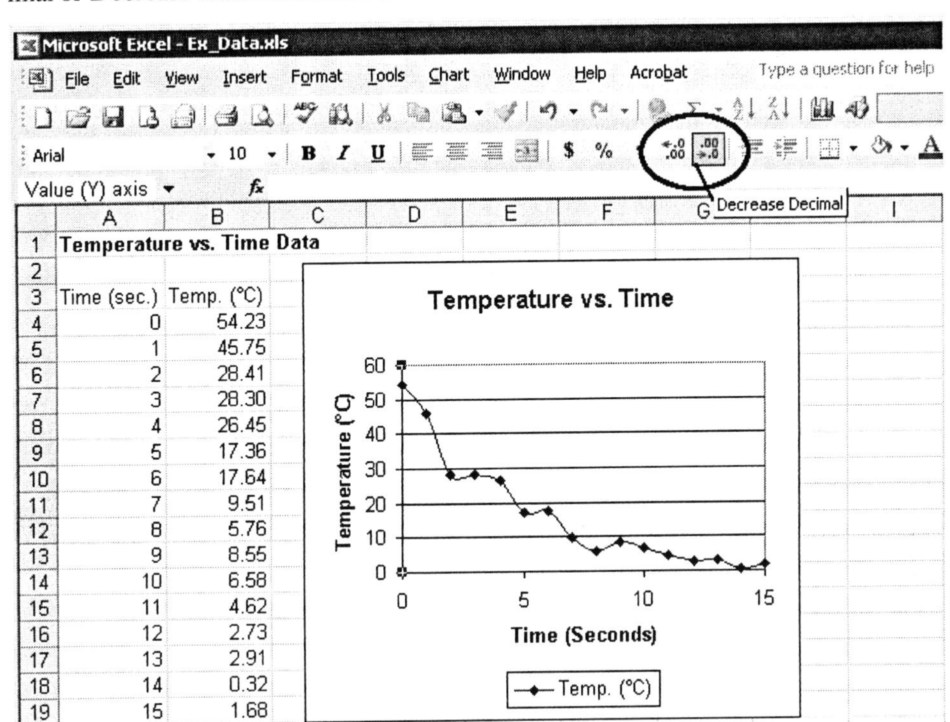

4.2 Adding a TrendLine

A *trendline* is a curve that has been fit to the data. Excel will automatically put several types of trendline on charts. To see the trendline clearly, we need to get rid of the original line connecting the dots.

Removing the Smooth Curve Connecting the Data Points To get rid of the current line, double click it. The Format Data Series dialog box is displayed. Select the Patterns panel. (It is the default panel and normally is displayed.) Set the Line pattern to None:

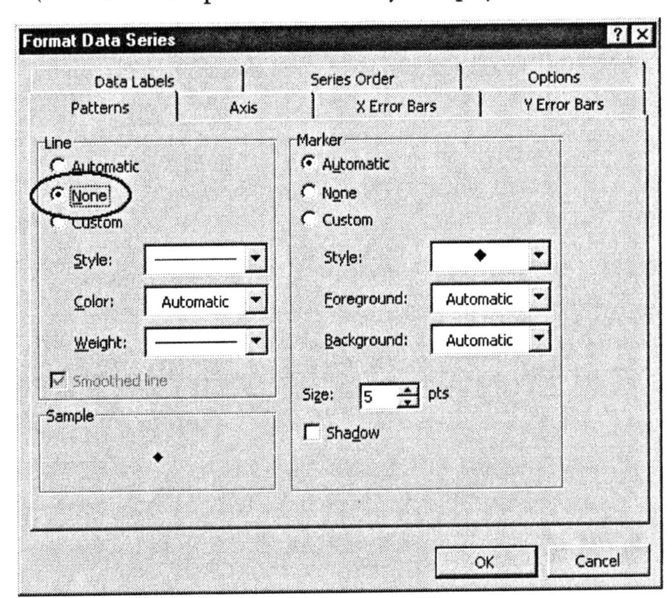

The graph should now resemble the following:

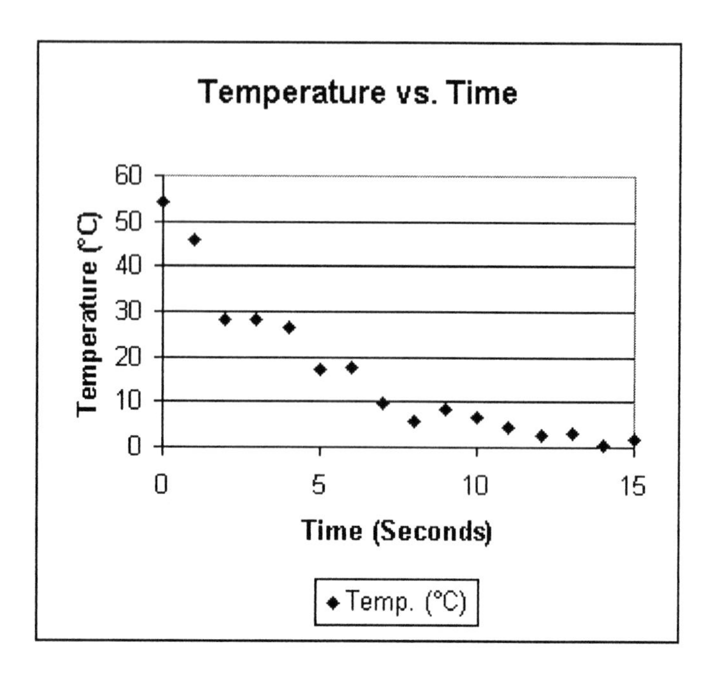

Adding a Trendline To add a trendline, right click any of the data markers and select Add Trendline . . . from the pop-up menu, as shown:

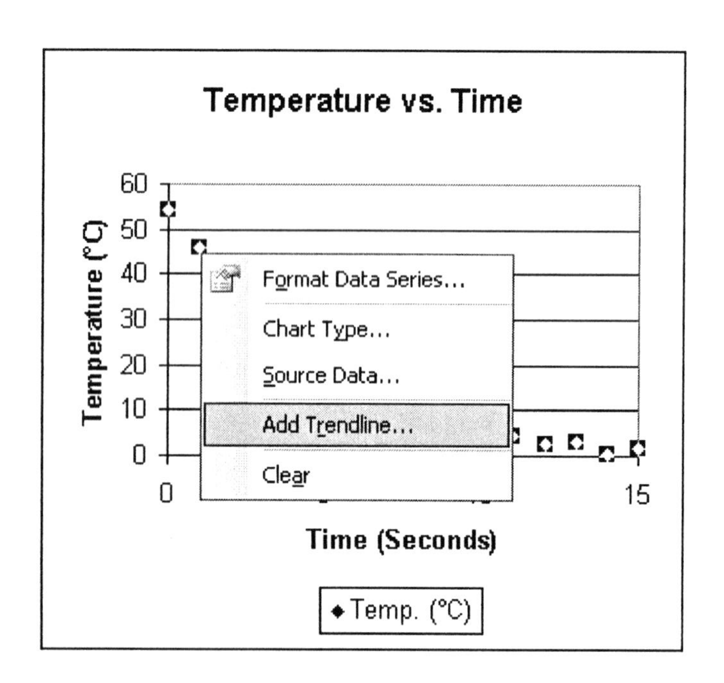

The Add Trendline dialog box is then displayed:

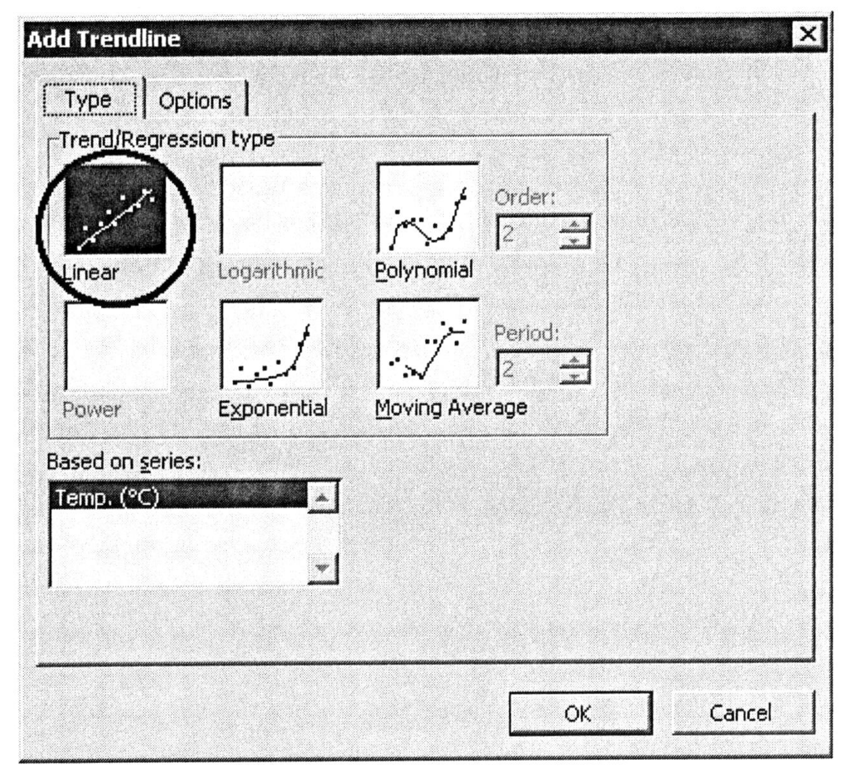

We'll start with a linear trendline. It's a very poor choice for this data, but will show how Excel fits trendlines to data.

Note: The options tab can be used if you want the equation of the trendline to be displayed on the graph.

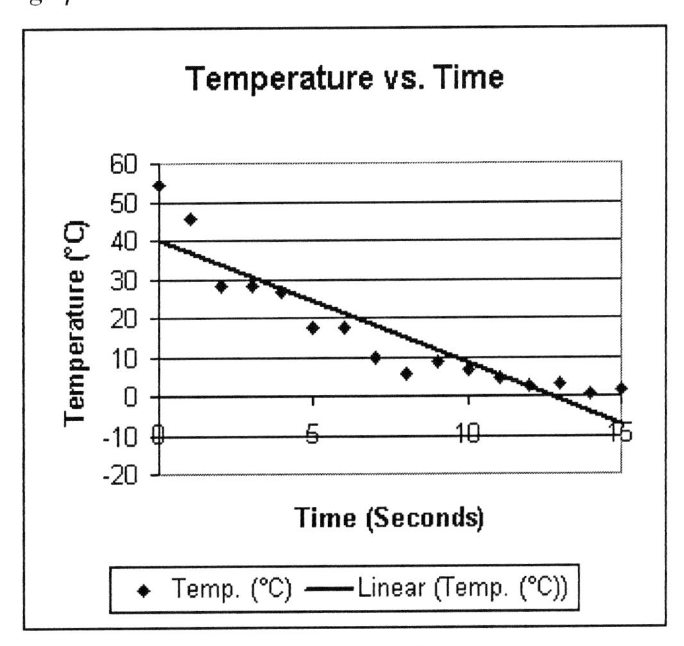

The linear trendline is the straight line that best fits the data. It doesn't fit very well, because the relationship between time and temperature shown in the data is not actually linear. Double click the trendline to edit its properties to change the type of trendline used, as follows:

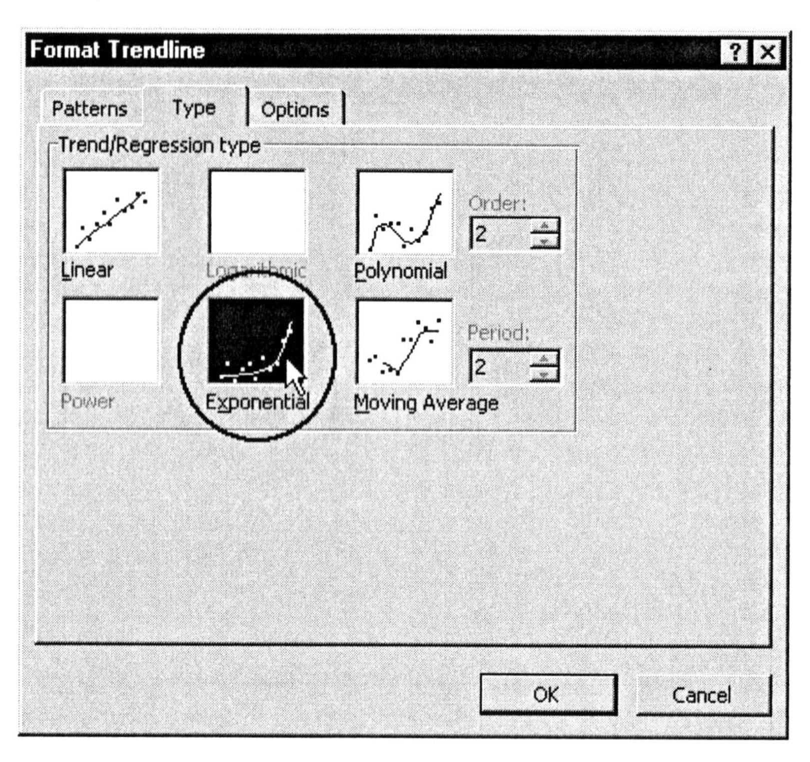

Use the Options panel to display the equation of the trendline and the R^2 value (coefficient of determination).

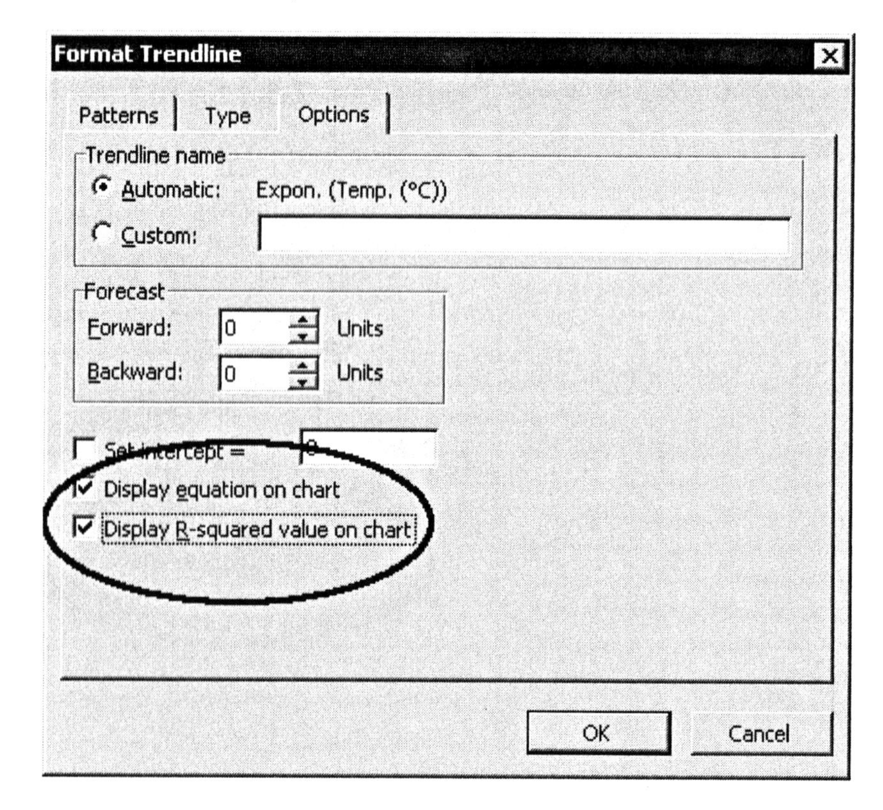

We'll select an exponential trendline, because the decline in temperature over time looks something like an exponential decay curve. The exponential trendline looks like a better fit to the data:

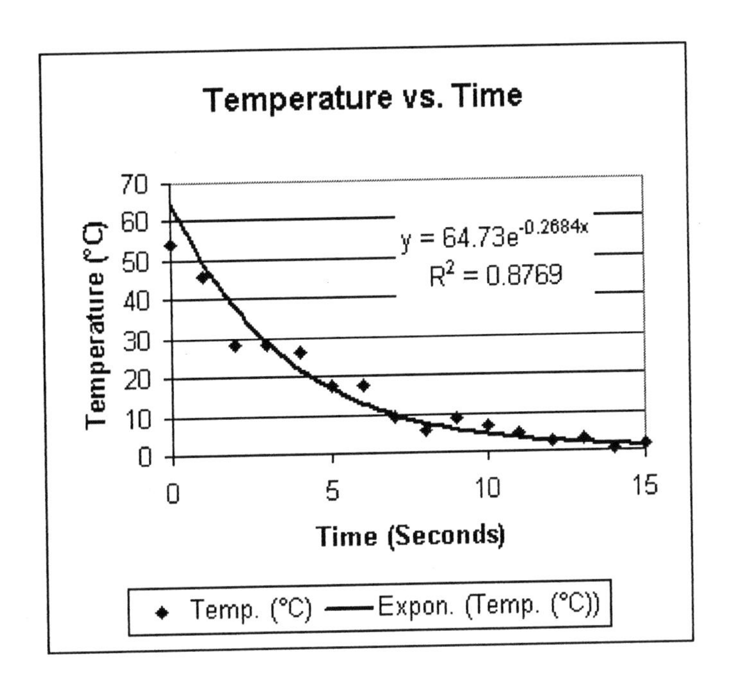

4.3 Adding Error Bars

Excel can automatically add *x*- or *y-error bars*, calculated from the data in several ways:

- Fixed Value: A fixed value is added to and subtracted from each data value and plotted as an error bar.
- Fixed Percentage: A fixed percentage is multiplied by each data value, and the result is added to and subtracted from the data value and plotted as an error bar.
- Standard Deviation: The selected standard deviation of all of the values in the data set is computed and then added to and subtracted from each data value and plotted as an error bar.
- Standard Error: The standard error of all of the values in the data set is computed and then added to and subtracted from each data value and plotted as an error bar.

Additionally, you can calculate the values you want plotted as error bars by using the Custom error bar option.

To demonstrate how to add error bars to a graph, fixed-percentage (30%) error bars will be added to the temperature values (*y* values).

To bring up the Format Data Series dialog, double click any of the data markers on the graph or select Series "Temp.(°C)" from the chart toolbar's drop-down list and click the Format Data Series button on the toolbar. Select the first display option to display error bars both above and below the data marker, and set the fixed percentage to 30%.

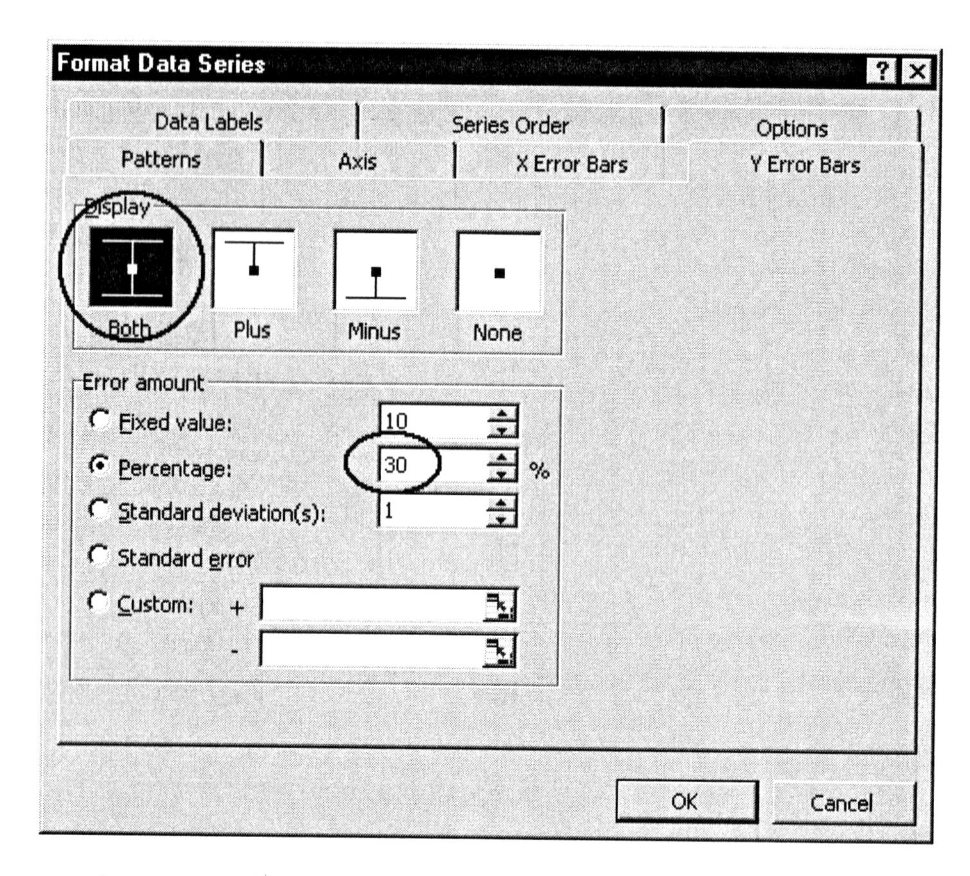

This process yields the following result:

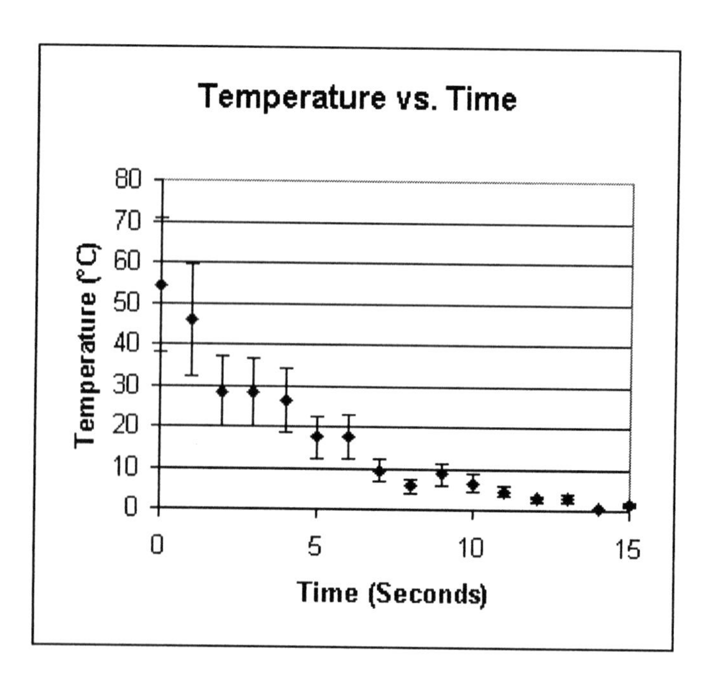

The trendline was removed from this graph to improve the visibility of the markers; the legend was removed to allow the plot area to be expanded.

5 CREATING GRAPHS WITH MULTIPLE CURVES

There is a particularly simple way to create an XY scatter graph with multiple curves *if only one column (or row) of* x *values is needed*: You simply select all of the columns (or rows) of data [one column (or row) of x values, multiple columns (or rows) of y values], and follow the Chart Wizard steps for creating the graph. Excel will assume that the left-most column (or top row) contains the x values and that all other columns (rows) contain y values. Each column (or row) of y values becomes a curve on the graph.

EXAMPLE 1

To demonstrate plotting multiple series on a single plot, we will graph sine and cosine curves over the range from 0 to 2π radians. The angle values in degrees are included in the data set but will not be plotted.

If the data are available in the spreadsheet, begin creating the graph by selecting the three columns of data. Include the column headings in the range of data values to be plotted if you want to make Excel use the headings to name the series.

	A	B	C	D	E
1	**Sine and Cosine Data**				
2					
3	**θ (degrees)**	**θ (radians)**	**Sin(θ)**	**Cos(θ)**	
4	0	0.000	0.000	1.000	
5	20	0.349	0.342	0.940	
6	40	0.698	0.643	0.766	
7	60	1.047	0.866	0.500	
8	80	1.396	0.985	0.174	
9	100	1.745	0.985	-0.174	
10	120	2.094	0.866	-0.500	
11	140	2.443	0.643	-0.766	
12	160	2.793	0.342	-0.940	
13	180	3.142	0.000	-1.000	
14	200	3.491	-0.342	-0.940	
15	220	3.840	-0.643	-0.766	
16	240	4.189	-0.866	-0.500	
17	260	4.538	-0.985	-0.174	
18	280	4.887	-0.985	0.174	
19	300	5.236	-0.866	0.500	
20	320	5.585	-0.643	0.766	
21	340	5.934	-0.342	0.940	
22	360	6.283	0.000	1.000	
23					

Note: The Greek letter θ (theta) was inserted into the spreadsheet by using Insert/Symbol. Including the column headings within the range of data to be plotted will make the Greek letters also appear in the graph's legend.

Start the Chart Wizard, and select an XY (Scatter) plot. The wizard will assume that the left column (column B, containing θ values in radians) is to be plotted on the x-axis and that the other columns [Sin(θ) and Cos(θ)] should be plotted as the y values for series 1 and series 2.

In the Wizard's Step 2 of 4—Chart Source Data—you can see that two series appear in the Series list. Because the Sin(θ) and Cos(θ) column headings were included in the selected data, the series are named Sin(θ) and Cos(θ).

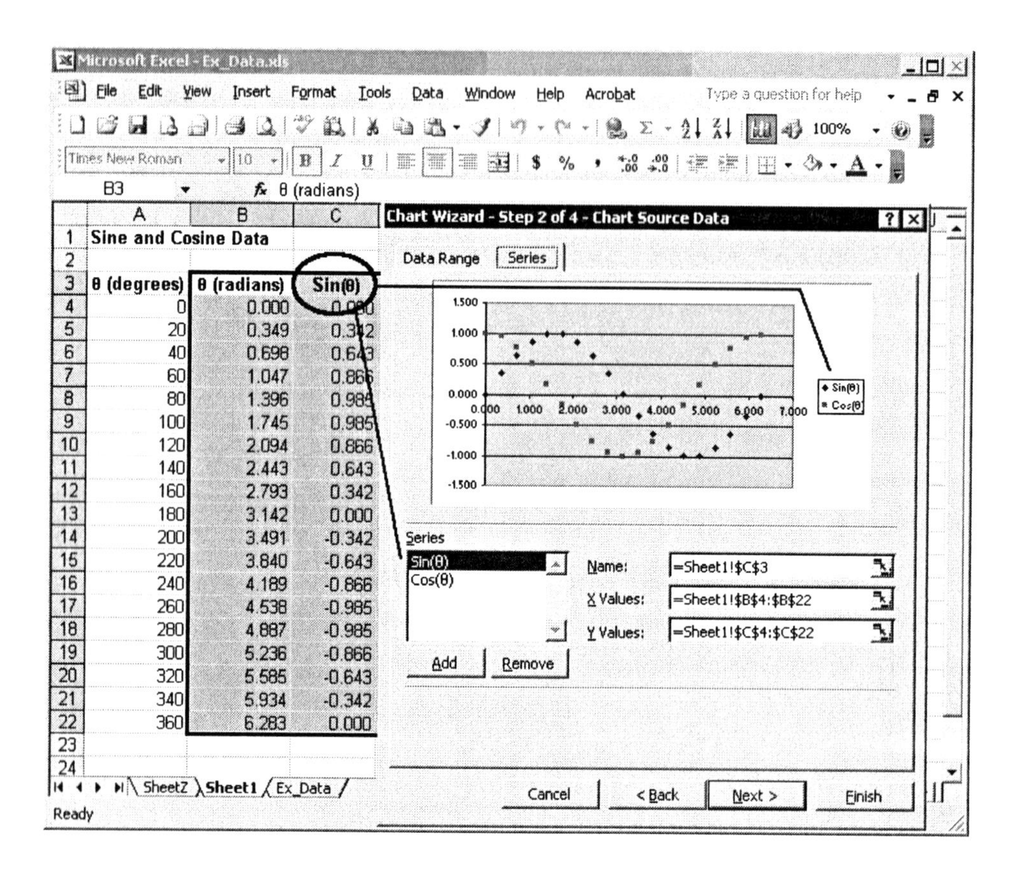

Note: If column headings were not included in the data range to be graphed, the series would have been given the default names: "Series 1" and "Series 2".

In the Chart Wizard's next step, the x-axis title was added. Insert/Symbol is not available while the Chart Wizard is running, so the word "Theta" was used in the axis label. This will be changed after the graph is created.

In the final step of the Chart Wizard, the chart was placed on the spreadsheet. Then the following cosmetic changes were made:

- The legend was moved over a blank spot in the graph.
- The plot area background color was changed to white.
- The line style for the Cosine series was changed to a dashed line.
- The number of displayed decimal places on the y-axis labels was reduced to one.
- The minimum and maximum values on the x-axis were set at 0 and 6.283 (2π), respectively.
- Labels on the x-axis were turned off (i.e., tick mark labels set to "None" on the Patterns panel of the Format Axis dialog).

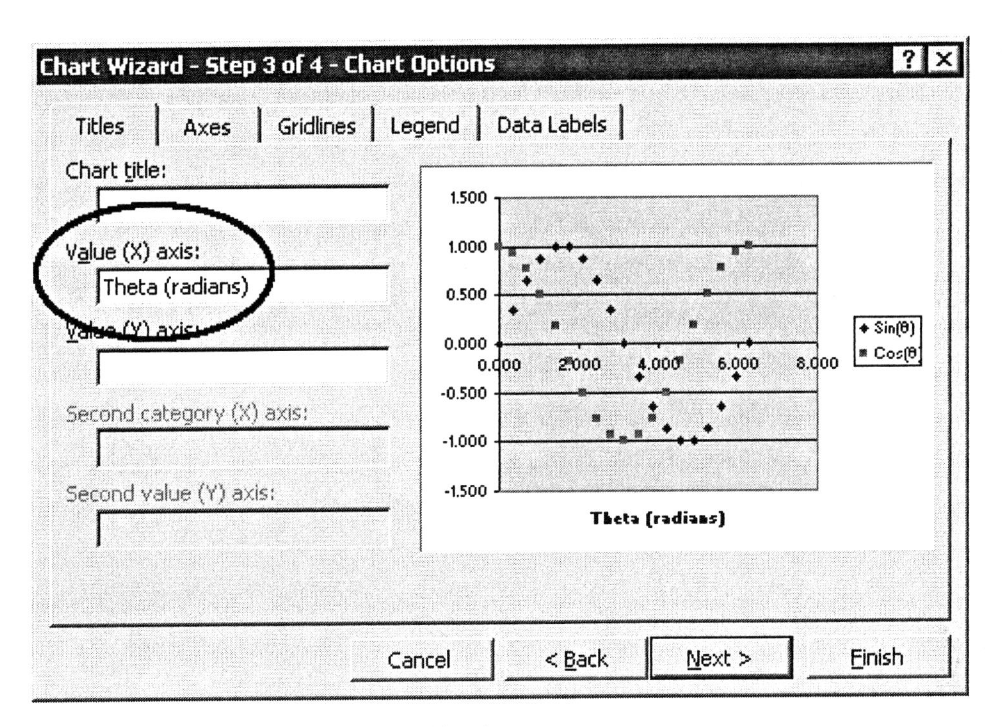

After these changes, the graph looks like this:

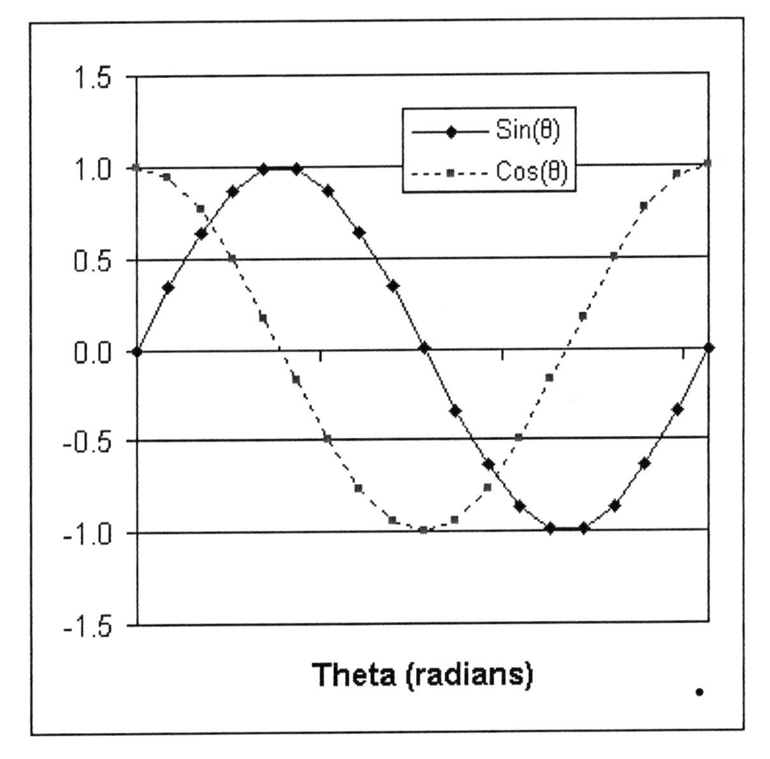

Now the x-axis title can be edited to replace "Theta" by the Greek symbol θ. To do this, you have to cheat a little, because Insert/Symbol is not available while editing the title. To work around this, first copy the symbol θ from any of the column headings (cells A3 through D3) to the Windows clipboard. Then the symbol can be pasted into the title while it is being edited.

To edit the title, click on the title to select it, then click it again to enter edit mode.

Note: This is two single clicks, not a double click. Leave a slight pause between the clicks. Double clicking on the title opens the Format Axis Title dialog, which is useful, but not for editing the contents of the axis title.

Once you are editing the x-axis title, select the word "Theta", then Edit/Paste (or [Ctrl-V]) the Greek letter θ from the Windows clipboard into the axis title. Click anywhere outside the axis title to leave edit mode.

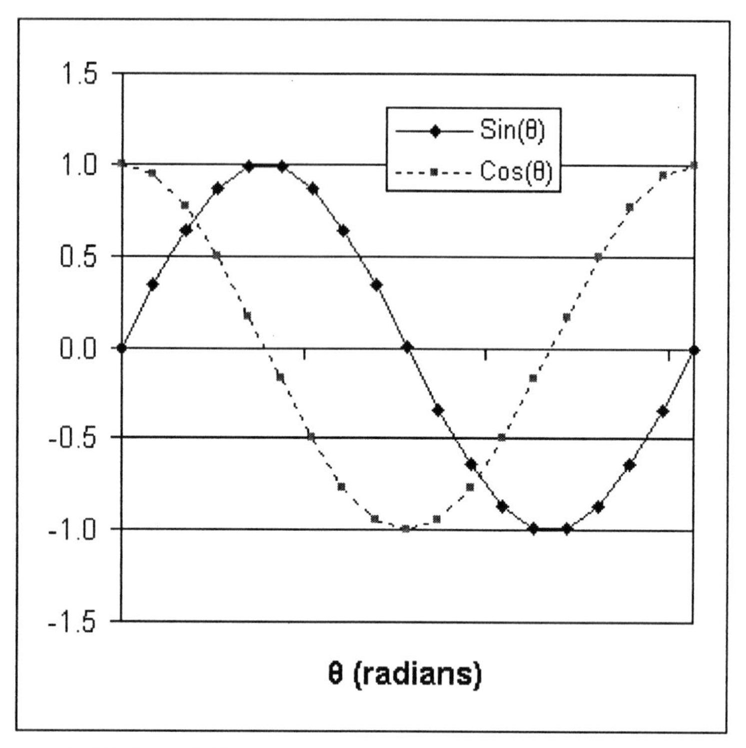

Adding an Additional Curve

If you have already created a graph and decide to add another curve, you can. For example, to add a $\sin^2(\theta)$ curve to the graph created in the previous example, we would need to add a new series of y values, but use the same x values as for the sine and cosine curves.

Once the $\sin^2(\theta)$ data are available in the spreadsheet (having been added in column E), you would begin by right clicking on the existing graph and selecting Source Data from the pop-up menu.

	A	B	C	D	E
1	Sine and Cosine Data				
2					
3	θ (degrees)	θ (radians)	Sin(θ)	Cos(θ)	Sin^2(θ)
4	0	0.000	0.000	1.000	0.000
5	20	0.349	0.342	0.940	0.117
6	40	0.698	0.643	0.766	0.413
7	60	1.047	0.866	0.500	0.750
8	80	1.396	0.985	0.174	0.970
9	100	1.745	0.985	-0.174	0.970
10	120	2.094	0.866	-0.500	0.750
11	140	2.443	0.643	-0.766	0.413
12	160	2.793	0.342	-0.940	0.117
13	180	3.142	0.000	-1.000	0.000
14	200	3.491	-0.342	-0.940	0.117
15	220	3.840	-0.643	-0.766	0.413
16	240	4.189	-0.866	-0.500	0.750
17	260	4.538	-0.985	-0.174	0.970
18	280	4.887	-0.985	0.174	0.970
19	300	5.236	-0.866	0.500	0.750
20	320	5.585	-0.643	0.766	0.413
21	340	5.934	-0.342	0.940	0.117
22	360	6.283	0.000	1.000	0.000
23					

Format Chart Area...
Chart Type...
Source Data...
Chart Options...
Location...
Chart Window
Cut
Copy
Clear
Bring to Front
Send to Back
Assign Macro...

On the Series panel of the Source Data dialog box, we need to add a new series to the list of Series. Set the Name of the new series to "Sin2(θ)" by pointing at cell E3 (specifically, `Sheet1!$E$3`). Use the small button at the right of the Name: field to return to the spreadsheet to point out the cell containing the series name.

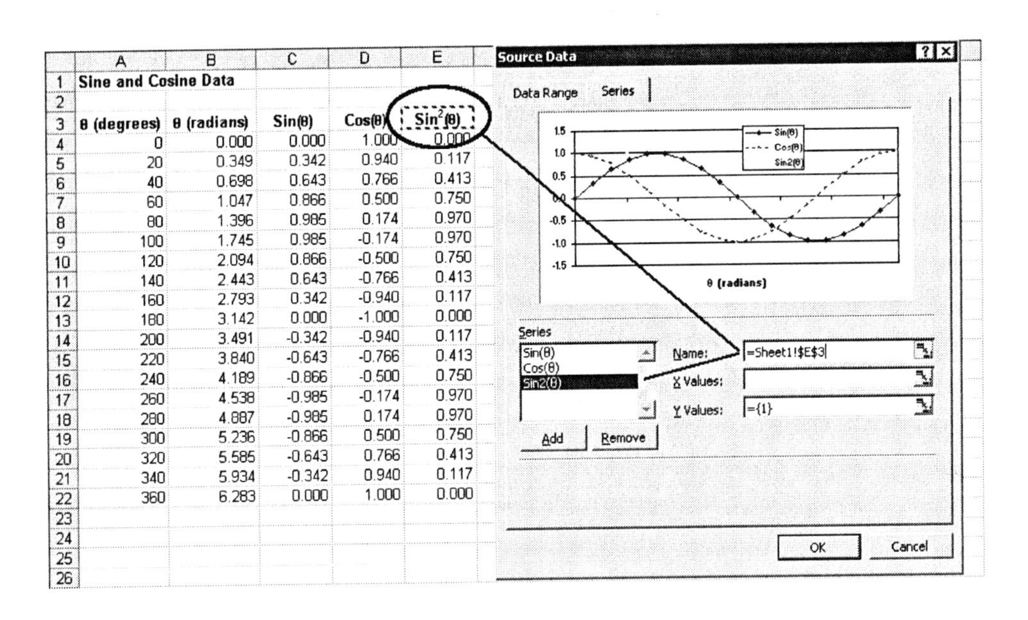

θ (degrees)	θ (radians)	Sin(θ)	Cos(θ)	Sin²(θ)
0	0.000	0.000	1.000	0.000
20	0.349	0.342	0.940	0.117
40	0.698	0.643	0.766	0.413
60	1.047	0.866	0.500	0.750
80	1.396	0.985	0.174	0.970
100	1.745	0.985	-0.174	0.970
120	2.094	0.866	-0.500	0.750
140	2.443	0.643	-0.766	0.413
160	2.793	0.342	-0.940	0.117
180	3.142	0.000	-1.000	0.000
200	3.491	-0.342	-0.940	0.117
220	3.840	-0.643	-0.766	0.413
240	4.189	-0.866	-0.500	0.750
260	4.538	-0.985	-0.174	0.970
280	4.887	-0.985	0.174	0.970
300	5.236	-0.866	0.500	0.750
320	5.585	-0.643	0.766	0.413
340	5.934	-0.342	0.940	0.117
360	6.283	0.000	1.000	0.000

Next, tell Excel where to find the x values for the new curve. Again, the small button at the right of the X Values field will take you back to the spreadsheet so that you can select the x values.

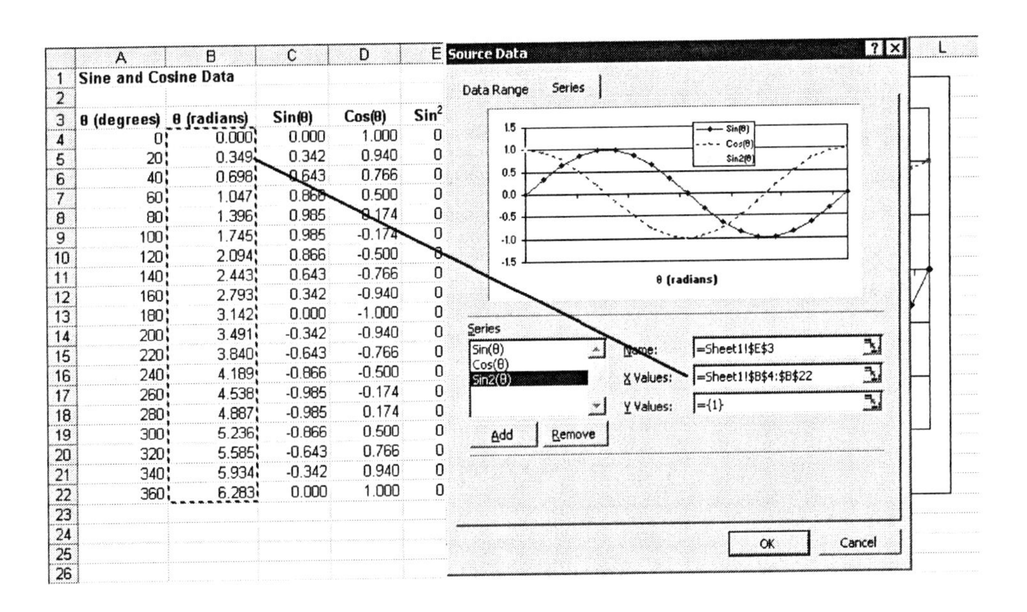

θ (degrees)	θ (radians)	Sin(θ)	Cos(θ)	Sin²
0	0.000	0.000	1.000	0
20	0.349	0.342	0.940	0
40	0.698	0.643	0.766	0
60	1.047	0.866	0.500	0
80	1.396	0.985	0.174	0
100	1.745	0.985	-0.174	0
120	2.094	0.866	-0.500	0
140	2.443	0.643	-0.766	0
160	2.793	0.342	-0.940	0
180	3.142	0.000	-1.000	0
200	3.491	-0.342	-0.940	0
220	3.840	-0.643	-0.766	0
240	4.189	-0.866	-0.500	0
260	4.538	-0.985	-0.174	0
280	4.887	-0.985	0.174	0
300	5.236	-0.866	0.500	0
320	5.585	-0.643	0.766	0
340	5.934	-0.342	0.940	0
360	6.283	0.000	1.000	0

Next, tell Excel where to find the y values for the new curve.

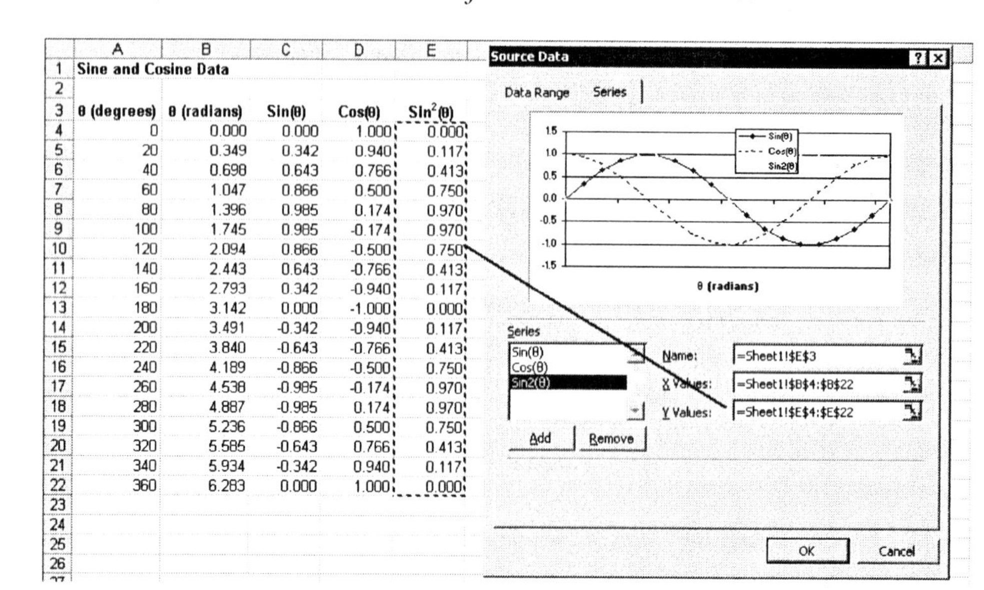

	A	B	C	D	E
1	Sine and Cosine Data				
2					
3	θ (degrees)	θ (radians)	Sin(θ)	Cos(θ)	Sin²(θ)
4	0	0.000	0.000	1.000	0.000
5	20	0.349	0.342	0.940	0.117
6	40	0.698	0.643	0.766	0.413
7	60	1.047	0.866	0.500	0.750
8	80	1.396	0.985	0.174	0.970
9	100	1.745	0.985	-0.174	0.970
10	120	2.094	0.866	-0.500	0.750
11	140	2.443	0.643	-0.766	0.413
12	160	2.793	0.342	-0.940	0.117
13	180	3.142	0.000	-1.000	0.000
14	200	3.491	-0.342	-0.940	0.117
15	220	3.840	-0.643	-0.766	0.413
16	240	4.189	-0.866	-0.500	0.750
17	260	4.538	-0.985	-0.174	0.970
18	280	4.887	-0.985	0.174	0.970
19	300	5.236	-0.866	0.500	0.750
20	320	5.585	-0.643	0.766	0.413
21	340	5.934	-0.342	0.940	0.117
22	360	6.283	0.000	1.000	0.000

At this point, the new series has the name "Sin2(θ)" (which came from cell E3), a specified range of cells containing x values (`=Sheet1!$B$4:$B$22`), and a range of y values (`=Sheet1!$E$4:$E$22`). Click the OK button to add the new curve to the existing graph.

The graph now includes three curves. The following modifications have been made:

- The legend has been moved to the lower left corner of the plot area.
- The color and line style of the new curve were changed from the default values.

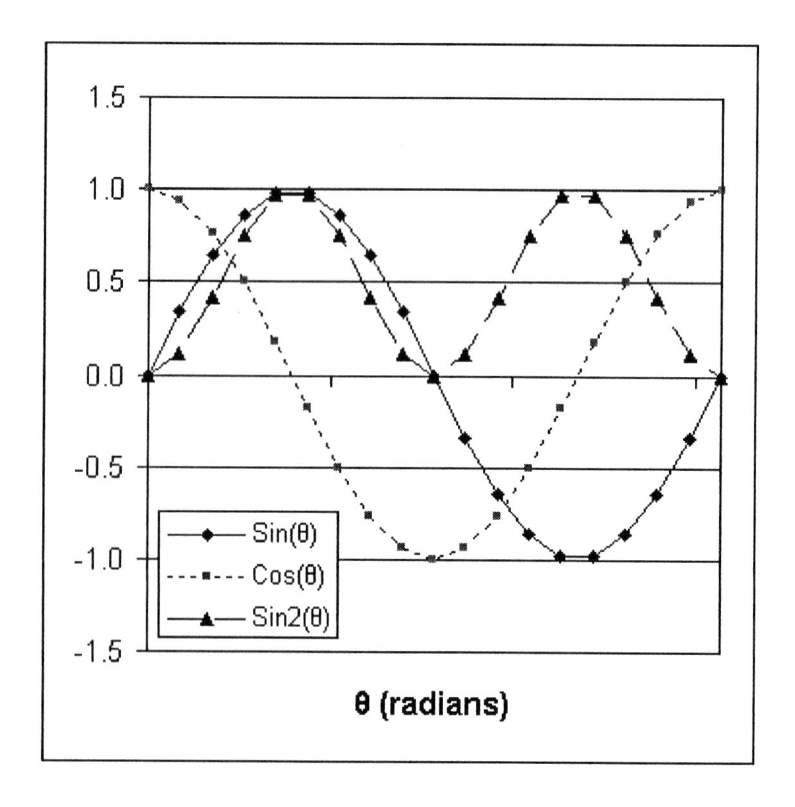

6 PRINTING THE GRAPH

There are two ways to get a graph onto paper:

1. Print the graph only.
2. Print the spreadsheet containing the graph.

To print only the graph, first click the graph to select it. (Handles will be displayed around the edge of the graph.) If you use the Print or Print Preview button on the standard toolbar or select File/Print... or File/Print Preview from the main menu, the graph will be printed or displayed on the preview page appropriately. The graph will be resized to fit the page. Use the Setup button on the preview page and select the Chart panel on the Page Setup dialog box to change the size of the printed graph.

To print the spreadsheet containing the graph, simply include the graph when you set the print area by selecting File/Print Area/Set Print Area. Then, when you use the Print or Print Preview button on the standard toolbar or select File/Print... or File/Print Preview, the spreadsheet with the graph will be printed or displayed on the preview page appropriately.

7 TYPES OF GRAPHS

Excel provides a number of chart types other than XY (Scatter) plots. XY (Scatter) plots are the most common type of graph for engineering work; however, several of the other chart types are also used. Other standard chart types include

- *Line Graphs*
- *Column* and *Bar Graphs*
- *Pie Charts*
- *Surface Plots*

WARNING: *A common error is to use a Line Graph when an XY Scatter plot is more appropriate. You will get away with this if the* x *values in your data set are uniformly spaced. But if the* x *values are not uniformly spaced, your curve will appear distorted on the Line Graph.*

EXAMPLE 2

The x values in the spreadsheet shown next are calculated as

$$x_{i+1} = 1.2 \cdot x_i. \tag{1}$$

This creates nonuniformly spaced x values. The y values are calculated from the x values as

$$y_i = 3 \cdot x_i, \tag{2}$$

so the relationship between x and y is linear. On an XY Scatter plot, the linear relationship is evident:

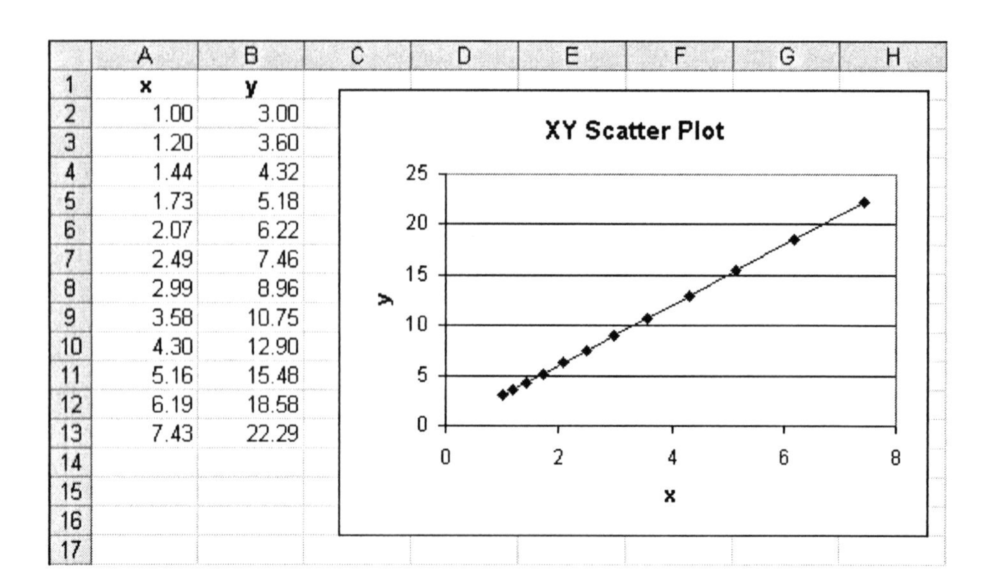

	A	B
1	x	y
2	1.00	3.00
3	1.20	3.60
4	1.44	4.32
5	1.73	5.18
6	2.07	6.22
7	2.49	7.46
8	2.99	8.96
9	3.58	10.75
10	4.30	12.90
11	5.16	15.48
12	6.19	18.58
13	7.43	22.29

However, on a Line Graph, the relationship between x and y appears to be nonlinear:

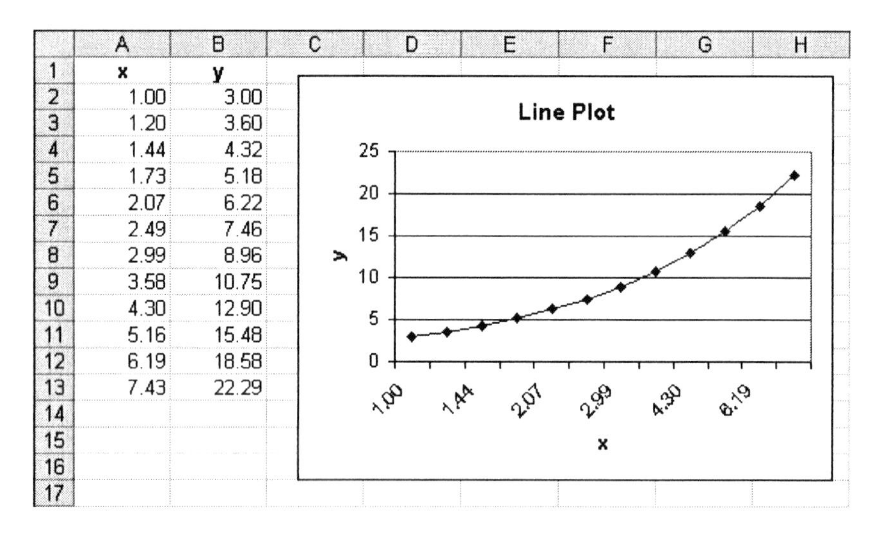

	A	B
1	x	y
2	1.00	3.00
3	1.20	3.60
4	1.44	4.32
5	1.73	5.18
6	2.07	6.22
7	2.49	7.46
8	2.99	8.96
9	3.58	10.75
10	4.30	12.90
11	5.16	15.48
12	6.19	18.58
13	7.43	22.29

This is an artifact of the Line Graph, because the x values were not used to plot the points on the graph. Excel's Line Graph simply causes the y values to be spread out evenly across the chart (effectively assuming uniform x spacing). If you include two columns of values when you create the chart, Excel assumes that the left column is a column of labels to use on the x-axis. This can be misleading on a Line Graph, because the x values are displayed on the x-axis, but they were not used to plot the data points.

Excel's Line, Column, Bar, and Pie Charts all require only y values to create the graph. If you provide two columns (or rows) of data, the left column (or top row) will be used as labels for the chart. If you need to plot x and y values on a graph, you must use an XY Scatter plot.

Surface Plots in Excel A surface plot takes the values in a two-dimensional range of cells and displays the values graphically.

EXAMPLE 3

The following surface plot shows the value of $F(x,y) = \sin(x)\cos(y)$ for $-1 \le x \le 2$ and $-1 \le y \le 2$:

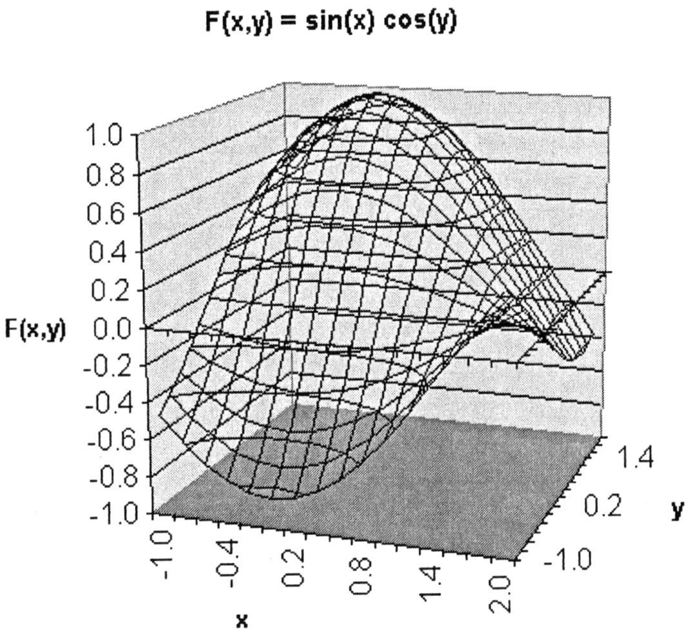

F(x,y) = sin(x) cos(y)

To create the plot, x values ranging from -1 to 2 were calculated in column A, and y values ranging from -1 to 2 were calculated in row 2:

C2 | fx =B2+0.2

	A	B	C	D	E	F	G	H	I	J	K	L	M	N	O	P	Q	R
1		y >>>																
2	x	-1.0	-0.8	-0.6	-0.4	-0.2	0.0	0.2	0.4	0.6	0.8	1.0	1.2	1.4	1.6	1.8	2.0	
3	-1.0																	
4	-0.8																	
5	-0.6																	
6	-0.4																	
7	-0.2																	
8	0.0																	
9	0.2																	
10	0.4																	
11	0.6																	
12	0.8																	
13	1.0																	
14	1.2																	
15	1.4																	
16	1.6																	
17	1.8																	
18	2.0																	
19																		

The first value for $F(x,y)$ is calculated in cell B3 by means of the formula `B3:=SIN($A3)*COS(B$2)`, as the following shows:

B3 ▾ fx =SIN($A3)*COS(B$2)

	A	B	C	D	E	F	G	H	I	J	K	L	M	N	O	P	Q	R
1		y >>>																
2	x	-1.0	-0.8	-0.6	-0.4	-0.2	0.0	0.2	0.4	0.6	0.8	1.0	1.2	1.4	1.6	1.8	2.0	
3	-1.0	-0.45																
4	-0.8																	
5	-0.6																	
6	-0.4																	
7	-0.2																	
8	0.0																	
9	0.2																	
10	0.4																	
11	0.6																	
12	0.8																	
13	1.0																	
14	1.2																	
15	1.4																	
16	1.6																	
17	1.8																	
18	2.0																	
19																		

The dollar signs on the A in `SIN($A3)` and the 2 in `COS(B$2)` allow the formula to be copied to the other cells in the range. After the formula is copied, the `SIN()` functions will always reference x values in column A, and `COS()` functions will always reference y values in row 2.

Next, the formula in cell B3 is copied to all of the cells in the range B3:Q18, to fill the two-dimensional array.

	A	B	C	D	E	F	G	H	I	J	K	L	M	N	O	P	Q	R
1		y >>>																
2	x	-1.0	-0.8	-0.6	-0.4	-0.2	0.0	0.2	0.4	0.6	0.8	1.0	1.2	1.4	1.6	1.8	2.0	
3	-1.0	-0.45	-0.59	-0.69	-0.78	-0.82	-0.84	-0.82	-0.78	-0.69	-0.59	-0.45	-0.30	-0.14	0.02	0.19	0.35	
4	-0.8	-0.39	-0.50	-0.59	-0.66	-0.70	-0.72	-0.70	-0.66	-0.59	-0.50	-0.39	-0.26	-0.12	0.02	0.16	0.30	
5	-0.6	-0.31	-0.39	-0.47	-0.52	-0.55	-0.56	-0.55	-0.52	-0.47	-0.39	-0.31	-0.20	-0.10	0.02	0.13	0.23	
6	-0.4	-0.21	-0.27	-0.32	-0.36	-0.38	-0.39	-0.38	-0.36	-0.32	-0.27	-0.21	-0.14	-0.07	0.01	0.09	0.16	
7	-0.2	-0.11	-0.14	-0.16	-0.18	-0.19	-0.20	-0.19	-0.18	-0.16	-0.14	-0.11	-0.07	-0.03	0.01	0.05	0.08	
8	0.0	0.00	0.00	0.00	0.00	0.00	0.00	0.00	0.00	0.00	0.00	0.00	0.00	0.00	0.00	0.00	0.00	
9	0.2	0.11	0.14	0.16	0.18	0.19	0.20	0.19	0.18	0.16	0.14	0.11	0.07	0.03	-0.01	-0.05	-0.08	
10	0.4	0.21	0.27	0.32	0.36	0.38	0.39	0.38	0.36	0.32	0.27	0.21	0.14	0.07	-0.01	-0.09	-0.16	
11	0.6	0.31	0.39	0.47	0.52	0.55	0.56	0.55	0.52	0.47	0.39	0.31	0.20	0.10	-0.02	-0.13	-0.23	
12	0.8	0.39	0.50	0.59	0.66	0.70	0.72	0.70	0.66	0.59	0.50	0.39	0.26	0.12	-0.02	-0.16	-0.30	
13	1.0	0.45	0.59	0.69	0.78	0.82	0.84	0.82	0.78	0.69	0.59	0.45	0.30	0.14	-0.02	-0.19	-0.35	
14	1.2	0.50	0.65	0.77	0.86	0.91	0.93	0.91	0.86	0.77	0.65	0.50	0.34	0.16	-0.03	-0.21	-0.39	
15	1.4	0.53	0.69	0.81	0.91	0.97	0.99	0.97	0.91	0.81	0.69	0.53	0.36	0.17	-0.03	-0.22	-0.41	
16	1.6	0.54	0.70	0.82	0.92	0.98	1.00	0.98	0.92	0.82	0.70	0.54	0.36	0.17	-0.03	-0.23	-0.42	
17	1.8	0.53	0.68	0.80	0.90	0.95	0.97	0.95	0.90	0.80	0.68	0.53	0.35	0.17	-0.03	-0.22	-0.41	
18	2.0	0.49	0.63	0.75	0.84	0.89	0.91	0.89	0.84	0.75	0.63	0.49	0.33	0.15	-0.03	-0.21	-0.38	
19																		

Then the array of values is selected before starting the Chart Wizard.

Microsoft Excel - ch02.xls

File Edit View Insert Format Tools Data Window Help — Type a question for help

100%

Arial 10 B I U $ % Chart Wizard

B3 ▾ fx =SIN($A3)*COS(B$2)

	A	B	C	D	E	F	G	H	I	J	K	L	M	N	O	P	Q	R
1		y>>>																
2	x	-1.0	-0.8	-0.6	-0.4	-0.2	0	0.2	0.4	0.6	0.8	1.0	1.2	1.4	1.6	1.8	2.0	
3	-1.0	-0.45	-0.59	-0.69	-0.78	-0.82	-0.84	-0.82	-0.78	-0.69	-0.59	-0.45	-0.30	-0.14	0.02	0.19	0.35	
4	-0.8	-0.39	-0.50	-0.59	-0.66	-0.70	-0.72	-0.70	-0.66	-0.59	-0.50	-0.39	-0.26	-0.12	0.02	0.16	0.30	
5	-0.6	-0.31	-0.39	-0.47	-0.52	-0.55	-0.56	-0.55	-0.52	-0.47	-0.39	-0.31	-0.20	-0.10	0.02	0.13	0.23	
6	-0.4	-0.21	-0.27	-0.32	-0.36	-0.38	-0.39	-0.38	-0.36	-0.32	-0.27	-0.21	-0.14	-0.07	0.01	0.09	0.16	
7	-0.2	-0.11	-0.14	-0.16	-0.18	-0.19	-0.20	-0.19	-0.18	-0.16	-0.14	-0.11	-0.07	-0.03	0.01	0.05	0.08	
8	0.0	0.00	0.00	0.00	0.00	0.00	0.00	0.00	0.00	0.00	0.00	0.00	0.00	0.00	0.00	0.00	0.00	
9	0.2	0.11	0.14	0.16	0.18	0.19	0.20	0.19	0.18	0.16	0.14	0.11	0.07	0.03	-0.01	-0.05	-0.08	
10	0.4	0.21	0.27	0.32	0.36	0.38	0.39	0.38	0.36	0.32	0.27	0.21	0.14	0.07	-0.01	-0.09	-0.16	
11	0.6	0.31	0.39	0.47	0.52	0.55	0.56	0.55	0.52	0.47	0.39	0.31	0.20	0.10	-0.02	-0.13	-0.23	
12	0.8	0.39	0.50	0.59	0.66	0.70	0.72	0.70	0.66	0.59	0.50	0.39	0.26	0.12	-0.02	-0.16	-0.30	
13	1.0	0.45	0.59	0.69	0.78	0.82	0.84	0.82	0.78	0.69	0.59	0.45	0.30	0.14	-0.02	-0.19	-0.35	
14	1.2	0.50	0.65	0.77	0.86	0.91	0.93	0.91	0.86	0.77	0.65	0.50	0.34	0.16	-0.03	-0.21	-0.39	
15	1.4	0.53	0.69	0.81	0.91	0.97	0.99	0.97	0.91	0.81	0.69	0.53	0.36	0.17	-0.03	-0.22	-0.41	
16	1.6	0.54	0.70	0.82	0.92	0.98	1.00	0.98	0.92	0.82	0.70	0.54	0.36	0.17	-0.03	-0.23	-0.42	
17	1.8	0.53	0.68	0.80	0.90	0.95	0.97	0.95	0.90	0.80	0.68	0.53	0.35	0.17	-0.03	-0.22	-0.41	
18	2.0	0.49	0.63	0.75	0.84	0.89	0.91	0.89	0.84	0.75	0.63	0.49	0.33	0.15	-0.03	-0.21	-0.38	
19																		

From the Chart Wizard, a Surface Plot is displayed that uses a *wire frame.*

Chart Wizard - Step 1 of 4 - Chart Type

Standard Types | Custom Types

Chart type: Column, Bar, Line, Pie, XY (Scatter), Area, Doughnut, Radar, Surface, Bubble, Stock

Chart sub-type:

Wireframe 3-D Surface. 3-D surface chart without color.

Press and Hold to View Sample

Cancel | < Back | Next > | Finish

The following is the resulting plot:

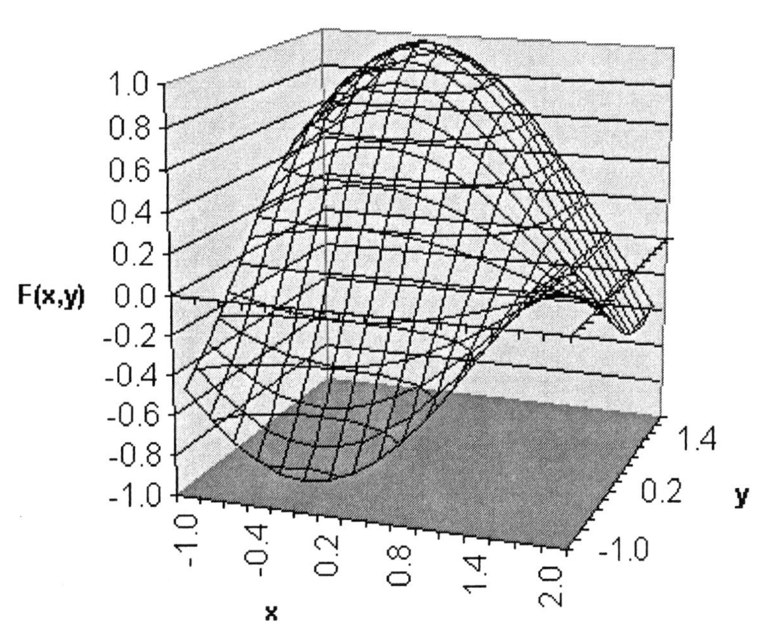

A few other things were added or changed during creation of the graph via the Chart Wizard:

- The labels (not values) displayed on the x-axis were added in Step 2 of the Chart Wizard by using the Series panel of the Source Data step. The contents of cells A3:A18 were used for these labels.
- The names of each of the data series (in Step 2 of the Chart Wizard on the Series panel of the Source Data step) were changed to "−1.0," "−0.8," "−0.6," . . . , "1.8," "2.0," so that these series names would display as labels (not values) on the y-axis of the final plot.
- The x- and y-axis labels "x" and "y" were added as axis titles, along with the z-axis label "F(x,y)" and the chart title "F(x, y) = sin(x) cos(y)."

Note that the x and y values on the spreadsheet (column A and row 2) were never used to plot the points on the surface plot. The $F(x, y)$ values in cells B3 through Q18 were plotted by assuming uniform spacing in the x- and y-directions. This is a significant limitation of surface plotting in Excel.

APPLICATIONS: MATERIALS TESTING

Stress–Strain Curve I

Strength testing of materials often involves a *tensile test* in which a sample of the material is held between two **mandrels** and increasing force—actually, *stress* (i.e., force per unit area)—is applied. A stress-vs.-strain curve for a typical ductile material is shown next. The sample first stretches reversibly (A to B). Then irreversible stretching occurs (B to D). Finally, the sample breaks (point D).

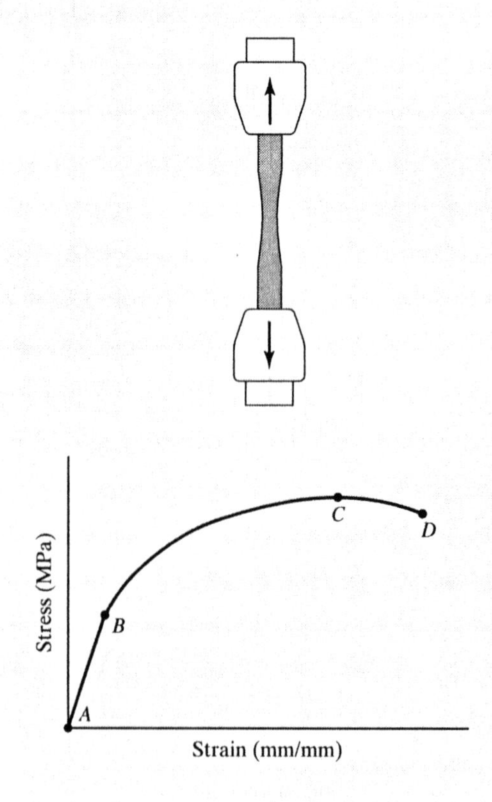

Point *C* is called the material's *ultimate stress*, or *tensile strength*, and represents the greatest stress that the material can endure (with deformation) before coming apart. The *strain* is the amount of elongation of the sample (mm) divided by the original sample length (mm).

The reversible stretching portion of the curve (*A* to *B*) is linear, and the proportionality constant relating stress and strain in this region is called *Young's modulus*, or the *modulus of elasticity*.

Tensile test data on a soft, ductile sample are tabulated as follows (and available electronically at *http://www.coe.montana.edu/che/Excel*):

Strain (mm/mm)	Stress (MPa)
0.000	0.00
0.003	5.38
0.006	10.76
0.009	16.14
0.012	21.52
0.014	25.11
0.017	30.49
0.020	33.34
0.035	44.79
0.052	52.29
0.079	57.08
0.124	59.79
0.167	60.10
0.212	59.58
0.264	57.50
0.300	55.42

As these test data are analyzed, there are some things we will want to do:

a. Plot the tensile test data as a stress-vs.-strain graph.
b. Evaluate the tensile strength from the graph (or the data set).
c. Create a second graph containing only the elastic-stretch (linear) portion of the data.
d. Add a linear trendline to the new plot to determine the modulus of elasticity for this material.

First, the data are entered into the spreadsheet:

	A	B	C	D	E	F	G	H
1	**Stress–Strain Curve I**							
2								
3		**Strain**	**Stress**					
4		(mm/mm)	(MPa)					
5		0.000	0.00					
6		0.003	5.38					
7		0.006	10.76					
8		0.009	16.14					
9		0.012	21.52					
10		0.014	25.11					
11		0.017	30.49					
12		0.020	33.34					
13		0.035	44.79					
14		0.052	52.29					
15		0.079	57.08					
16		0.124	59.79					
17		0.167	60.10					
18		0.212	59.58					
19		0.264	57.50					
20		0.300	55.42					
21								

Then, a graph is prepared. The ultimate tensile stress can be read from the graph or the data set:

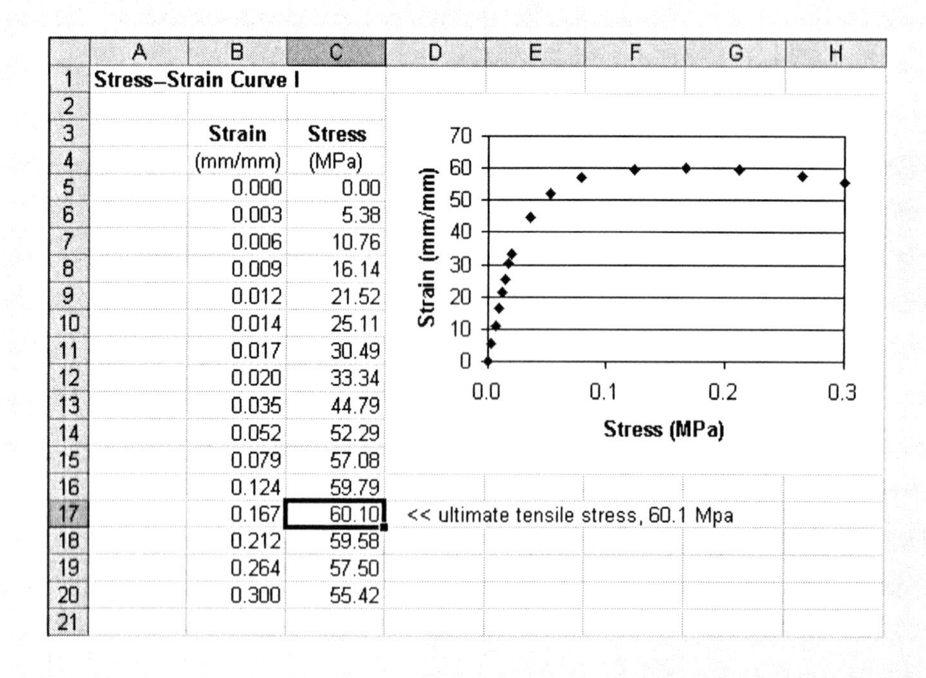

	A	B	C	D	E	F	G	H
1	**Stress–Strain Curve I**							
2								
3		**Strain**	**Stress**					
4		(mm/mm)	(MPa)					
5		0.000	0.00					
6		0.003	5.38					
7		0.006	10.76					
8		0.009	16.14					
9		0.012	21.52					
10		0.014	25.11					
11		0.017	30.49					
12		0.020	33.34					
13		0.035	44.79					
14		0.052	52.29					
15		0.079	57.08					
16		0.124	59.79					
17		0.167	60.10	<< ultimate tensile stress, 60.1 Mpa				
18		0.212	59.58					
19		0.264	57.50					
20		0.300	55.42					
21								

Finally, another graph is prepared, one that contains only the linear portion of the data (the first eight data points). A linear trendline with the intercept forced through the origin is added to the graph. We will use the slope from the equation for the trendline to compute the modulus of elasticity; the R^2 value, 1, provides reassurance that we have indeed plotted the linear portion of the test data:

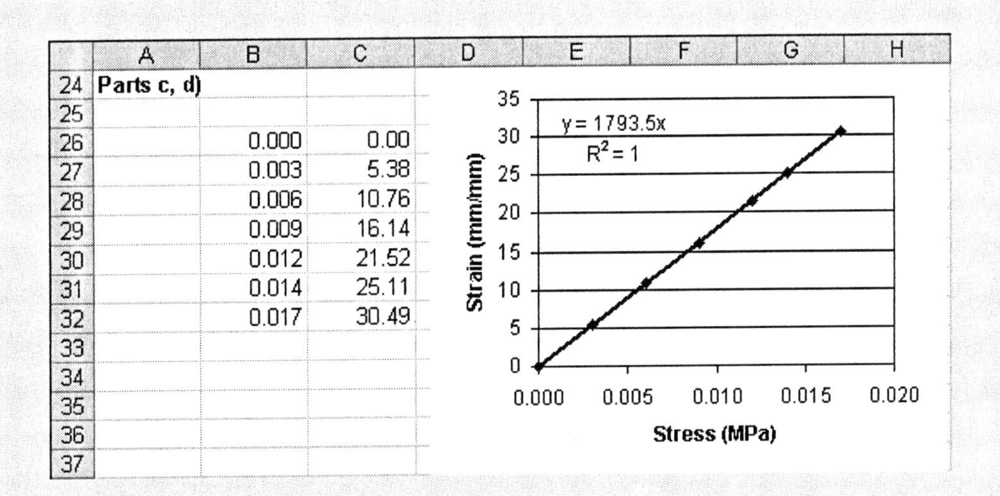

From slope of the regression line, we see that the modulus of elasticity for this material is 1793.7 MPa, or 1.79 GPa.

8 GRAPHING WEB DATA

The Internet's World Wide Web is becoming an increasingly common place to locate data, but those data may be in many different forms. Web pages may provide links to data files or embed the data as HTML tables. There is no single way to move Web data into Excel for graphing, but the following two methods frequently work:

1. Copy and paste; or
2. Save the data file, then import into Excel.

The first method is described in this section; the second method is introduced, then described more fully, in Section 9.

8.1 Copying and Pasting Web Data

Data sets presented on the Web are often HTML tables. It is usually possible to copy the information from such tables and paste it into Excel, but you have to copy entire rows; you can't select portions. Then, when you want to paste the data into Excel, you might need to use Paste Special... to instruct Excel to paste the values as text and ignore the HTML format information.

The temperature vs. time data used at the beginning of this chapter is available on the website in two forms: as an HTML table, and as text file Ex_Data.prn. The text's website is located at

http://www.coe.montana.edu/che/excel

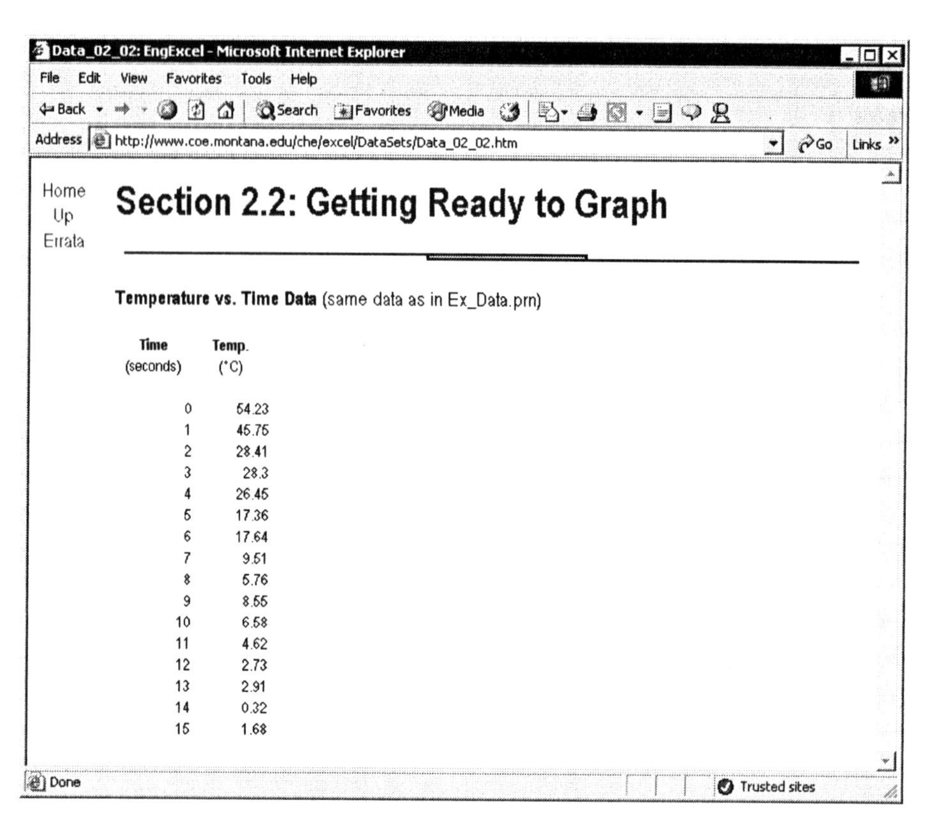

To copy the data from the HTML table, simply select all of the rows (and headings, if desired) and use Edit/Copy (or [Ctrl-C]) to copy the data to the Windows clipboard.

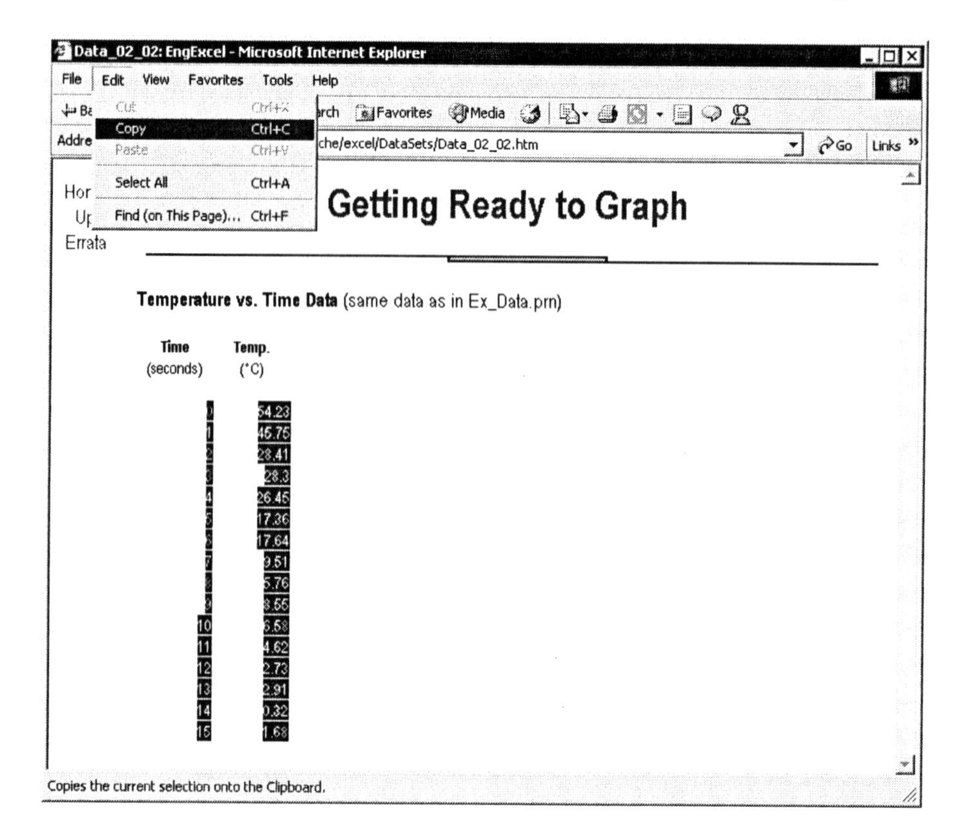

Then, you can paste the information into Excel by using Edit/Paste or [Ctrl-V].

B3 ▾ fx 28.41

	A	B	C	D
1	0	54.23		
2	1	45.75		
3	2	28.41		
4	3	28.3		
5	4	26.45		
6	5	17.36		
7	6	17.64		
8	7	9.51		
9	8	5.76		
10	9	8.55		
11	10	6.58		
12	11	4.62		
13	12	2.73		
14	13	2.91		
15	14	0.32		
16	15	1.68		
17				

With this data set, using Edit/Paste worked fine. Sometimes, you will find it necessary to use Edit/Paste Special... to paste the data into the spreadsheet as "Text." This tells Excel to ignore HTML formatting information and paste just the data into the cells.

8.2 Importing Data Files from the Web

A Web page could provide a link to a data file, such as the links to file Ex_Data.prn from the text's website. What happens when you click on a link to a .prn file depends on how your browser is configured:

1. The browser might display the contents of the file on the screen.
2. The browser might present an option box asking whether you want to open the file or save it.

If your browser displays the file contents on the screen, you can try copying and pasting the data. The process is exactly like that used in the previous section. If copying and pasting the data fails (or if your browser will not display the data file contents), then you might need to save the file to your computer and import the file into Excel.

If you right click on the data-file link, a pop-up menu will offer a Save Target As... option. This option allows you to save a copy of the link's target (the data file) to your own computer.

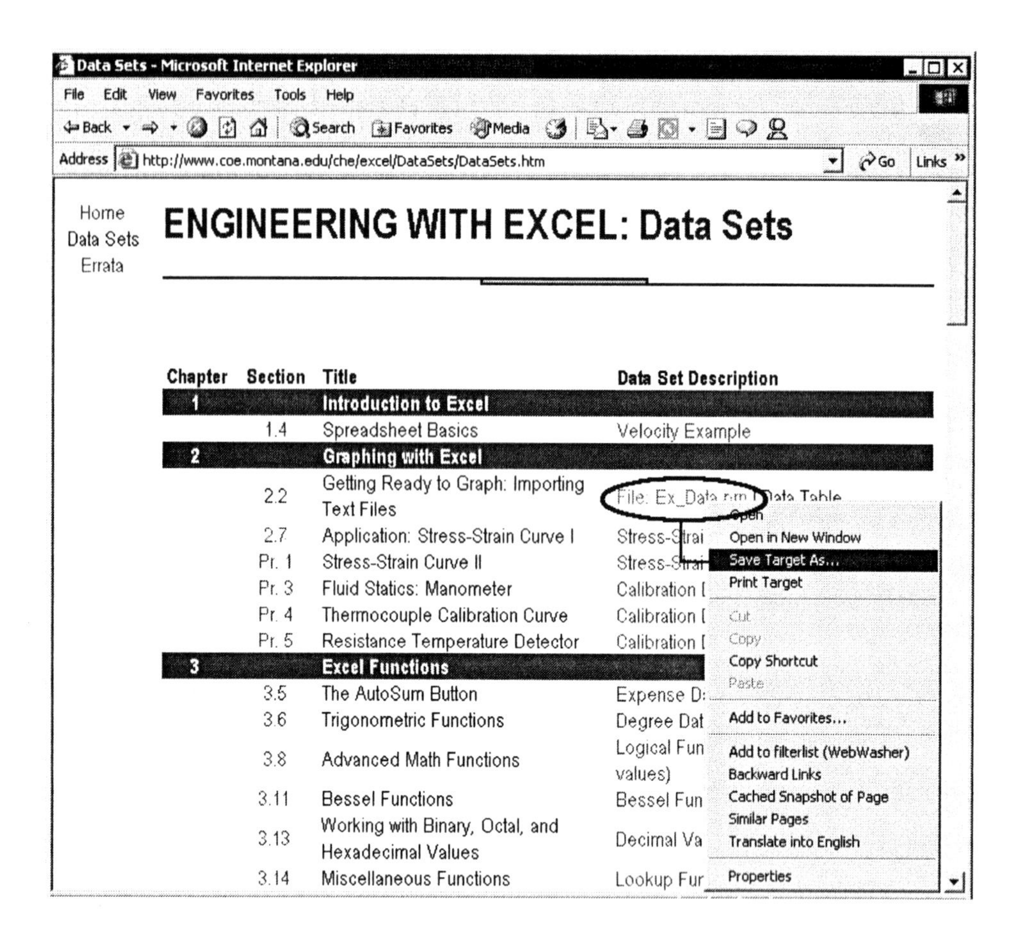

Once the data file has been saved on your own computer, it can be imported into Excel by Excel's Text Import Wizard. That process is described in the next section.

9 IMPORTING TEXT FILES

Text files are a common way to move data from one program to another, and Excel is good at creating graphs that use data from other programs. Importing a text file is one way to get the data to be plotted into Excel. Excel provides a Text Import Wizard to make it easy to import data from text files.

Two types of text files are used to store data:

- delimited
- fixed width

Delimited data has a special character, called a *delimiter*, between data values. Commas, spaces and tabs are the most common delimiters, but any nonnumeric character can be used. Quotes are frequently used as text-string delimiters.

The following is an example of comma-delimited data:

0, 54.23
1, 45.75
2, 28.41

Fixed width files align the data values in columns and use character position to distinguish individual data values. The comma-delimited data shown previously would look quite different in a fixed-width data file. In the following example, the data have been written to the file with 8-character fields, using 4 decimal places (a couple of header lines have been included to show the layout of the data fields):

```
Field 1 Field 2
1234567812345678

  0.0000 54.2300
  1.0000 45.7500
  2.0000 28.4100
```

Excel can read the data from either type of file, but Excel must know the format used in the data file before the data can be imported. The Text Import Wizard allows you to select the appropriate format as part of the import process. Fixed-width files were once very common, but delimited data seems to be more common at this time. Both types of data files are used regularly, and Excel's Text Import Wizard can handle either type of file.

9.1 Using the Text Import Wizard

The data set used in Section 2 of this chapter consists of 16 temperature values measured at 1-second intervals from 0 to 15 seconds. The values are available as a space-delimited text file called Ex_Data.prn. The file is available at the text's website, *http://www.coe.montana.edu/che/excel.* The following example assumes that the data file is available on the C: drive of the computer that is running Excel, in a folder called "ch_02".

You begin importing a text file into Excel by attempting to open the file. Select File/Open ... and enter the name of the data file—or, to select the data file from the files on the drive, change the file type (near the bottom of the Open File dialog box) to "Text Files (*.prn; *.txt; *.csv)" and browse for the file.

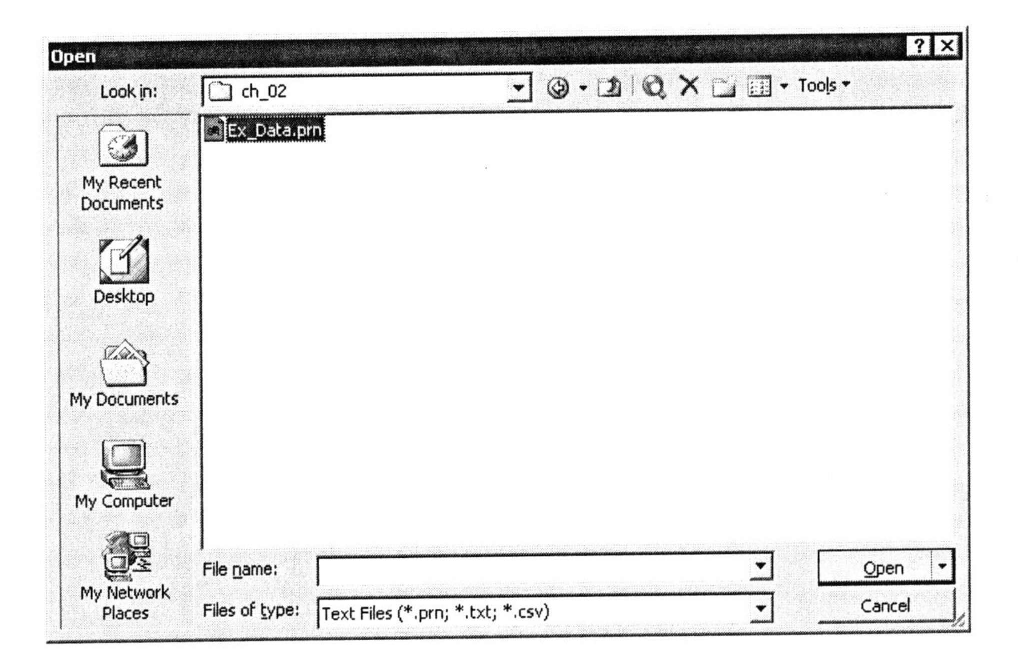

When Excel attempts to open the file and finds that it is not saved as an Excel workbook, it starts the Text Import Wizard to guide you through the import process. The steps in the process are as follows:

Select the Type of Text File First, select the data format that best fits your data, either delimited or fixed width. Excel will analyze the file contents and make a recommendation, but you should verify the data format. The data in Ex_Data.prn is space delimited, so we select Delimited.

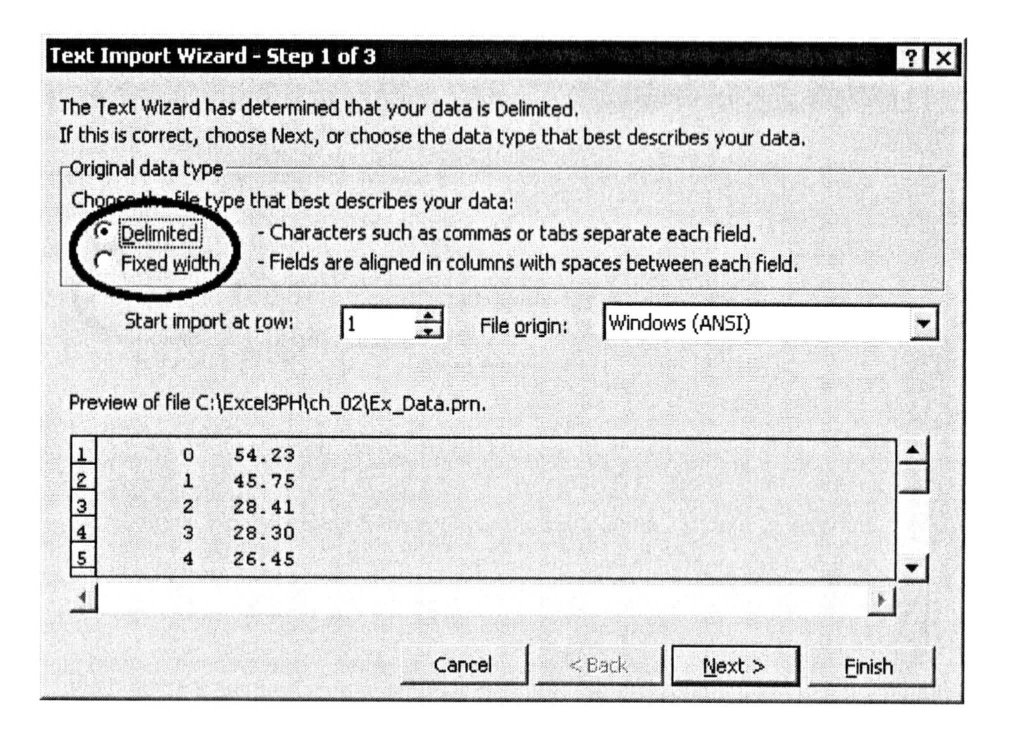

Notice that the text-import dialog allows you to begin importing data at any row (by using the Start import at row: field.) This is very useful if your data file contains heading or title information that you do not want to import into the spreadsheet.

Click Next > to go to the next step in the process.

Select the Type of Delimiter(s) If you selected "Delimited" data in the previous step, then you can choose the type(s) of delimiters. In file Ex_Data.prn, the values have leading spaces at the left of each line and spaces between two columns of values. When "Space" delimiter is checked, Excel treats the spaces in the files as delimiters and adds lines in the Data preview panel to show how the values will be separated into columns:

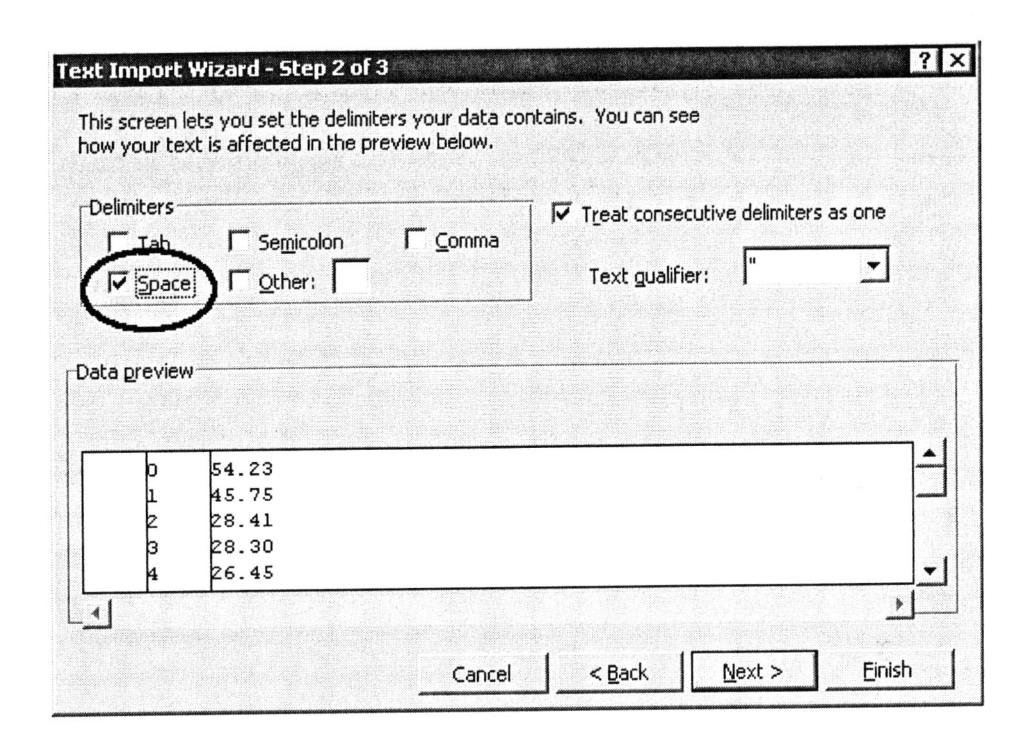

Click Next > to go to the next step in the process.

Select the Data to Be Imported and the Data Formats to be Used The dialog box for the final import step allows you to tell Excel the number format you want used for each imported column. You can also select not to import one or more columns. To select a column, click on the column heading. Then indicate the data format to be used for the data in that column, or select "Do not import column (skip)" to elect not to import the selected column. In the following figure, I chose to skip the first column (because Excel

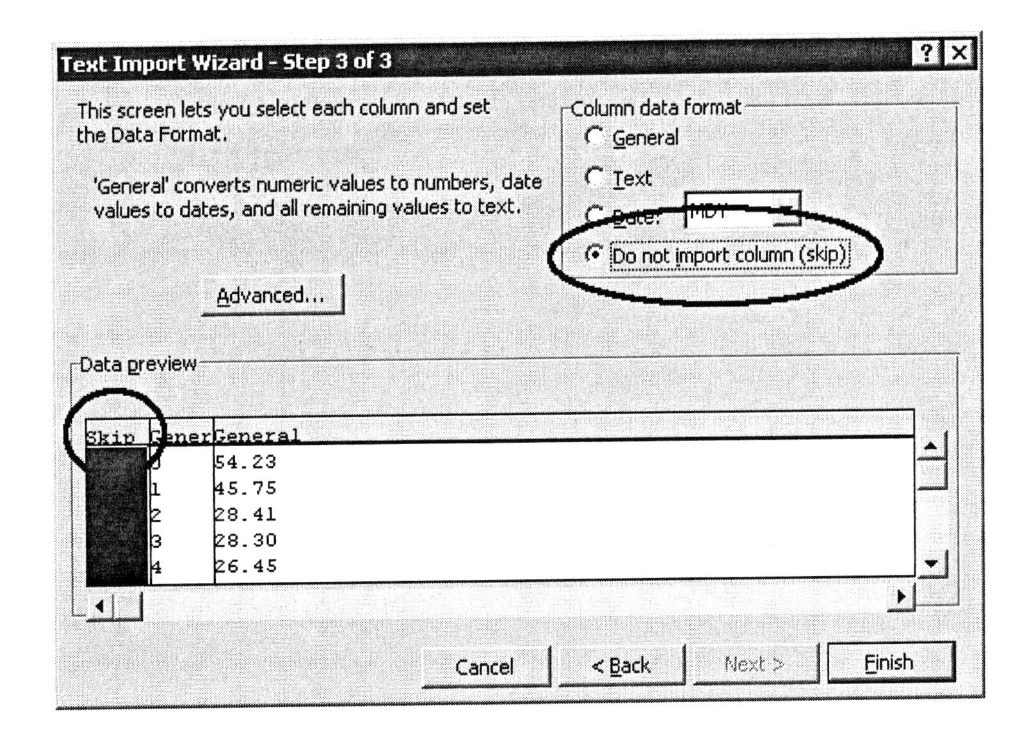

interpreted leading spaces on each line as an empty column) and to import the other two columns, saving them in the spreadsheet with a general number format.

When the correct formats have been specified for each column to be imported, click "Finish" to complete the import process. The values are placed at the top left corner of the spreadsheet:

	A	B	C
1	0	54.23	
2	1	45.75	
3	2	28.41	
4	3	28.3	
5	4	26.45	
6	5	17.36	
7	6	17.64	
8	7	9.51	
9	8	5.76	
10	9	8.55	
11	10	6.58	
12	11	4.62	
13	12	2.73	
14	13	2.91	
15	14	0.32	
16	15	1.68	
17			

You can move the cells to a different location within the same spreadsheet or copy and paste them to another spreadsheet. In the following example, the values were moved down a few rows to make room for titles:

	A	B	C
1	**Time**	**Temp.**	
2	(seconds)	(°C)	
3			
4	0	54.23	
5	1	45.75	
6	2	28.41	
7	3	28.3	
8	4	26.45	
9	5	17.36	
10	6	17.64	
11	7	9.51	
12	8	5.76	
13	9	8.55	
14	10	6.58	
15	11	4.62	
16	12	2.73	
17	13	2.91	
18	14	0.32	
19	15	1.68	
20			

Note: Since file Ex_Data.prn was opened, the workbook is called Ex_Data.prn. Excel will allow you to use the workbook just as you would a standard .xls file, but any nonalphanumeric content (e.g., graphs) will be lost if the file is saved as a .prn file. Excel will show a warning if you attempt to save the file with a .prn extension.

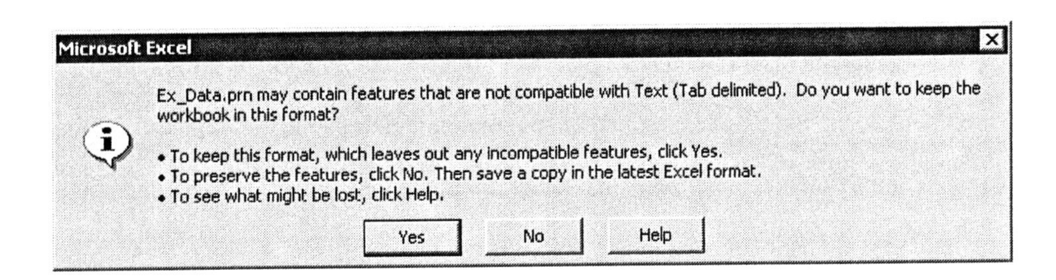

After the importing of a text file, the Excel workbook normally should be saved with the file extension .xls.

KEY TERMS

Automatic scaling	Legend	Tensile strength
Bar Graph	Line Graph	Tensile test
Column Graph	Modules of elasticity	Text file
Chart Wizard	Pie chart	Trendline
Delimited	Plot area	Ultimate stress
Error bars	Surface plot	Wire frame
Fixed width	Strain	Young's modulus
Handles	Stress	XY Scatter plot

SUMMARY

Creating an XY Scatter Plot from Existing Data

Before Starting the Chart Wizard, select the data range (x values in left column or top row).

The following are the Chart Wizard steps:

1. Select Chart Type XY (Scatter) and Basic Features (markers or no markers and no lines, straight lines, or smoothed lines)
2. Check the Data Series. Use Step 2 (Series panel) to add names to the series (displayed in the legend) or add additional curves to the graph.
3. Format the Graph (Add titles, turn grid lines on or off, turn the legend on or off, etc.)
4. Graph Placement. Indicate where the graph should be placed (on new spreadsheet or in the current spreadsheet).

Editing an Existing Graph

Double click the item you wish to modify. Items that can be modified include

- Axes
- Grid lines
- Legend
- Markers and Lines
- Plot Area
- Titles

Add Another Curve or Modify Existing Data Series Right click in some white space on the graph, and select Source Data Series from the pop-up menu.

Add New Titles Right click in some white space on the graph, and select Chart Options from the pop-up menu.

Printing a Graph

There are two ways to print a graph:

1. Select the graph (click on it) and use the Print or Print Preview buttons on the toolbar. (Or select File/Print... or File/Print Preview.)
   This method causes only the graph to be printed.

2. Select a cell range on the spreadsheet that includes the graph and then use the Print or Print Preview buttons on the toolbar. (Or select File/Print... or File/Print Preview.)

This causes the graph to be printed with the selected range of the spreadsheet.

Available Graph Types

- XY Scatter Plots
- Line Graphs
- Column and Bar Graphs
- Pie Charts
- Surface Plots

Problems

Stress–Strain Curve II

1. The following tabulated data represent stress–strain data from an experiment on an unknown sample of a white metal (modulus of elasticity values for various white metals are also listed):
   a. Graph the stress–strain data. If the data include values outside the elastic-stretch region, discard those values.
   b. Use a linear trendline to compute the modulus of elasticity for the sample.
   c. What type of metal was tested?

STRESS (MM/MM)	STRAIN (MPA)
0.0000	0
0.0015	168
0.0030	336
0.0045	504
0.0060	672

MATERIAL	MODULUS OF ELASTICITY (GPA)
Mg Alloy	45
Al Alloy	70
Ag	71
Ti Alloy	110
Pt	170
SS	200

Note: The modulus of elasticity depends on the type of alloy or purity of a nonalloyed material. The values listed here are typical.

Tank Temperature During a Wash-Out

2. One evening, a few friends come over for a soak, and you discover that the water in the hot tub is at 115°F (46°C)—too hot to use. As your friends turn on the cold water to cool down the tub, the engineer in you wants to know how long this is going to take, so you write an energy balance on a well-mixed tank (ignoring heat losses to the air). You end up with the following differential equation relating the temperature in the tank, T, to the temperature of the cold water flowing into the tank, T_{in}, the volume of the tank, V, and the volumetric flow rate of the cold water, $\dot{V}$:

$$\frac{dT}{dt} = \frac{\dot{V}}{V}(T_{in} - T). \quad (3)$$

Integrating, you get an equation for the temperature in the tank as a function of time:

$$T = T_{in} - (T_{in} - T_{init.})e^{\frac{-\dot{V}}{V}t}. \quad (4)$$

If the initial temperature $T_{init.}$ is 115°F, the cold water temperature is 35°F (1.7°C), and the volume and volumetric flow rate are 3,000 liters and 30 liters per minute, respectively,

a. calculate the expected water temperature at 5-minute intervals for the first 60 minutes after the flow of cold water is established;
b. plot the water temperature in the hot tub as a function of time;
c. calculate how long it should take for the water in the tub to cool to 100°F (37.8°C);
d. explain whether a hot tub is really a well-mixed tank. If it is not, will your equation predict a time that is too short or too long? Explain your reasoning.

Fluid Statics: Manometer

3. Manometers used to be common pressure-measurement devices, but, outside of laboratories, electronic pressure transducers are now more common. Manometers are sometimes still used to calibrate the pressure transducers.

In the calibration system shown in the accompanying figure, the mercury manometer on the right and the pressure transducer on the left are both connected to a piston-driven pressure source filled with hydraulic oil ($\rho = 880\ kg/m^3$). The bulbs connected to the transducer and the right side of the manometer are both evacuated ($\rho = 0$).

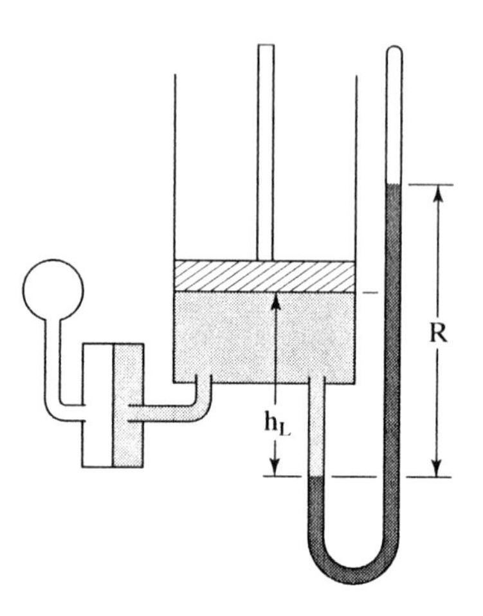

During the calibration, the piston is moved to generate a pressure on both the manometer and the transducer. The manometer reading R is recorded, along with the output of the pressure transducer A (assuming a 4- to 20-mA output current from the transducer).

Consider the following calibration data:

CALIBRATION DATA

PISTON SETTING	h_L (MM OIL)	MANOMETER READING (MM HG)	TRANSDUCER OUTPUT (MA)
1	300	0	4.0
2	450	150	5.6
3	600	300	7.2
4	750	450	8.8
5	900	600	10.4
6	1050	750	12.0
7	1200	900	13.6
8	1350	1050	15.2
9	1500	1200	16.8
10	1650	1350	18.4
11	1800	1500	20.0

a. Calculate pressures from the manometer readings.

b. Create a calibration table and graph showing the transducer output (mA) as a function of measured pressure.

Thermocouple Calibration Curve

4. A type J (iron/constantan) thermocouple was calibrated by using the system illustrated in the accompanying figure. The thermocouple and a thermometer were dipped into a beaker of water on a hot plate. The power level was set at a preset level (known only as 1, 2, 3, ... on the dial) and the thermocouple readings were monitored on a computer screen. When steady state had been reached, the thermometer was read, and 10 thermocouple readings were recorded. Then the power level was increased and the process repeated.

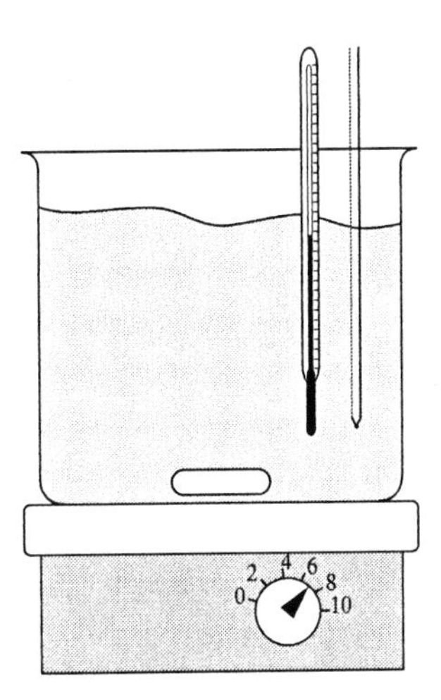

The accumulated calibration data (steady-state data only) are as follows (available electronically at *http://www.coe.montana.edu/che/Excel*):

	THERMOMETER	THERMOCOUPLE	
POWER SETTING	**(°C)**	**AVERAGE (mV)**	**STD. DEV. (mV)**
0	24.6	1.264	0.100
1	38.2	1.841	0.138
2	50.1	2.618	0.240
3	60.2	2.900	0.164
4	69.7	3.407	0.260
5	79.1	4.334	0.225
6	86.3	4.506	0.212
7	96.3	5.332	0.216
8	99.8	5.084	0.168

a. Plot the thermocouple calibration curve with temperature on the x-axis and average thermocouple reading on the y-axis.

b. Add a linear trendline to the graph and have Excel display the equation for the trendline and the R^2 value.

c. Use the standard-deviation values to add error bars (± 1 std. dev.) to the graph.

d. The millivolt output of an iron/constantan thermocouple can be related to temperature by the correlation equation[1]

$$T = aV^b, \tag{5}$$

where

T is temperature in °C,
V is the thermocouple output in millivolts,
a is 19.741 for iron/constantan, and
b is 0.9742 for iron/constantan.

Use this equation to calculate predicted thermocouple outputs at each temperature, and add these to the graph as a second data series. Do the predicted values appear to agree with the average experimental values?

Resistance Temperature Detector

5. The *linear temperature coefficient* α of a *resistance temperature detector* (RTD) is a physical property of the metal used to make the RTD that indicates how the electrical resistance of the metal changes as the temperature increases. The equation relating temperature to resistance is

$$R_T = R_0[1 + \alpha T], \tag{6}$$

or

$$R_T = R_0 + (R_0\alpha)T \qquad \textit{(in linear-regression form)}, \tag{7}$$

where

R_T is the resistance at the unknown temperature, T,
R_0 is the resistance at 0°C (known, one of the RTD specifications), and
α is the linear temperature coefficient (known, one of the RTD specifications).

The common grade of platinum used for RTDs has an α value equal to 0.00385 ohm/ ohm/°C (sometimes written simply as 0.00385°C^{-1}), but older RTDs used a different grade of platinum and operated with α = 0.003902°C^{-1}, and laboratory grade RTDs use very high-purity platinum with α = 0.003923°C^{-1}. If the wrong α value is used to compute temperatures from RTD readings, the computed temperatures will be incorrect.

[1]Thermocouple correlation equation from *Transport Phenomena Data Companion*, L.P.B.M. Janssen and M.M.C.G. Warmoeskerken, Arnold DUM, London, 1987, p. 20.

The following data show the temperature vs. resistance for an RTD:

TEMPERATURE	RESISTANCE
°C	OHMS
0	100.0
10	103.9
20	107.8
30	111.7
40	115.6
50	119.5
60	123.4
70	127.3
80	131.2
90	135.1
100	139.0

a. Use Excel to graph the data and add a trend line to evaluate the linear temperature coefficient.

b. Is the RTD of laboratory grade?

6

Linear Regression in Excel

Sections

Objectives

After reading this chapter, you will know

- How to use regression functions to calculate slopes, intercepts, and R^2 values for data sets
- How to perform simple regression analyses directly from a graph of your data, using trendlines
- A general approach that can handle any linear-regression model

1 INTRODUCTION

When most people think of *linear regression*, they think about finding the slope and intercept of the best-fit straight line through some data points. While that is linear regression, it's only the beginning. The "linear" in linear regression means that the equation used to fit the data points must be linear in the coefficients; it does not imply that the curve through the data points must be a straight line or that the equation can have only two coefficients (i.e., slope and intercept).

Excel provides several methods for performing linear regressions making possible both very simple and quick analyses and highly detailed advanced regression models.

2 LINEAR REGRESSION BY USING EXCEL FUNCTIONS

When all you need is the *slope* and *intercept* of the best-fit straight line through your data points, Excel's `SLOPE()` and `INTERCEPT()` functions are very handy. Include the `RSQ()` function to calculate the *coefficient of determination*, or R^2 value, and a lot of simple data analysis problems are covered.

2.1 A Simple Example

The following temperature and time values are a simple data set that we can use to investigate the basics of regression analysis in Excel:

	A	B	C	D	E
1	**Linear Regression Using Excel Functions**				
2					
3	**Time**	**Temp.**			
4	(min.)	(K)			
5					
6	0	298			
7	1	299			
8	2	301			
9	3	304			
10	4	306			
11	5	309			
12	6	312			
13	7	316			
14	8	319			
15	9	322			
16					

The `SLOPE()` function can be used to determine the slope of the best-fit straight line through these data. The `SLOPE()` function takes two arguments: the cell range containing the y-values (*dependent variable* values) and the cell range containing the x-values (*independent variable* values)—in that order.

Here, temperature depends on time, not the other way around, so temperature (cells B6:B15) is the dependent variable, and time (A6:A15) is the independent variable:

D6 fx =SLOPE(B6:B15,A6:A15)

	A	B	C	D	E
1	**Linear Regression Using Excel Functions**				
2					
3	**Time**	**Temp.**			
4	(min.)	(K)			
5					
6	0	298	**Slope:**	2.78	
7	1	299	**Intercept:**		
8	2	301	**R^2:**		
9	3	304			
10	4	306			
11	5	309			
12	6	312			
13	7	316			
14	8	319			
15	9	322			
16					

Similarly, the intercept can be obtained by using the `INTERCEPT()` function, with the same arguments:

D7 | f_x =INTERCEPT(B6:B15,A6:A15)

	A	B	C	D	E
1	**Linear Regression Using Excel Functions**				
2					
3	**Time**	**Temp.**			
4	(min.)	(K)			
5					
6	0	298	**Slope:**	2.78	
7	1	299	**Intercept:**	296.1	
8	2	301	**R²:**		
9	3	304			
10	4	306			
11	5	309			
12	6	312			
13	7	316			
14	8	319			
15	9	322			
16					

Next, the coefficient of determination (R^2) can be computed by using the `RSQ()` function with the same arguments:

D8 | f_x =RSQ(B6:B15,A6:A15)

	A	B	C	D	E
1	**Linear Regression Using Excel Functions**				
2					
3	**Time**	**Temp.**			
4	(min.)	(K)			
5					
6	0	298	**Slope:**	2.78	
7	1	299	**Intercept:**	296.1	
8	2	301	**R²:**	0.9864	
9	3	304			
10	4	306			
11	5	309			
12	6	312			
13	7	316			
14	8	319			
15	9	322			
16					

This tells us that the best-fit line through the data has the slope (b_1) 2.7758 K/min (the units were inferred from the data) and the intercept (b_0) 296.1 K. The R^2 value is 0.9864.

Thus, we have a slope, an intercept, and an R^2 value. Is the straight line a good fit to the data? It is always a good idea to plot the data and the regression line to verify the fit visually; but, if you are going to graph your data, Excel provides an even easier way to perform a linear regression: the trendline.

3 LINEAR REGRESSION BY USING EXCEL'S TRENDLINE CAPABILITY

Performing a linear-regression analysis in Excel is incredibly simple. Once the data have been graphed, regression takes just a few mouse clicks. This ease of use creates a situation in which people sometimes use linear regression because it is easy, even when the relationship between their independent and dependent variables might be nonlinear. A rule of thumb for fitting curves to data: *always graph the fitted curve against the original data to inspect the quality of the fit visually.* When the regression is done with a *trendline*, the fitted curve is automatically added to the graph of the original data.

3.1 Simple Slope–Intercept Linear Regression

The process of performing a linear regression for a slope and intercept requires the computation of various sums involving the x-(independent) and y-(dependent) values in your data set. With these sums, you could use the following equations to calculate the slope b_1 and intercept b_0 of the straight line that best fits your data, *but Excel will do it for you:*

$$b_1 = \frac{\sum_i x_i y_i - \frac{1}{N_{\text{data}}} \sum_i x_i \sum_i y_i}{\sum_i (x_i^2) - \frac{1}{N_{\text{data}}} \left(\sum_i x_i \right)^2},$$

$$b_0 = \frac{\sum_i y_i - b_1 \sum_i x_i}{N_{\text{data}}}. \tag{1}$$

In these equations, $\sum_i$ implies summation over all data points, $i = 1$ to N_{data}.

When you add a trendline to a graph, Excel calculates all of the required summations, then calculates the slope b_1, the intercept b_0, and the coefficient of determination R^2. The trendline is added to the graph so that you can see how well the fitted equation matches the data points. By default, the equation of the trendline and the R^2 value are not shown on the graph. You have to request them by using the Options panel on the Trendline dialog box.

To see how to use trendlines, we will again use the temperature-vs.-time data. The first step in using a trendline to obtain a regression equation is to plot the data, using an *XY (Scatter) plot* with the data points indicated by data markers.

Note: It is customary to plot data values with markers and fitted results with curves, so that it is easy to see whether the fitted line actually goes through the data points.

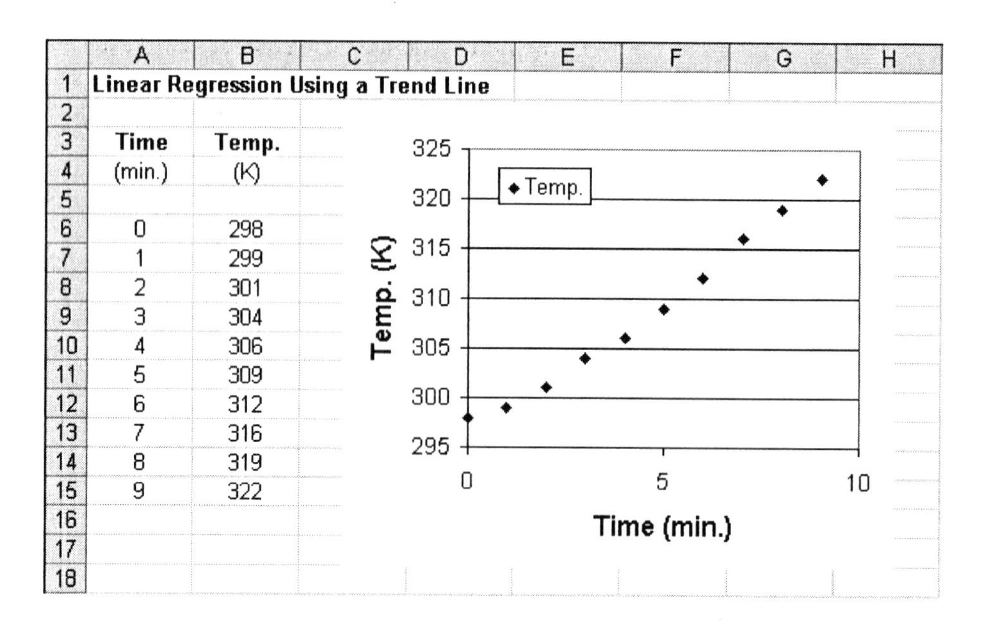

Then right click on any data point on the graph and select Add Trendline . . . from the pop-up menu:

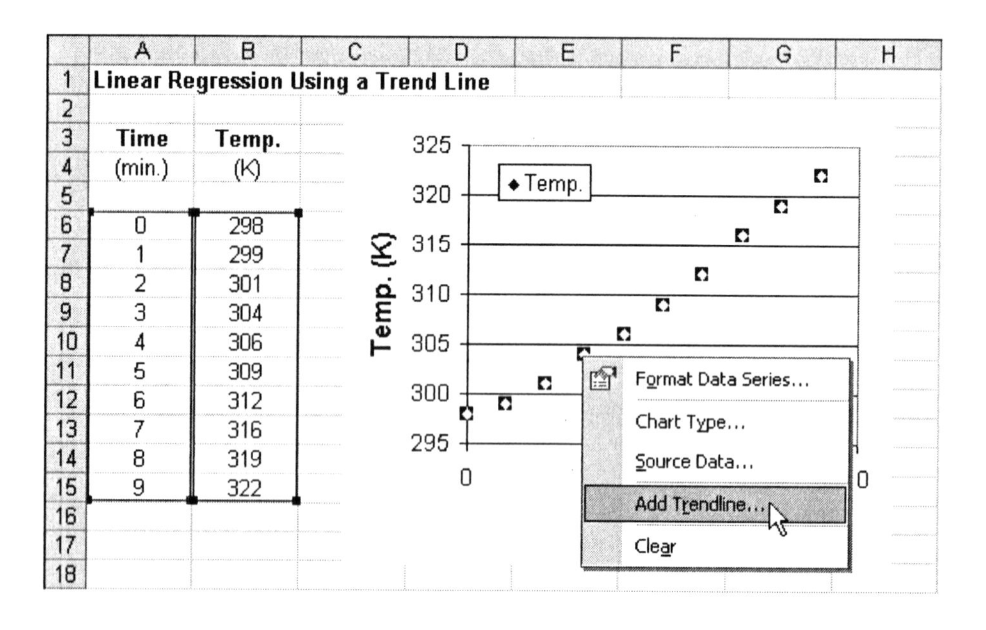

In the Add Trendline dialog box, select Linear from the Type panel:

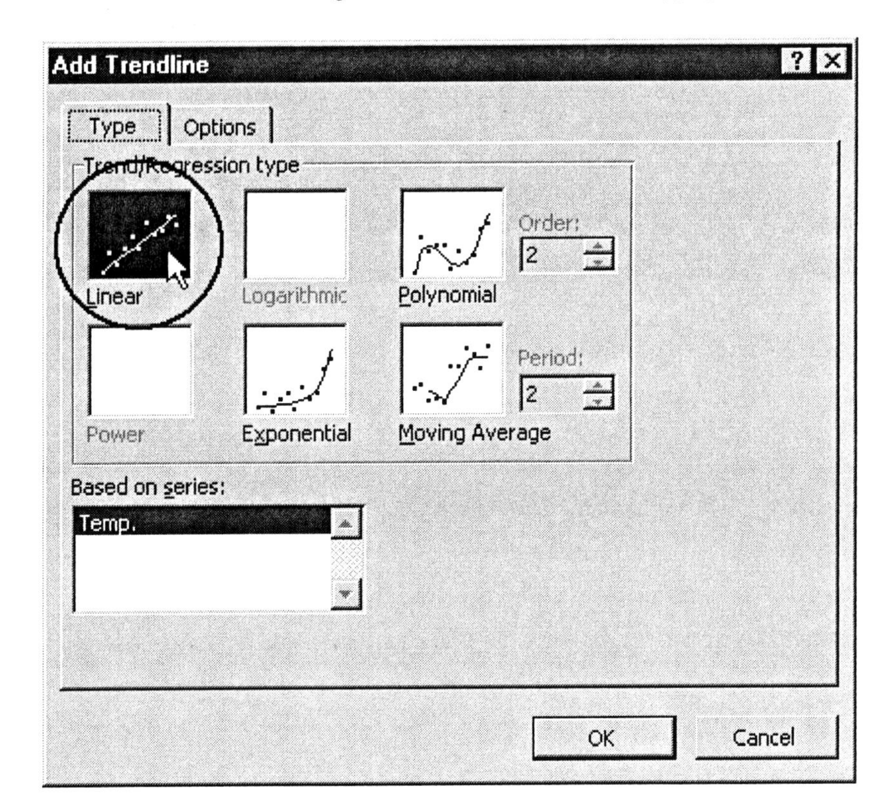

Press OK to close the Add Trendline dialog box and add the trendline to the plot:

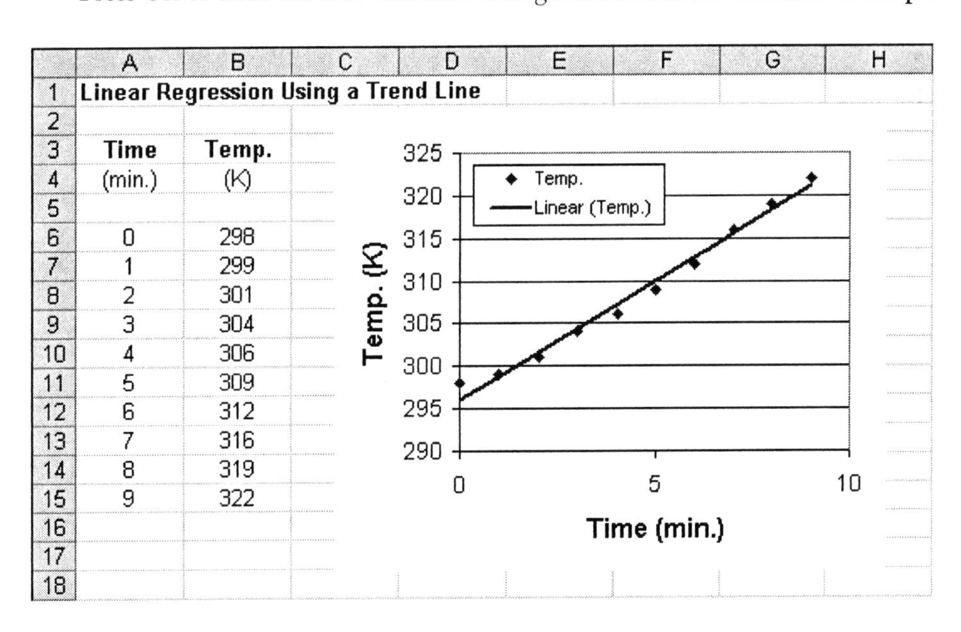

Excel has added the trendline to the graph. To create the line, Excel performed a linear regression on the graphed data. The equation of the regression line is available; you need only ask Excel to display it. Double click on the trendline to bring up the Format Trendline dialog box.

In the Options panel, check "Display equation on chart" and "Display R-squared value on chart" to have these items included on the graph. Also, you can see where the trendline text in the plot's legend could be defined in the Custom field on the Trendline name box:

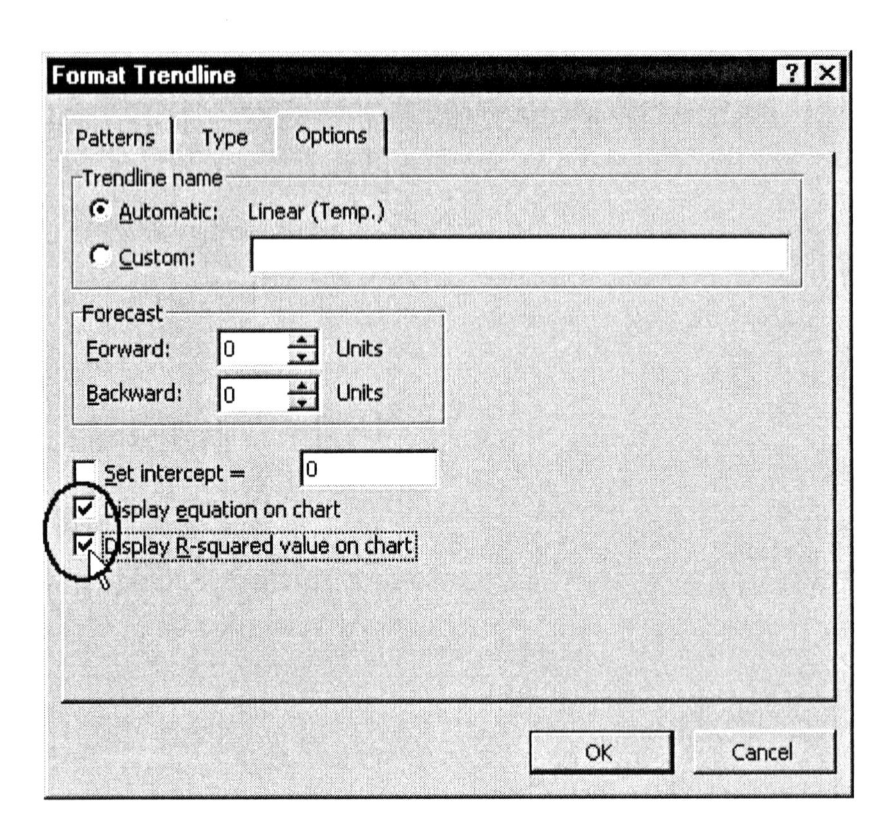

When you press OK, Excel will add the regression equation and the R^2 value to the plot:

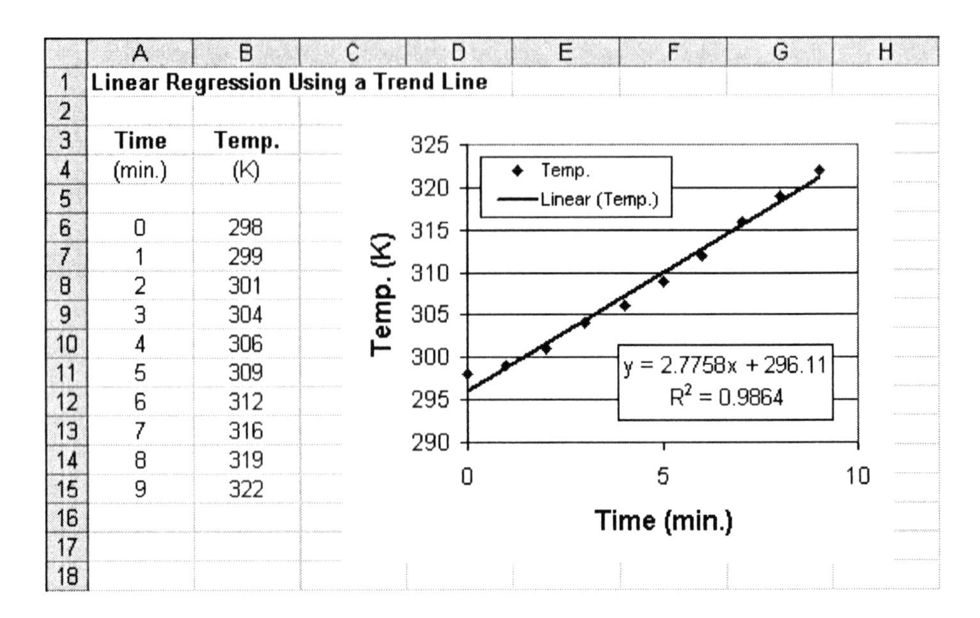

Linear Regression Using a Trend Line

Time (min.)	Temp. (K)
0	298
1	299
2	301
3	304
4	306
5	309
6	312
7	316
8	319
9	322

From the graph, we see that the regression equation is

$$y = 2.7758x + 296.11, \tag{2}$$

with the R^2 value 0.9864. (These are the same results we obtained by using the `SLOPE()`, `INTERCEPT()`, and `RSQ()` functions.) This tells us that the best-fit line through the data has the slope (b_1) 2.7758 K/min (the units were inferred from the data), the intercept (b_0) 296.1 K, and R^2 value 0.9864. The R^2 value 1 means a perfect fit, so the value 0.9864 indicates that this is a less-than-perfect fit. The plotted trendline allows you to verify visually that the best-fit line really does (or doesn't) fit the data. In this case, the straight trendline is not fitting the data well. We need to try to find a regression equation that allows for some curvature.

3.2 Forcing the Regression Line through the Origin (0,0)

If you do not want Excel to compute an intercept (i.e., if you want to force the curve to go through $y = 0$ when $x = 0$), there is a check box you can select on the Options panel of the Format Trendline (or Add Trendline) dialog box.

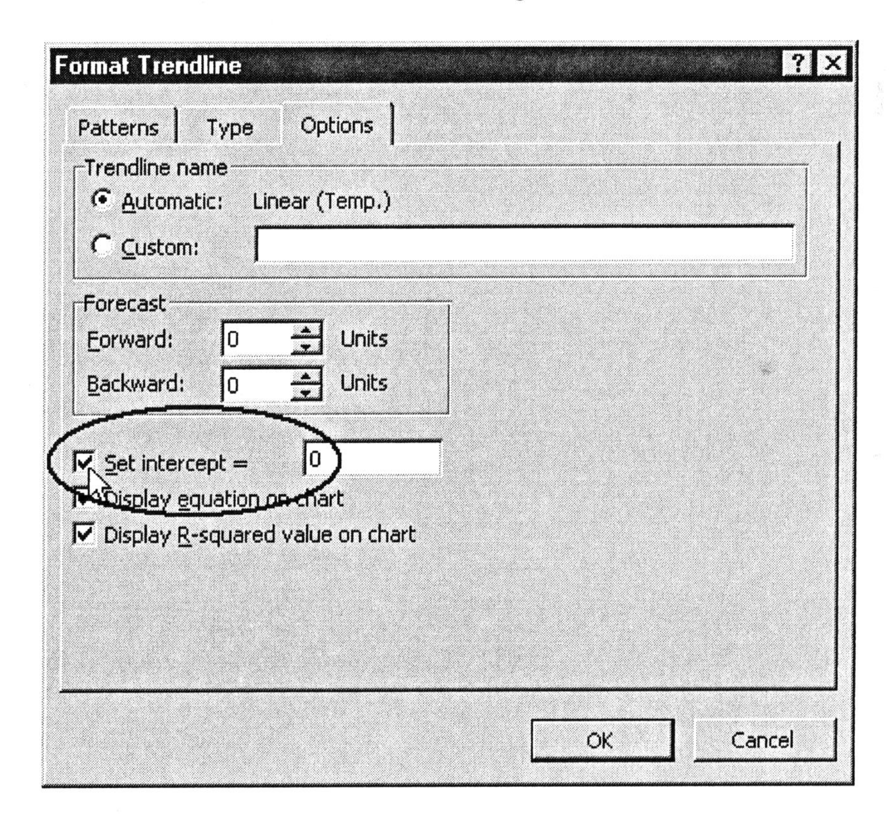

The temperature in our data set does not go to zero at time zero, so there is no reason to force the intercept through the origin for this data.

4 OTHER TWO-COEFFICIENT LINEAR-REGRESSION MODELS

Any equation relating x-values to y-values that is linear in the coefficients can be used in regression analysis, but there are a number of two-coefficient models that are commonly used for linear regression. These include the following:

NAME	EQUATION	LINEAR FORM	DATA MANIPULATION
Exponential Fit	$y = k_0 e^{k_1 x}$	$\ln(y) = \ln(k_0) + k_1 x$ $= b_0 + b_1 x$ $b_0 = \ln(k_0)$ $b_1 = k_1$	Take the natural log of all y-values prior to performing regression. Regression returns b_0 and b_1 which can be related to k_0 and k_1 through the equations on the left.
Logarithmic Fit	$y = k_0 + k_1 \ln(x)$	$y = k_0 + k_1 \ln(x)$ $b_0 = k_0$ $b_1 = k_1$	Take the natural log of all x-values prior to performing regression.
Power Fit	$y = k_0 x^{k_1}$	$\ln(y) = \ln(k_0) + k_1 \ln(x)$ $= b_0 + b_1 \ln(x)$ $b_0 = \ln(k_0)$ $b_1 = k_1$	Take the natural log of all x and y-values prior to performing regression.

Note: Excel will manipulate the data as needed to create these trendlines. You simply need to select the type of trendline you want to use.

Each of these is available as a regressed trendline in Excel. You select the type of regression you want Excel to perform, using the Type panel of the Format Trendline (or Add Trendline) dialog box.

The slight upward bending visible in the data suggests an exponential fit might work. It's easy to give it a try; just double click on the existing trendline to bring up the Format Trendline dialog box:

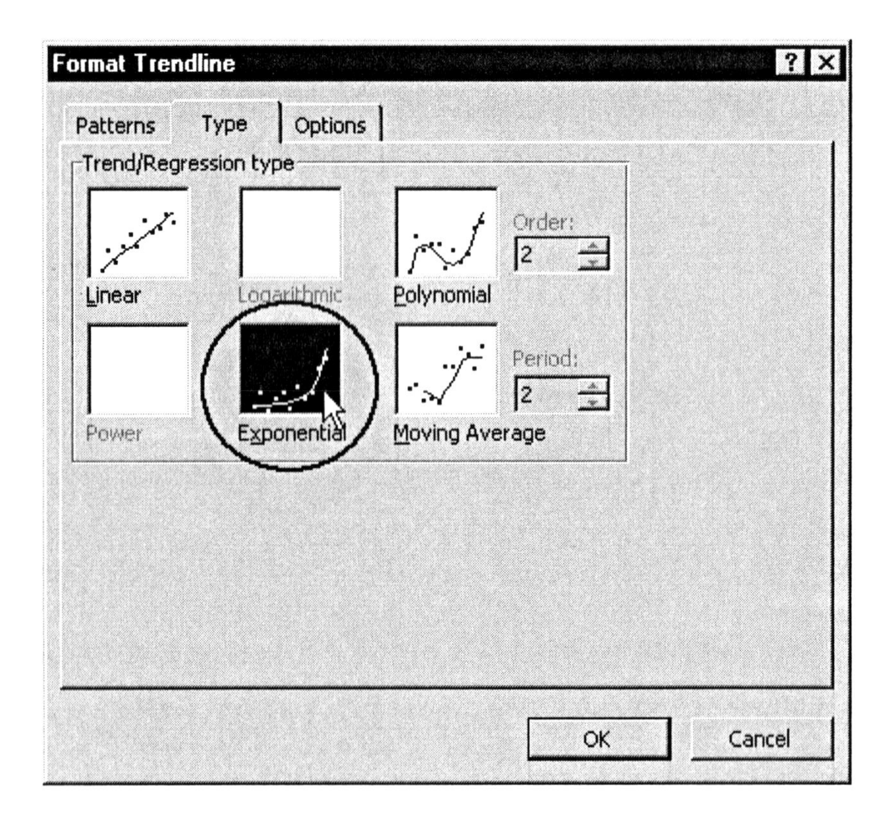

Then select Exponential from the Type panel. When you click the OK button, Excel will perform the regression, using an exponential fit.

Note: The Logarithmic and Power types are not available for this data set, because it contains x = 0 *(i.e.,* time = 0*). Both of those regression equations take the natural log of* x*. Because ln(0) is not defined, these regression equations cannot be used with this data set.*

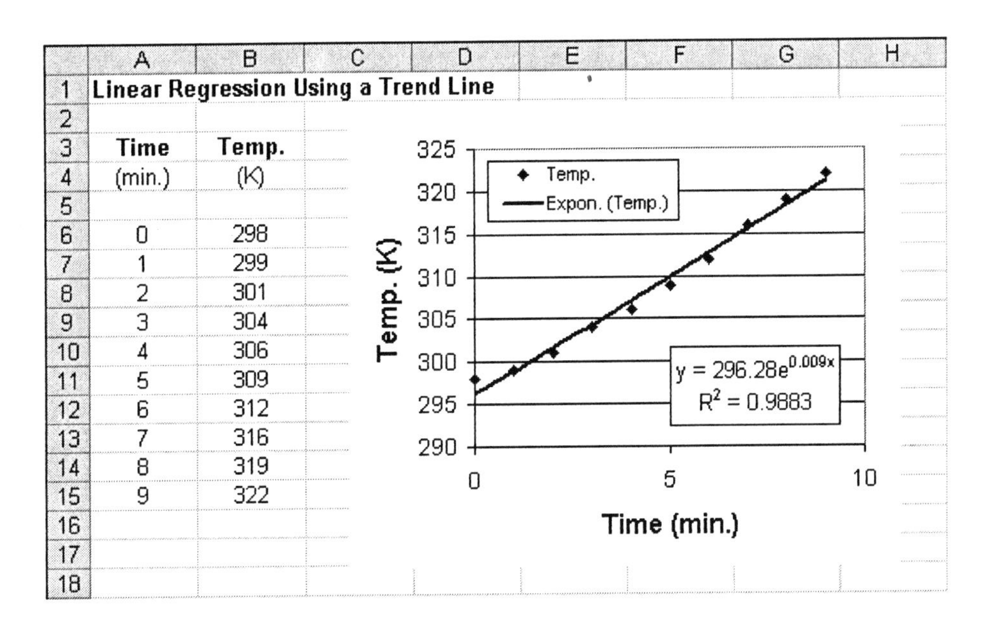

The result from using an exponential fit doesn't look much better, and the R^2 value is about the same as what we obtained with the linear model. (Excel offers one more type of regression on the Format Trendline (or Add Trendline) dialog: polynomial regression.)

5 POLYNOMIAL REGRESSION

Polynomial regression is still a linear regression, because the regression polynomials are linear in the coefficients (the b-values). Since, during a regression analysis, all of the x values are known, each of the polynomial equations listed next is a linear equation, so regression using any of these equations is a linear regression. It differs from the other regression models in that there are more than two coefficients. Technically, simple slope–intercept regression is also a polynomial regression, but the term is usually reserved for polynomials of order two or higher. Excel's polynomial trendlines can be of order 2 through 6:

ORDER	REGRESSION MODEL	NUMBER OF COEFFICIENTS
2	$y_p = b_0 + b_1x + b_2x^2$	3
3	$y_p = b_0 + b_1x + b_2x^2 + b_3x^3$	4
4	$y_p = b_0 + b_1x + b_2x^2 + b_3x^3 + b_4x^4$	5
5	$y_p = b_0 + b_1x + b_2x^2 + b_3x^3 + b_4x^4 + b_5x^5$	6
6	$y_p = b_0 + b_1x + b_2x^2 + b_3x^3 + b_4x^4 + b_5x^5 + b_6x^6$	7

Note: It is fairly standard nomenclature to write polynomials with the higher powers to the right. However, Excel reports polynomial trendline equations with the high powers first. It's not a big deal, but read the equations carefully.

To request a second-order polynomial regression, bring up the Format Trendline dialog box by double clicking on the existing trendline:

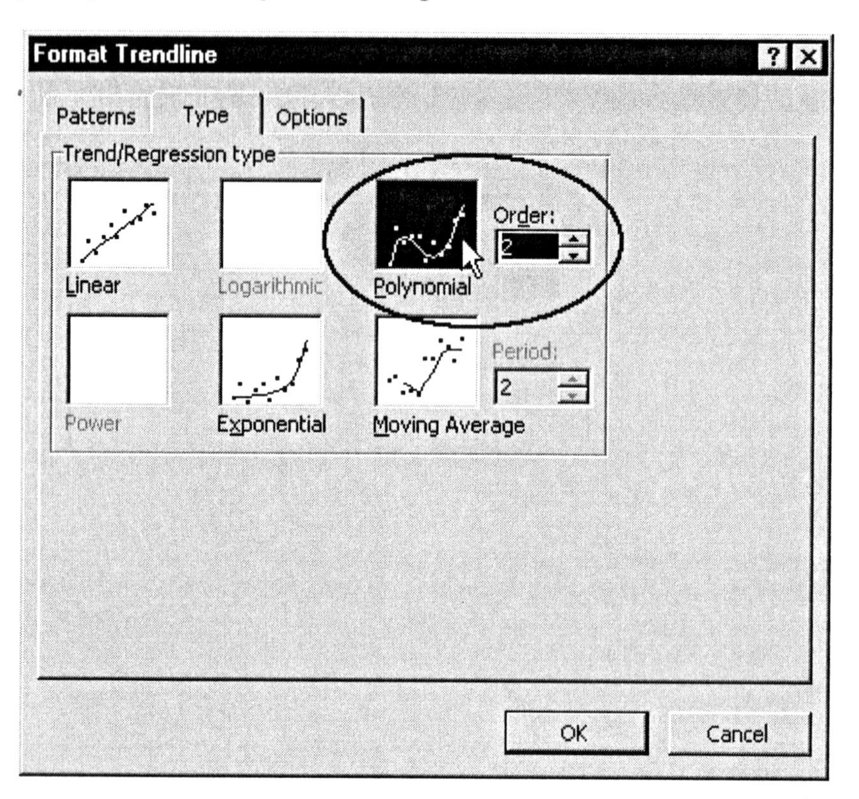

Select Polynomial type, and set the order to 2. Click the OK button to have Excel perform the regression:

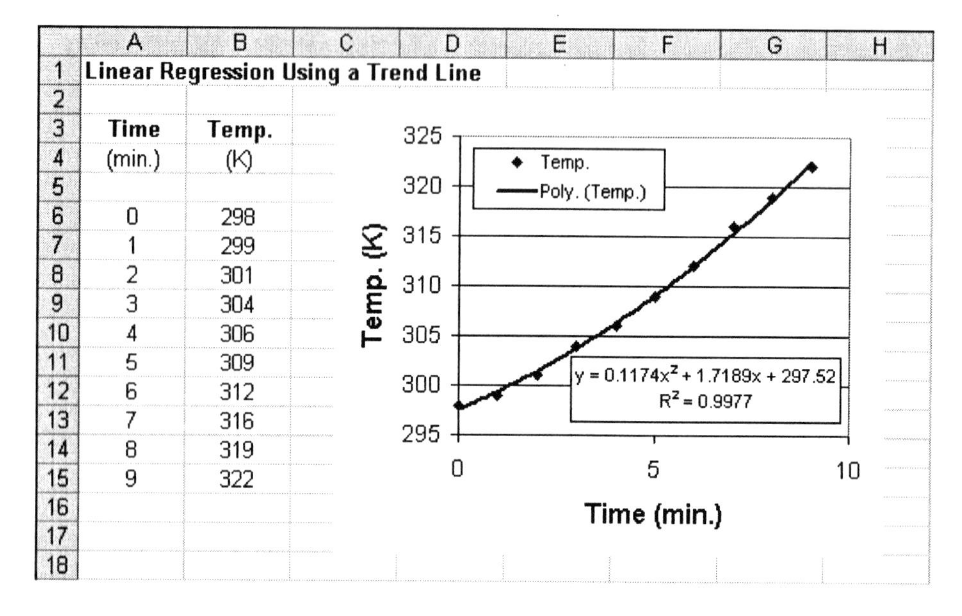

The second-order polynomial trendline appears to fit the data well, and the R^2 value is much closer to unity.

Polynomial regression using trendlines is as easy and simple as slope–intercept regression. But what happens if you want a 7th-order fit, and Excel's trendline capability can't be used? You can still use Excel's regression-analysis package, which is available from the main menu under Tools/Data Analysis/Regression. You also might want to use the regression-analysis package if you want more details about the regression results than are available with the use of trendlines.

6 LINEAR REGRESSION BY USING EXCEL'S REGRESSION-ANALYSIS PACKAGE

Excel's regression analysis package is fairly easy to use, but is more involved than simply asking for a trendline on a graph. There are two reasons why you might want to use the more complex approach:

1. You want to use a regression model that is not available as a trendline. The regression-analysis package can handle any linear-regression model.
2. You want more details about the regression process than are provided by using trendlines.

6.1 A Simple Linear Regression for Slope and Intercept

As a first example of working with the regression-analysis package, we will regress the temperature-vs.-time data to calculate the slope and intercept:

Step 1. Open the Data Analysis list box.

Regression is one of the data-analysis tools available on the Tools menu. Select Tools/Data Analysis ... to bring up the Data Analysis list box.

Note: By default, the data-analysis package is installed, but not an activated part of Excel. If the Data Analysis menu option does not appear under the Tools menu, it has not been activated. Select Tools/Add-Ins ..., and activate the Analysis option. (This need be done only once.)

Step 2. Select Regression from the Data Analysis list box.

Click Regression, and then OK.

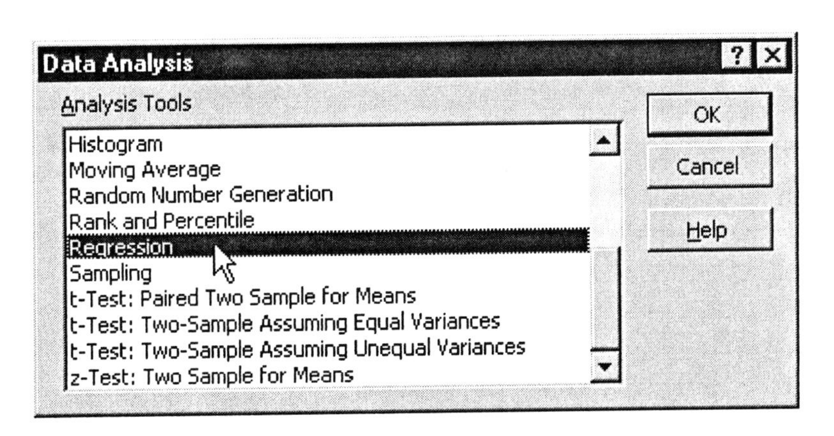

This will open the Regression dialog box:

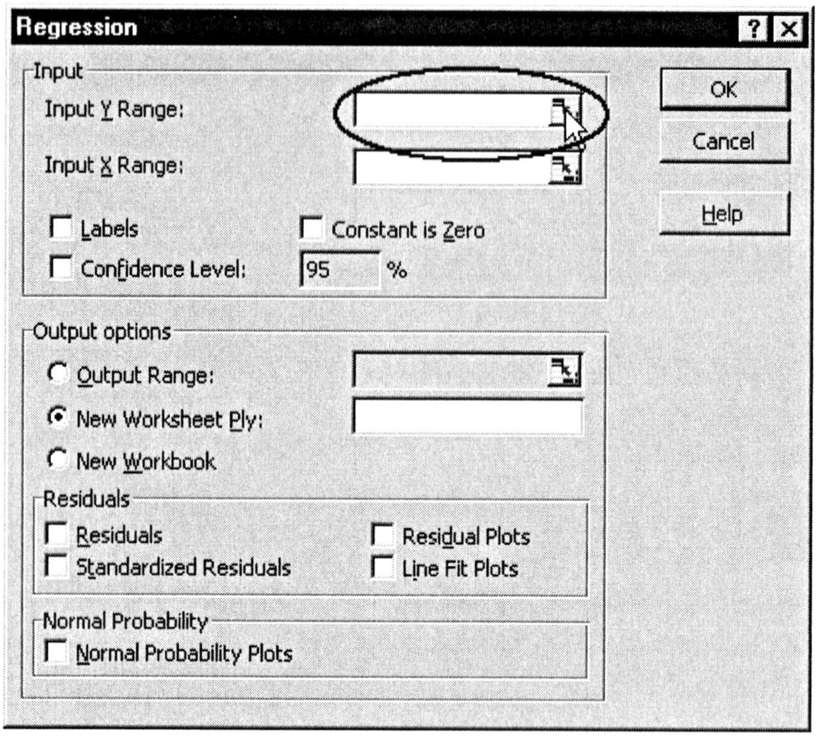

Step 3(a). Tell Excel where to find the *y*-values for the regression: Use the "to the spreadsheet" button.

The Regression dialog box has a field labeled "Input Y Range" as shown before. At the right side of the input field, there is a small button that will take you to the spreadsheet (so you can select the cells containing *y*-values). Click the "to the spreadsheet" button.

Note: Common linear regression assumes that all of the uncertainty in the data is in the y*-values and that the* x*-values are known precisely. It is important, therefore, to call the values that are imprecise the* y*-values for regression analysis.*

Step 3(b). Select the cells containing the *y*-values.

When the spreadsheet is displayed, drag the mouse to indicate the cells containing the *y*-values. When the *y*-values have been selected, click on the "return to dialog" button (circled in the figure below) or press [Enter] to return to the Regression dialog box.

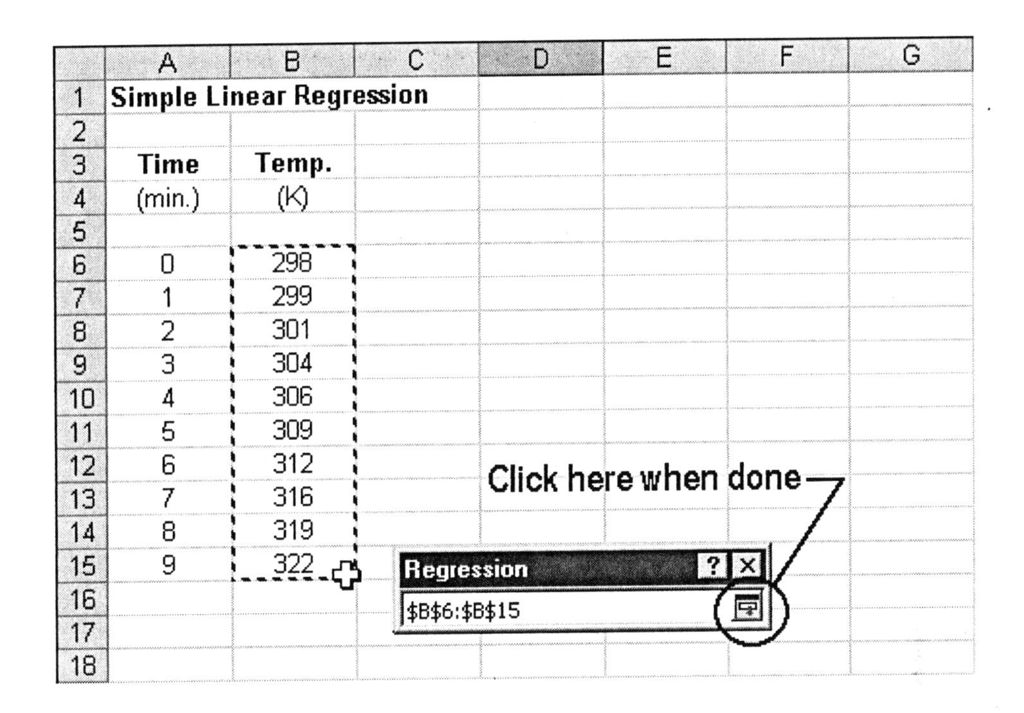

Step 4(a). Tell Excel where to find the *x*-values: Use the "to the spreadsheet" button.

Similarly, indicate the *x*-values:

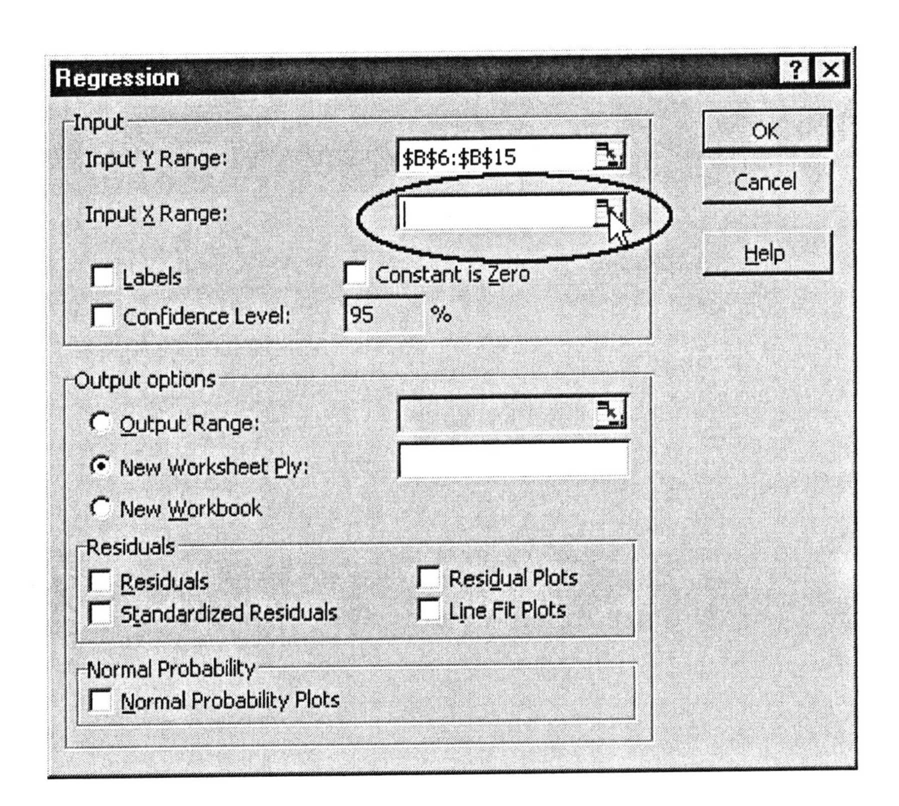

Step 4(b). Select the cells containing the *x*-values.

Use the mouse to indicate which cells contain the x-values, then return to the Regression dialog box:

	A	B	C	D	E	F	G
1	**Simple Linear Regression**						
2							
3	**Time**	**Temp.**					
4	(min.)	(K)					
5							
6	0	298					
7	1	299					
8	2	301					
9	3	304					
10	4	306					
11	5	309					
12	6	312					
13	7	316					
14	8	319					
15	9	322					
16							
17							

Regression
$A$6:$A$15

Step 5. Choose a location for the results of the regression analysis.

Because the results take up quite a bit of space, putting the output on a new worksheet ply (a new spreadsheet) is the most common. Do this by clicking the button next to "New Worksheet Ply:"

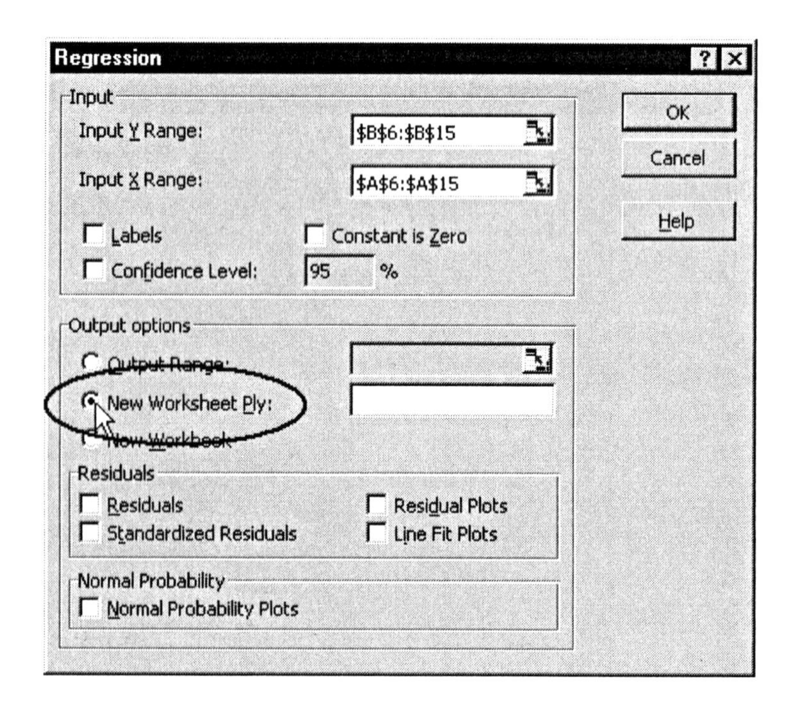

Step 6. Indicate whether you want the results to be graphed.

It is always a good idea to look at the residual plot and the line-fit plot to check visually on whether the regression line actually fits the data:

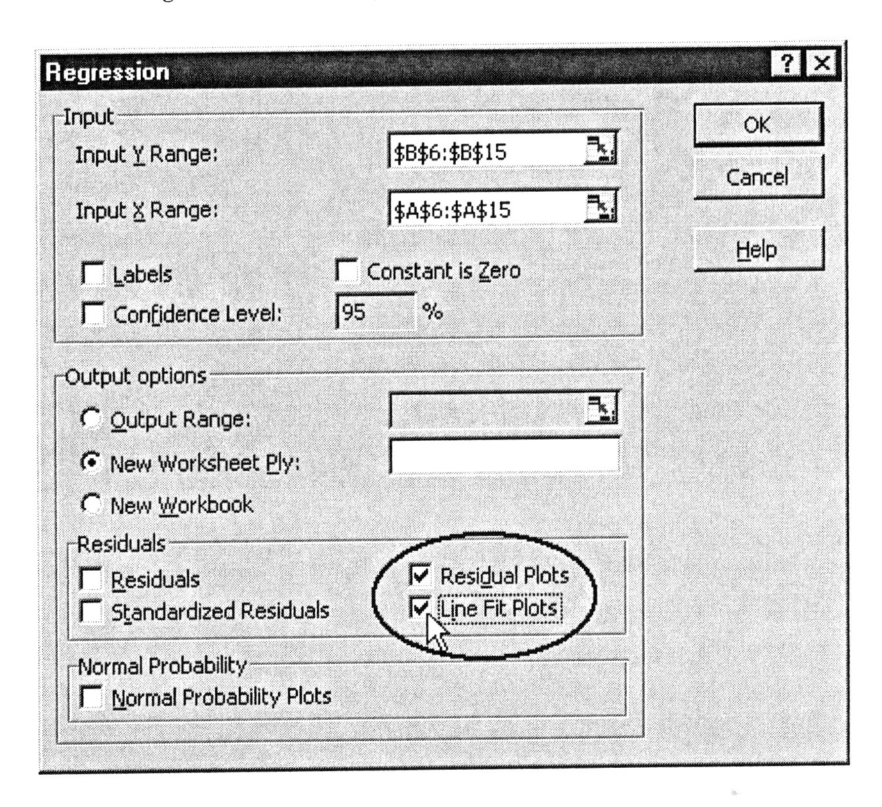

Step 7. Perform the regression.

Click the [OK] button to perform the regression. The results are presented as tables and graphs (if you requested them.) Only a portion of the output is shown here:

	A	B	C	D	E	F
1	SUMMARY OUTPUT					
2						
3	*Regression Statistics*					
4	Multiple R	0.99318635				
5	R Square	0.98641913				
6	Adjusted R Square	0.98472152				
7	Standard Error	1.04591558				
8	Observations	10				
9						
10	ANOVA					
11		*df*	*SS*	*MS*	*F*	*Significance F*
12	Regression	1	635.6484848	635.6485	581.0637	9.35281E-09
13	Residual	8	8.751515152	1.093939		
14	Total	9	644.4			
15						
16		*Coefficients*	*Standard Error*	*t Stat*	*P-value*	*Lower 95%*
17	Intercept	296.109091	0.614740869	481.6812	3.86E-19	294.691495
18	X Variable 1	2.77575758	0.115151515	24.10526	9.35E-09	2.510217534
19						

The output page tells us that the best-fit line through the data has slope (b_1) 2.775 K/min (the units were inferred from the data) and intercept (b_0) 296.1 K. The R^2 value is 0.9864. These are the same results we obtained with the other methods.

The plots allow you to verify visually that the best-fit line really does (or doesn't) fit the data. The line-fit plot was created by Excel and placed on the output page:

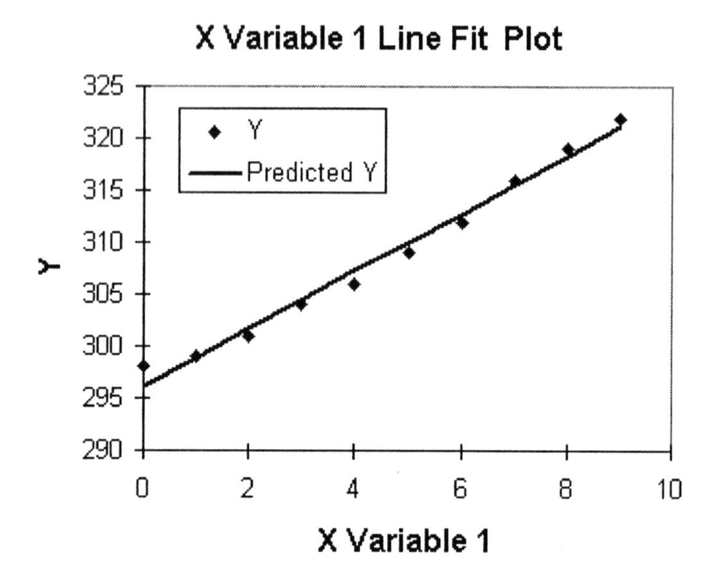

This is essentially the same as the plot created by using the linear trendline. Poor fits become even more apparent when you look at the residual plot:

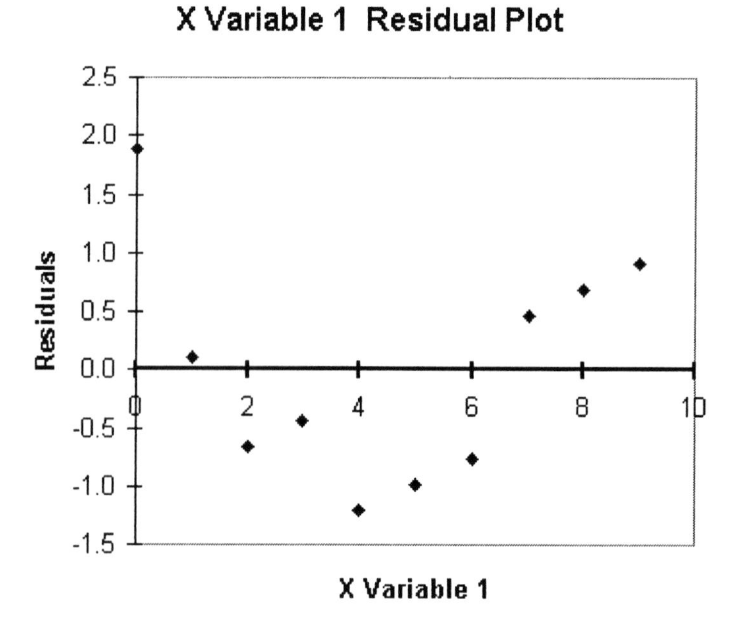

The *residual* is the difference between the data point y-value and the regression line y-value at each x-value. A *residual plot* highlights poor fits and makes them easy to spot. Strong patterns in a residual plot, such as the "U" shape shown here, indicate that there is something happening in your data that the model (the straight line) is not accounting for. It's a strong hint that you should look for a better regression model.

This example was included as a reminder that, although you can perform a simple (straight-line) linear regression on any data set, it is not always a good idea. Nonlinear data require a more sophisticated curve-fitting approach.

6.2 Polynomial Regression by Using the Regression Analysis Package

The best fit we obtained to the temperature–time data by using trendlines was obtained by using the second-order polynomial

$$y_p = b_0 + b_1 x + b_2 x^2 \tag{3}$$

or, in terms of temperature, T, and time, t,

$$T_p = b_0 + b_1 t + b_2 t^2. \tag{4}$$

We will use this polynomial to demonstrate how to solve for more than two coefficients when using Excel's regression-analysis package.

The regression-analysis package in Excel allows you only one column of y-values (dependent variables), but you can have multiple columns of x-values (independent variables). These can be completely independent variables [e.g., enthalpy (dependent) as a function of temperature (independent) and pressure (independent)], or they can be the same variable in multiple forms [e.g., x and x^2 or z and $\ln(z)$]

For this second-order polynomial, we'll need two columns of independent values, containing t and t^2. The dependent values (T-values) have been moved to column A to allow the t- and t^2-values to be placed next to each other in columns B and C:

C9 f_x =B9^2

	A	B	C	D
1	**Generalized Linear Regression**			
2				
3	**Temp.**	**Time**	**Time^2**	
4	(K)	(min.)	(min.^{2})	
5				
6	298	0	0	
7	299	1	1	
8	301	2	4	
9	304	3	9	
10	306	4	16	
11	309	5	25	
12	312	6	36	
13	316	7	49	
14	319	8	64	
15	322	9	81	
16				

The procedure for getting Excel to regress this data is almost the same as that used in the previous example, except in step 4 when you tell Excel where to find the x-values. In this case, you need to indicate *both* column B and column C:

	A	B	C	D	E	F	G
1	**Generalized Linear Regression**						
2							
3	**Temp.**	**Time**	**Time²**				
4	(K)	(min.)	(min.²)				
5				**Regression**			
6	298	0	0	$B$6:$C$15			
7	299	1	1				
8	301	2	4				
9	304	3	9				
10	306	4	16				
11	309	5	25				
12	312	6	36				
13	316	7	49				
14	319	8	64				
15	322	9	81				
16							

The rest of the regression process is unchanged. The regression output page shows the results (again, only part of it is shown here):

	A	B	C	D	E	F
1	SUMMARY OUTPUT					
2						
3	*Regression Statistics*					
4	Multiple R	0.99885781				
5	R Square	0.99771693				
6	Adjusted R Square	0.99706462				
7	Standard Error	0.45844646				
8	Observations	10				
9						
10	ANOVA					
11		*df*	*SS*	*MS*	*F*	*Significance F*
12	Regression	2	642.9287879	321.4644	1529.522	5.68616E-10
13	Residual	7	1.471212121	0.210173		
14	Total	9	644.4			
15						
16		*Coefficients*	*Standard Error*	*t Stat*	*P-value*	*Lower 95%*
17	Intercept	297.518182	0.36045142	825.4044	1.01E-18	296.6658503
18	X Variable 1	1.71893939	0.186520848	9.215803	3.66E-05	1.277887988
19	X Variable 2	0.11742424	0.019951321	5.885537	0.000608	0.070246898
20						

Again, the results obtained by using the regression-analysis package are the same as those obtained by using the polynomial trendline. One piece of information that is available only from the regression-analysis package is the residual plot:

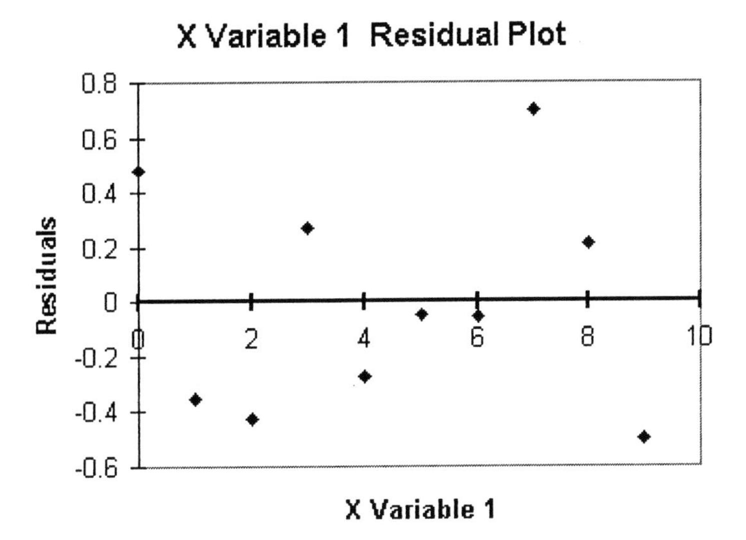

The residual plot shows no obvious trends. This suggests that the model is doing about as good a job of fitting these data as can be done.

6.3 Other Linear Models

The models used in the preceding examples,

$$T_p = b + b_1 t \text{ and}$$
$$T_p = b_0 + b_1 t + b_2 t^2, \tag{5}$$

are both linear models (linear in the coefficients, not in time). Excel's regression-analysis package works with any linear model, so you could try fitting equations such as

$$T_p = b_0 + b_1 \sinh(t) + b_2 \operatorname{atan}(t^2) \tag{6}$$

or

$$T_p = b_0 \exp(t^{0.5}) + b_1 \ln(t^3). \tag{7}$$

There is no reason to suspect that either of these last two models would be a good fit to the temperature-vs.-time data, but both equations are linear in the coefficients (the b's) and are compatible with generalized regression analysis. (There is one problem: The natural logarithm in the last model won't work with the $t = 0$ that appears in the data set.) In general, you choose a linear model either from some theory that suggests a relationship between your variables or from looking at a plot of the data set.

You could also use a regression equation that has multiple independent variables, such as

$$V_p = b_0 + b_1 P + b_2 T, \tag{8}$$

which says that the volume of a gas depends on pressure and temperature.

6.4 Forcing the Regression Line through the Origin (0,0)

If you do not want Excel to compute an intercept (i.e., if you want to force the curve to go through $y = 0$ when $x = 0$ by setting $b_0 = 0$), there is a check box you can select on the Regression dialog box:

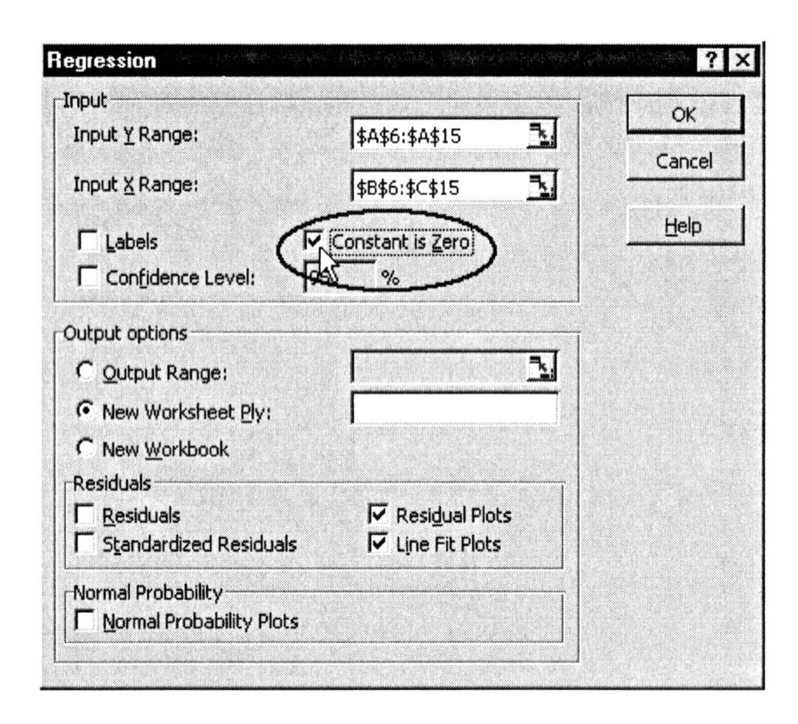

There are times when theory predicts that the curve should go through (0,0). In such a situation, you force the regression line through the origin by setting the Constant is Zero check box.

PRACTICE!

In the accompanying table, two sets of y-values are shown. The noisy data were calculated from the clean data by adding random values. Try linear regression on these data sets. What is the impact of noisy data on the calculated slope, intercept, and R^2-value?

X	Y_{CLEAN}	Y_{NOISY}
0	1	0.85
1	2	1.91
2	3	3.03
3	4	3.96
4	5	5.10
5	6	5.90

EXAMPLE 1

Thermocouple output voltages are commonly considered to be directly proportional to temperature. But, over large temperature ranges, a power fit can do a better job. Compare the simple linear fit and the exponential fit for copper–constantan output voltages (reference junction at 0°C) between 10 and 400°C.[1]

First, create a simple linear regression for a slope and intercept:

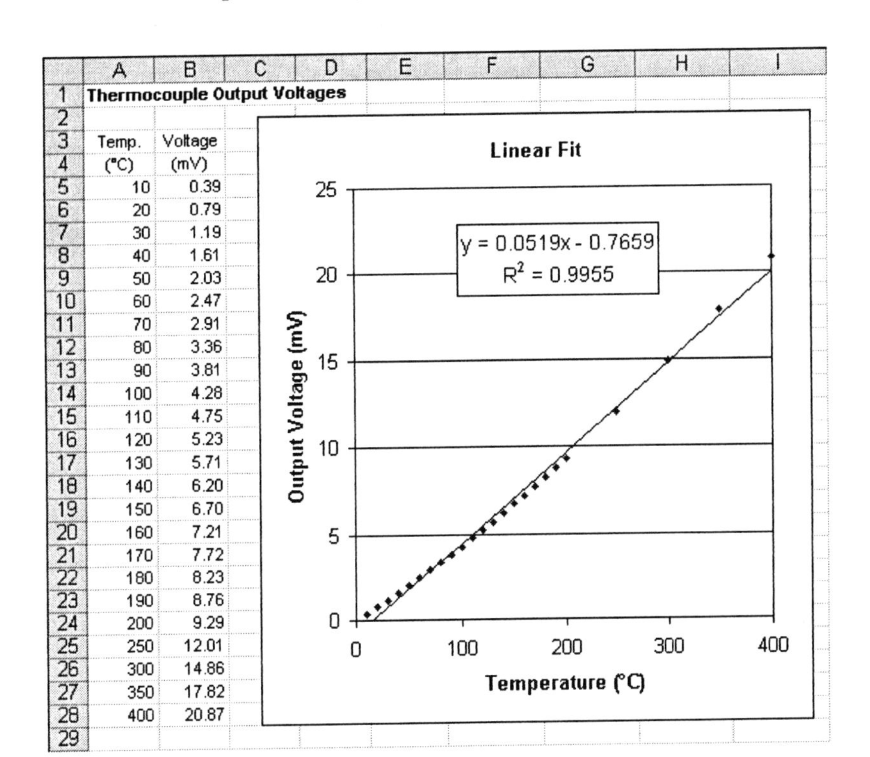

Thermocouple Output Voltages

Temp. (°C)	Voltage (mV)
10	0.39
20	0.79
30	1.19
40	1.61
50	2.03
60	2.47
70	2.91
80	3.36
90	3.81
100	4.28
110	4.75
120	5.23
130	5.71
140	6.20
150	6.70
160	7.21
170	7.72
180	8.23
190	8.76
200	9.29
250	12.01
300	14.86
350	17.82
400	20.87

The R^2 value, 0.9955, looks OK, but there is some difference between the data values and the regression line.

Now try the power fit:

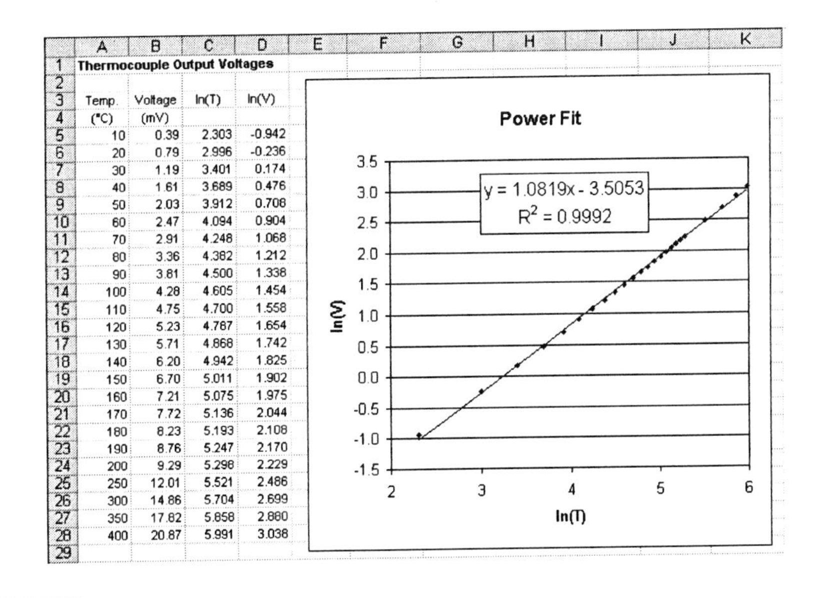

Thermocouple Output Voltages

Temp. (°C)	Voltage (mV)	ln(T)	ln(V)
10	0.39	2.303	-0.942
20	0.79	2.996	-0.236
30	1.19	3.401	0.174
40	1.61	3.689	0.476
50	2.03	3.912	0.708
60	2.47	4.094	0.904
70	2.91	4.248	1.068
80	3.36	4.382	1.212
90	3.81	4.500	1.338
100	4.28	4.605	1.454
110	4.75	4.700	1.558
120	5.23	4.787	1.654
130	5.71	4.868	1.742
140	6.20	4.942	1.825
150	6.70	5.011	1.902
160	7.21	5.075	1.975
170	7.72	5.136	2.044
180	8.23	5.193	2.108
190	8.76	5.247	2.170
200	9.29	5.298	2.229
250	12.01	5.521	2.486
300	14.86	5.704	2.699
350	17.82	5.858	2.880
400	20.87	5.991	3.038

---

[1]Data from *Transport Phenomena Data Companion* by L.P.B.M. Janssen and M.M.C.G. Warmoeskerken, Arnold D.U.M. (1987). Copper–constantan was selected for this example because its performance is the least linear of the commonly used thermocouple types.

The R^2 value is closer to unity, although there is still some difference between the plotted data points [ln(T) and ln(V)]. Let's see how the power model does at predicting voltages:

$$b_0 = -3.5053, \quad \text{so}, \quad k_0 = e^{b_0} = 0.03004,$$
$$b_1 = 1.0819, \quad \text{so}, \quad k_1 = b_1 = 1.0819.$$

Thus, the power model gives $V = k_0 T^{k_1} = 0.03004T^{1.0819}$.

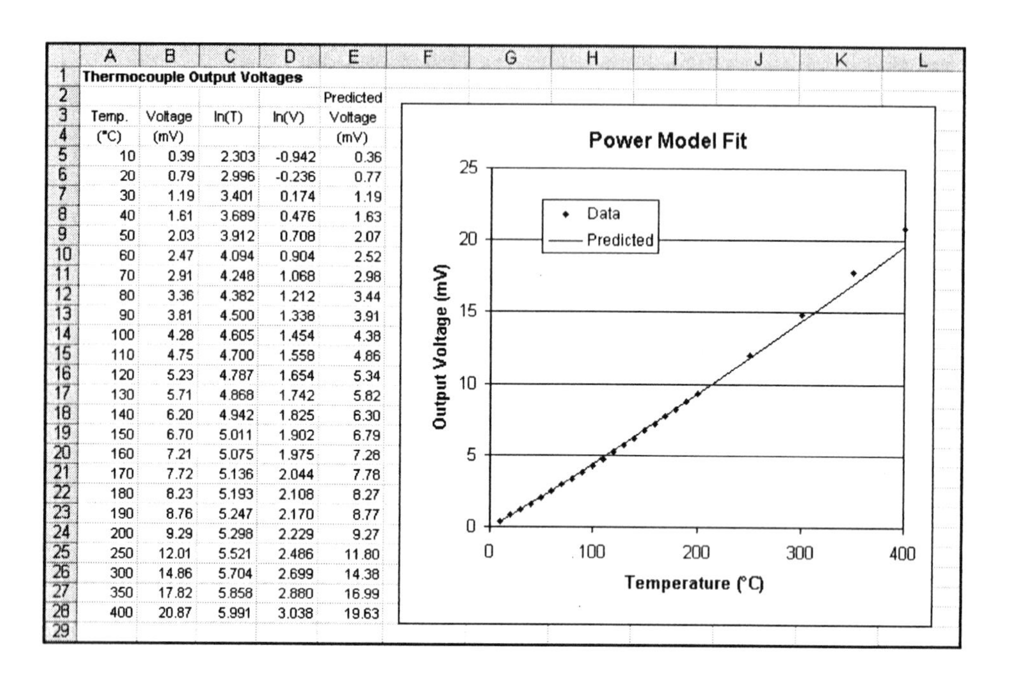

Thermocouple Output Voltages

Temp. (°C)	Voltage (mV)	ln(T)	ln(V)	Predicted Voltage (mV)
10	0.39	2.303	-0.942	0.36
20	0.79	2.996	-0.236	0.77
30	1.19	3.401	0.174	1.19
40	1.61	3.689	0.476	1.63
50	2.03	3.912	0.708	2.07
60	2.47	4.094	0.904	2.52
70	2.91	4.248	1.068	2.98
80	3.36	4.382	1.212	3.44
90	3.81	4.500	1.338	3.91
100	4.28	4.605	1.454	4.38
110	4.75	4.700	1.558	4.86
120	5.23	4.787	1.654	5.34
130	5.71	4.868	1.742	5.82
140	6.20	4.942	1.825	6.30
150	6.70	5.011	1.902	6.79
160	7.21	5.075	1.975	7.28
170	7.72	5.136	2.044	7.78
180	8.23	5.193	2.108	8.27
190	8.76	5.247	2.170	8.77
200	9.29	5.298	2.229	9.27
250	12.01	5.521	2.486	11.80
300	14.86	5.704	2.699	14.38
350	17.82	5.858	2.880	16.99
400	20.87	5.991	3.038	19.63

The power model fits the data better at lower temperatures, but it misses at the higher end.

KEY TERMS

Coefficient of Determination (R^2)
Dependent variable (y-axis)
Independent variable (x-axis)
Intercept
Linear regression
Polynomial regression
Residual
Residual plot
Slope
Trendline
XY Scatter plot

SUMMARY

Using Excel's Regression Functions

For simple slope–intercept calculations, Excel's built-in regression functions are useful. The drawback is they don't show you the regression line superimposed on the data values, and verifying the fit visually is always a good idea. If you plot the data, it is faster to use a trendline to find the slope and intercept, but, although the trendline displays the values, it does not make them available for use in the rest of the spreadsheet.

`SLOPE(y, x)`	Returns the slope of the straight line through the x- and y-values.
`INTERCEPT(y, x)`	Returns the intercept of the straight line through the x- and y-values.
`RSQ(y, x)`	Returns the coefficient of determination (R^2) for the straight line through the x- and y-values.

APPLICATIONS: RECALIBRATING A FLOW METER

Flow meters in industrial situations come with calibration charts for standard fluids (typically air or water), but, for critical applications, the calibration must be checked periodically to see whether the instrument still provides a reliable reading.

When purchased, the calibration sheet for a turbine flow meter provided the following equation relating the meter output (frequency, Hz) to water flow velocity (m/s):

$$v = 0.0023 + 0.0674f$$

After the meter had been in use for a period of one year, it was removed from service for recalibration. During a preliminary test, the following data were obtained from a test system:

Velocity	Frequency
(m/s)	(Hz)
0.05	0.8
0.27	4.2
0.53	8.2
0.71	10.9
0.86	13.1
1.10	16.8
1.34	20.5
1.50	23.0
1.74	26.6
1.85	28.4
2.15	32.9
2.33	35.6
2.52	38.5
2.75	42.1

Does the meter need to be recalibrated? If so, what is the new calibration equation?

First, we can use the original calibration equation to calculate predicted velocity values and plot the results to see whether the original calibration equation is still working.

C6 f_x =0.0023+0.0674*A6

	A	B	C	D
1	**Flow Meter Calibration Test**			
2		**Experimental**	**Predicted**	
3	**Frequency**	**Velocity**	**Velocity**	
4	(Hz)	(m/s)	(m/s)	
5				
6	0.8	0.05	0.1	
7	4.2	0.27	0.3	
8	8.2	0.53	0.6	
9	10.9	0.71	0.7	
10	13.1	0.86	0.9	
11	16.8	1.10	1.1	
12	20.5	1.34	1.4	
13	23.0	1.50	1.6	
14	26.6	1.74	1.8	
15	28.4	1.85	1.9	
16	32.9	2.15	2.2	
17	35.6	2.33	2.4	
18	38.5	2.52	2.6	
19	42.1	2.75	2.8	
20				

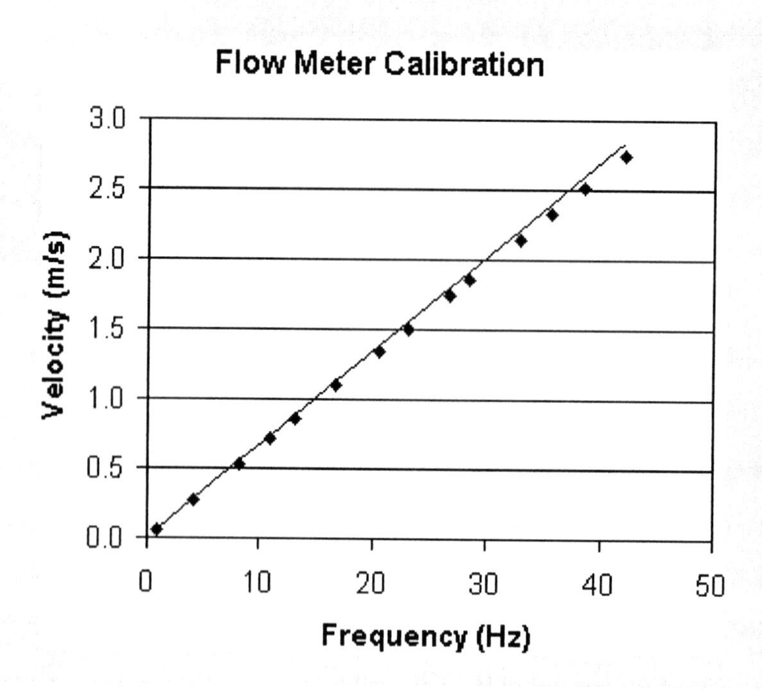

The data values do not seem to agree with the original calibration line at higher velocities, so it is time to recalibrate. To do so, simply add a linear trendline to the graph and ask Excel to display the equation of the line. The result (without the original calibration line) is

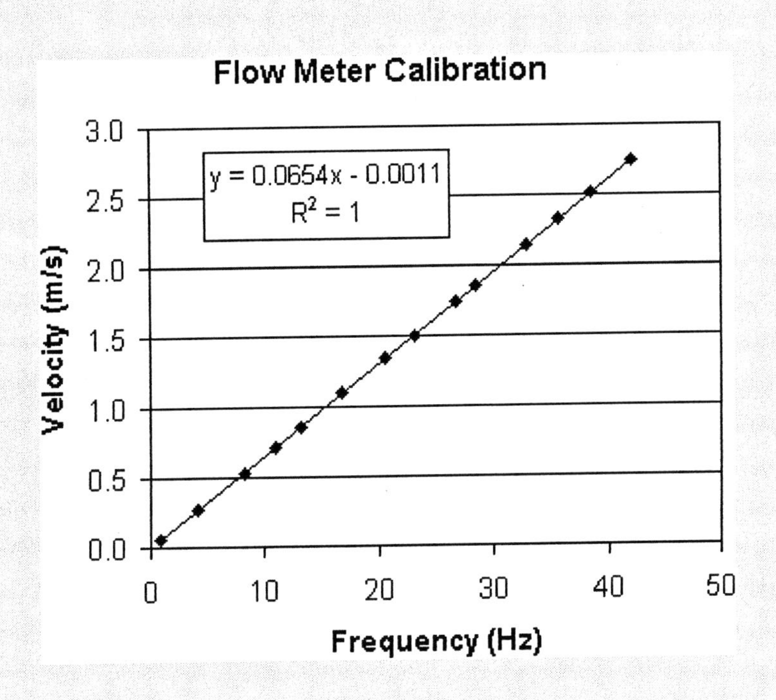

The new calibration equation is

$$v = -0.0011 + 0.0654f$$

Using TrendLines

If you don't need a lot of information about the regression results—just the equation and the R^2 value—then trendlines are fast and easy. To add a trendline, do the following:

1. Graph your data.
2. Right click on any data point, and select Trendline from the pop-up menu.
3. Use the Type tab to select the type of trendline. (Set the order of the polynomial, if needed.)
4. Use the Options tab to force the intercept through the origin or to have Excel display the equation of the line and the R^2 value, if desired.

Using the Regression-Analysis Package

General Procedure

1. Choose a linear regression model: The model must be linear in the coefficients.
2. Set up the required columns of x- and y-values in the spreadsheet:
   - You may have only one column of y-values, but multiple columns of x-values (e.g., x, x^2, x^3, etc., as required for the regression model you want to fit).
3. Have Excel perform the regression analysis.
4. Find your regression results in the output table created by Excel. As a minimum, check for
   - The coefficients are listed as Intercept (if you asked Excel to compute one) and the Coefficients for X Variable 1, X Variable 2, and so on (as many as are needed for your model).
   - The R^2 value; the value 1.0 indicates a perfect fit.
5. Check the line-fit plot and residual plots (if you requested them) to verify visually that your model does (or does not) fit the data.

Using the Regression-Analysis Package

1. Open the Data Analysis List Box by selecting Tools/Data Analysis . . . .
2. Select Regression from the list.
3. Show Excel where to find the y-values.
   a. Click on the "go to spreadsheet button" at the right side of the Input Y Range field.
   b. When the spreadsheet is displayed, drag the mouse over the cells containing the y-values to select those cells.
   c. Click the "go to dialog" button on the small Regression box to return to the Regression dialog box.
4. Show Excel where to find the x-values.
5. Choose a location for the regression results; on a new worksheet ply is the most common location.
6. Indicate whether you want the line-fit plot and residual plot prepared (generally recommended).
7. Click [OK] on the Regression dialog box to have Excel perform the regression and produce the output summary tables, and any graphs you requested.

Problems

Graphing Functions

1. Graph the following common regression functions, using the specified coefficients and ranges:

   a. $y = a + bx, \qquad a = 2, \quad b = 0.3, 0 \le x \le 5.$

b. $y = a + b/x$ $a = 2,\ b = 0.3, 1 \le x \le 5.$

c. $y = ae^{bx}$, $a = 2,\ b = 0.3, 0 \le x \le 5.$

d. $y = ae^{-bx}$, $a = 2,\ b = 0.3, 0 \le x \le 5.$

Compare the general shape of the curves produced by the regression functions with the following plot:

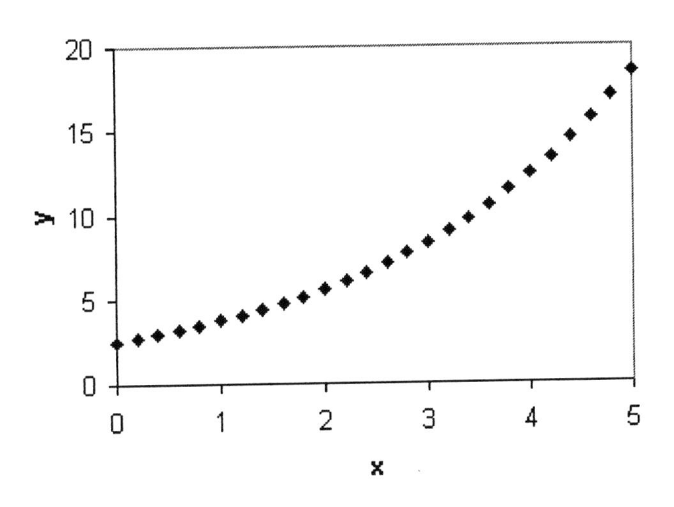

Which regression function is most likely to provide a good fit to the data?

Simple Linear Regression

2. Plot each of the three data sets presented in the accompanying table to see whether a straight line through each set of points seems reasonable. If so, add a linear trendline to the graph and have Excel display the equation of the line and the R^2 value on the graph.

   The same x-data have been used in each example, to minimize typing.

X	Y_1	Y_2	Y_3
0	2	0.4	10.2
1	5	3.6	4.2
2	8	10.0	12.6
3	11	9.5	11.7
4	14	12.0	28.5
5	17	17.1	42.3
6	20	20.4	73.6
7	23	21.7	112.1

Thermocouple Calibration Curve

3. Thermocouples are made by joining two dissimilar metal wires. The contact of the two metals results in a small, but measurable, voltage drop across the junction. This voltage drop changes as the temperature of the junction changes; thus, the thermocouple can be used to measure temperature if you know the

relationship between temperature and voltage. Equations for common types of thermocouples are available, or you can simply take a few data points and prepare a calibration curve. This is especially easy for thermocouples, because, for small temperature ranges, the relationship between temperature and voltage is nearly linear.

Use a linear trendline to find the coefficients of a straight line through the data shown here:

T(°C)	V (mV)
10	0.397
20	0.798
30	1.204
40	1.612
50	2.023
60	2.436
70	2.851
80	3.267
90	3.682

Note: The thermocouple voltage changes because the temperature changes—that is, the voltage depends on the temperature. For regression, the independent variable (temperature) should always be on the x*-axis, and the dependent variable (voltage) should be on the* y*-axis.*

Conduction Heat Transfer

4. Thermal conductivity is a property of a material related to the material's ability to transfer energy by conduction. Materials with high thermal conductivities, such as copper and aluminum, are good conductors. Materials with low thermal conductivities are used as insulating materials.

   The next figure depicts a device that could be used to measure the thermal conductivity of a material. A rod of the material to be tested is placed between a resistance heater (on the right) and a block containing a cooling coil (on the left). Five thermocouples are inserted into the rod at evenly spaced intervals. The entire apparatus is placed under a bell jar, and the space around the rod is evacuated to reduce energy losses.

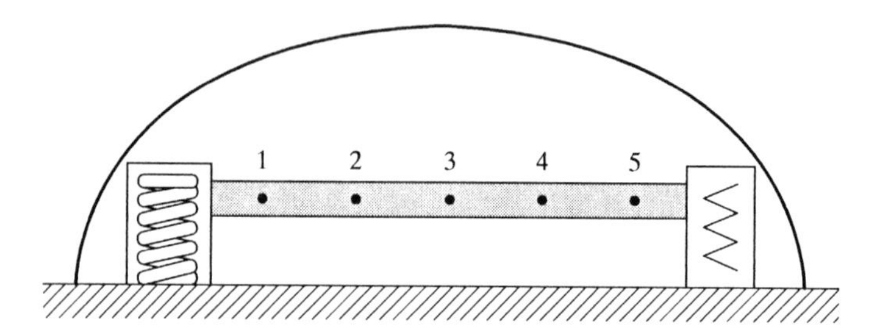

To run the experiment, a known amount of power is sent to the heater, and the system is allowed to reach steady state. Once the temperatures are steady, the power level and the temperatures are recorded. A data sheet from an experiment with the device is reproduced next.

Thermal Conductivity Experiment	
Rod Diameter: 2 cm Thermocouple Spacing: 5 cm Power: 100 watts	
THERMOCOUPLE	**TEMPERATURE (K)**
1	348
2	387
3	425
4	464
5	503

The thermal conductivity can be determined by using Fourier's law,

$$\frac{q}{A} = -k\frac{dT}{dx}, \tag{9}$$

where

q is the power applied to the heater
A is the cross-sectional area of the rod

The q/A is the energy flux and is a vector quantity, having both magnitude and direction. With the energy source on the right, the energy moves to the left or in the negative x-direction, so the flux in this problem is negative.

a. From the information supplied on the data sheet, prepare a table of position, x, and temperature T, values, in a spreadsheet, with the position of thermocouple 1 set as $x = 0$.
b. Graph the temperature-vs-position data, and add a linear trendline to the data. Ask Excel to display the equation of the line and the R^2 value.
c. Use Fourier's law and the slope of the regression line to compute the material's thermal conductivity.

Thermal conductivity is usually a function of temperature. Does your graph indicate that the thermal conductivity of this material changes significantly over the temperature range in this problem? Explain your reasoning.

Calculating Heat Capacity

5. The heat capacity at constant pressure is defined as

$$C_p = \left(\frac{\partial \hat{H}}{\partial T}\right)_p, \tag{10}$$

where

$\hat{H}$ is specific enthalpy
T is absolute temperature

If enthalpy data are available as a function of temperature at constant pressure, the heat capacity can be computed. For steam, these data are readily available.[2] For example, the following table shows the specific enthalpy for various absolute temperatures at a pressure of 5 bars:

T (°C)	$\hat{H}$ (kJ/kg)
200	2855
250	2961
300	3065
350	3168
400	3272
450	3379
500	3484
550	3592
600	3702
650	3813
700	3926
750	4040

a. Plot the specific enthalpy on the y-axis against absolute temperature on the x-axis.

b. Add a linear trendline to the data, and ask Excel to display the equation of the line and the R^2 value.

c. Compute the heat capacity of steam from the slope of the trendline.

d. The ideal gas (assumed) heat capacity for steam is approximately 2.10 kJ/kg K at 450°C. How does your result compare with this value?

e. Does it appear that the heat capacity of steam is constant over this temperature range? Why or why not?

Vapor–Liquid Equilibrium

6. When a liquid mixture is boiled, the vapor that leaves the vessel is enriched in the more volatile component of the mixture. The vapor and liquid in a boiling vessel are in equilibrium, and vapor–liquid equilibrium (VLE) data are available for many mixtures. The data are usually presented in tabular form, as in the table shown next, which represents VLE data for mixtures of methanol (MeOH) and ethanol (EtOH) boiling at 1 atm. From the graph of the VLE data, we see that, if a 50:50 liquid mixture of the alcohols is boiled, the vapor will contain about 60% methanol:

[2]The data are from a steam table in *Elementary Principles of Chemical Engineering*, 3d ed., by R. M. Felder and R. W. Rousseau, New York: Wiley, 2000. These data are also available at *http://www.coe.montana.edu/che/Excel*.

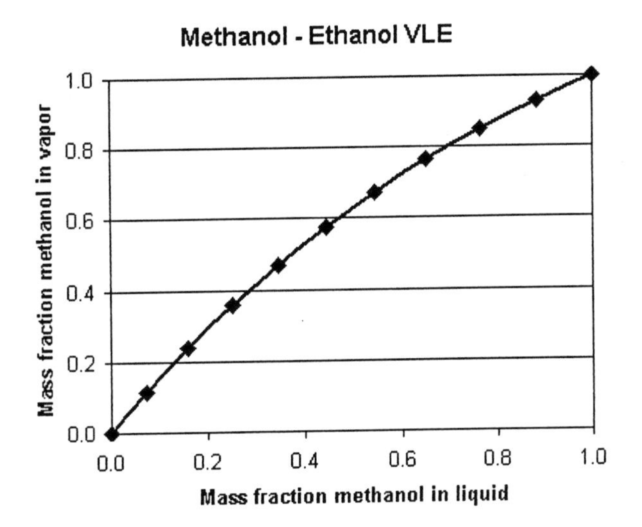

VLE data are commonly used in designing distillation columns, but an equation relating vapor mass fraction to liquid mass fraction is a lot more handy than tabulated values.

Use trendlines on the tabulated VLE data to obtain an equation relating the mass fraction of methanol in the vapor (y) to the mass fraction of vapor in the liquid (x). Test several different linear models (e.g., polynomials) to see which model gives a good fit to the experimental data.

Data The VLE values shown next were generated by using Excel, with the assumption that these similar alcohols form an ideal solution. The x-column represents the mass fraction of methanol in the boiling mixture. (Mass fraction of ethanol in the liquid is calculated as $1 - x$ for any mixture.) The mass fraction of methanol in the vapor leaving the solution is shown in the y-column.

These data are available in electronic form at the text's website *http://www.coe.montana.edu/che/Excel*:

x_{MeOH}	y_{MeOH}
1.000	1.000
0.882	0.929
0.765	0.849
0.653	0.764
0.545	0.673
0.443	0.575
0.344	0.471
0.250	0.359
0.159	0.241
0.072	0.114
0.000	0.000

Calculating Latent Heat of Vaporization

7. The Clausius–Clapeyron equation can be used to determine the latent heat (or enthalpy change) of vaporization, $\Delta \hat{H}_v$. The equation is

$$\ln(p_{\text{vapor}}) = -\frac{\Delta \hat{H}_v}{R\,T} + k, \tag{11}$$

where

p_{vapor} is the vapor pressure of the material,
R is the ideal gas constant,
T is the absolute pressure,
k is a constant of integration.

There are a few assumptions built into this equation:

1. The molar volume of the liquid must be much smaller than the molar volume of the gas (not true at high pressures).
2. The gas behaves as an ideal gas.
3. The latent heat of vaporization is not a function of temperature.

Water vapor data from the website of an Honors Chemistry class[3] is reported in the table shown next. A plot of the natural log of vapor pressure vs. T^{-1} should, if the assumptions are valid, produce a straight line on the graph.

a. Create a plot of natural log of vapor pressure of water on the y-axis, against T^{-1} on the x-axis.
b. Add a linear trendline, and have Excel show the equation of the line and the R^2 value.
c. What is the latent heat of vaporization of water, as computed from the slope of the trendline?
d. Does it look as if the assumptions built into the Clausius–Clapeyron equation are valid for this data set? Why, or why not?

T (°C)	p_{vapor}(mm Hg)	ln(p_{vapor})
90	525.8	6.265
92	567.0	6.340
94	610.9	6.415
96	657.6	6.489
98	707.3	6.561
100	760.0	6.633
102	815.9	6.704
104	875.1	6.774
106	937.9	6.844
108	1004.4	6.912
110	1074.6	6.980

[3]Dr. Tom Bitterwolf's Honors Chemistry class at the University of Idaho. Data used with the permission of Dr. Bitterwolf.

Note: What do you do with the units on vapor pressure inside that natural logarithm? In this problem, it doesn't matter; the units you choose for vapor pressure change the value of k, but not the slope of the trendline.

Orifice Meter Calibration

8. Orifice meters are commonly used to measure flow rates, but they are highly nonlinear devices. Because of this, special care must be taken when preparing calibration curves for these meters. The equation relating volumetric flow rate, V, to the measured pressure drop, ΔP, across the orifice is

$$\dot{V} = \frac{A_O C_O}{\sqrt{1 - \beta^4}} \sqrt{\frac{2g_c \Delta P}{\rho}}. \quad (12)$$

For purposes of creating a calibration curve, the details of the equation are unimportant (as long as the other terms stay constant). It is necessary that we see the theoretical relationship between flow rate and pressure drop:

$$\dot{V} \propto \sqrt{\Delta P}. \quad (13)$$

Also, the pressure drop across the orifice plate depends on the flow rate, not the other way around. So, the $\sqrt{\Delta P}$ should be regressed as the dependent variable (y-values) and the volumetric flow rate as the independent variable (x-values):

$\dot{V}$ (ft³ · MIN)	ΔP (psi)
3.9	0.13
7.9	0.52
11.8	1.18
15.7	2.09
19.6	3.27
23.6	4.71
27.5	6.41
31.4	8.37
35.3	10.59
39.3	13.08

a. Calculate $\sqrt{\Delta P}$ values at each flow rate from the tabulated data.
b. Regress $\dot{V}$ and $\sqrt{\Delta P}$, using Excel's regression package (found by selecting Tools/Data Analysis . . .) to create a calibration curve for this orifice meter.
c. Check the line-fit and residual plots to make sure your calibration curve really fits the data.

7

Excel's Statistics Functions

1 OVERVIEW

Data analysis is a standard part of an engineer's day-to-day work, aimed at understanding a process better and making better products. Whenever you try to glean information from data sets, you soon find yourself needing some *statistics*.

A statistical analysis is performed on a data set, and the rows and columns of values fit naturally into a spreadsheet. Perhaps it is no surprise, then, that Excel has a variety of built-in functions to help out with statistical calculations. Because of these features, Excel has become a commonly used tool for statistical analysis.

2 POPULATIONS AND SAMPLES

If a dairyman has 238 cows that he milks every day, those 238 cows form a *population*—his herd. If he keeps track of the daily milk production for each cow, he has a data set that represents the daily milk production for a population.

If, one day, he's running behind and decides to record the milk production for only 24 cows and then use the values from those 24 cows to estimate the total milk production for the entire herd, then his data set represents a *sample* of the total population.

Whenever a sample is used to predict something about a population, the *sampling method* must be carefully considered. If the hired hand, not understanding what the farmer planned to do with the data, recorded data for the 24 cows that gave the most milk, the data set's not much good for predicting the total milk production for the herd. The farmer needs a *representative sample*. The usual way to try to achieve this is to choose a *random sample*. The key to getting a random sample is to try to make sure that every cow has an equal chance of being a part of the sample.

SECTIONS

OBJECTIVES

After reading this chapter, you will know

- How to distinguish samples and populations and how to select a representative sample
- How to use Excel for common statistical calculations, including means, standard deviations, and variances
- How to create histograms with Excel's Data Analysis Package
- How to calculate confidence intervals about Sample Mean Values

2.1 Alternative Example

If cows aren't your cup of tea, consider mice—computer mice. If every mouse coming off the assembly line during November was tested (for ease of rolling, button functionality, cursor tracking, etc.), then the data set represents a population: mice produced in November. (It could also represent a sample of mice produced in the fourth quarter.) If the company decided to test only part of the mice coming off the assembly line, the mice that were tested would represent a sample of the total population. If the sample is to be considered a representative sample, some care must be taken in designing the sampling protocol. For example, if mice are collected for testing only during the day shift, defects introduced by sleepy employees on the night shift will never be observed. Again, the usual way to try to get a representative sample is to choose a random sample. The key to getting a random sample is to make sure that every mouse produced has an equal chance of being a part of the sample.

2.2 Multiple Instrument Readings

Instruments, such as digital thermometers and scales, are imperfect measuring devices. It is common to weigh something several times to try to get a "better" value than would be obtained from a single measurement. Any time you record multiple readings from an instrument, you are taking a sample from an infinite number of possible readings. The multiple readings should be treated as a sample, not a population. The impact of this will become apparent when the equations for standard deviations and variances are presented.

PRACTICE!

The SO_2 content in the stack gas from a coal-fired boiler is measured halfway up the stack at six different positions across the diameter, and the concentration values are averaged.

- Do these data represent a sample or a population?
- If it's a sample, is it a representative sample? Is it a random sample? Why, or why not?

2.3 Arithmetic Mean, or Average

The formulas for the *population mean*, μ (mu), and *sample mean*, $\bar{x}$, are

$$\mu = \frac{\sum_{i=1}^{N_{\text{pop}}} x_i}{N_{\text{pop.}}},$$

$$\bar{x} = \frac{\sum_{i=1}^{N_{\text{sample}}} x_i}{N_{\text{sample}}}. \tag{1}$$

Both equations add up all of the values in their respective data set and then divide by the number of values in their data set. The same Excel function, AVERAGE ( ), is used for computing the population mean and the sample mean. Different symbols are used for these means as a reminder that they have different meanings: The population mean is the *arithmetic average* value for the data set; the sample mean should be interpreted as the best estimate of the population mean.

Excel provides the AVERAGE(*range*) function for computing arithmetic means, or averages. The range in the function represents a range of cells in a spreadsheet. The average of the values in a small data set consisting of six random integers is computed in the following spreadsheet:

B10 ▾ f_x =AVERAGE(B3:B8)

	A	B	C	D	E
1	**Small Data Set**				
2					
3		3			
4		9			
5		1			
6		3			
7		4			
8		6			
9					
10	**mean:**	4.33			
11					

```
B10: =AVERAGE(B3:B8)
```

3 STANDARD DEVIATIONS AND VARIANCES

The same function is used to calculate both sample and population means, but separate functions are needed for sample and population *standard deviations* and *variances*. The computational formulas for standard deviations and variances are slightly different for populations and samples, and this is accounted for in the spreadsheet functions.

The variance (and standard deviation, which is just the square root of the variance) provides information about the spread of the values (or dispersion) about the mean. A small variance or standard deviation suggests that all of the data values are clustered closely around the mean value; a large standard deviation tells you that there is a wide range of values in the data set. For example, the two data sets shown in the following spreadsheet have the same mean value, but quite different standard deviations:

C12 ▾ f_x =STDEV(C3:C9)

	A	B	C	D	E
1		**Set A**	**Set B**		
2					
3		4.02	6.12		
4		3.98	2.53		
5		4.04	5.27		
6		3.93	4.24		
7		3.89	3.50		
8		4.16	5.10		
9		3.95	1.22		
10					
11	**mean:**	4.00	4.00		
12	**stdev:**	0.089	1.71		
13	**var:**	0.008	2.92		
14					

The greater spread around the mean value (4.00) in Set B is easily seen if the data are plotted:

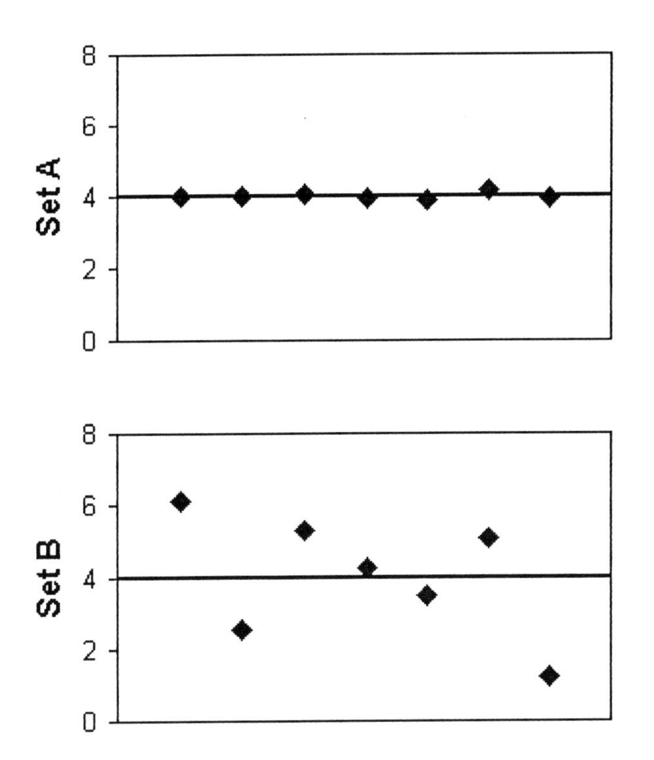

3.1 Population Statistics

The Greek symbol σ (sigma) is used for the standard deviation of a population. The population variance is indicated as σ^2:

$$\sigma^2 = \frac{\sum_{i=1}^{N_{\text{pop.}}} (x_i - \mu)^2}{N_{\text{pop.}}},$$
$$\sigma = \sqrt{\sigma^2}. \tag{2}$$

Excel provides functions for computing the variance and standard deviation of a population:

```
VARP(range)
STDEVP(range)
```

In the following spreadsheet, these two functions have been used to calculate the standard deviation and variance in the small data set (assumed here to be a population):

B12 =VARP(B3:B8)

	A	B	C	D	E
1	**Small Data Set**				
2					
3		3			
4		9			
5		1			
6		3			
7		4			
8		6			
9					
10	**mean:**	4.33			
11	**stdev:**	2.56			
12	**var:**	6.56			
13					

3.2 Samples of a Population

The denominator of the variance equation changes to $N_{\text{sample}} - 1$ when your data set represents a sample. The symbol s is used for the standard deviation of a sample, and the sample variance is indicated as s^2:

$$s^2 = \frac{\sum_{i=1}^{N_{\text{sample}}} (x_i - \bar{x})^2}{N_{\text{sample}} - 1}, \tag{3}$$

$$s = \sqrt{s^2}.$$

Excel provides functions for computing the variance and standard deviation of a sample:

```
VAR(range)
STDEV(range)
```

Applying these formulas to the small data set (treated here as a sample) produces the following results:

B12 f_x =VAR(B3:B8)

	A	B	C	D	E	F
1	**Small Data Set**					
2						
3		3				
4		9				
5		1				
6		3				
7		4				
8		6				
9						
10	**mean:**	4.33				
11	**stdev:**	2.80	<< formula changed to STDEV( )			
12	**var:**	7.87	<< formula changed to VAR( )			
13						

PRACTICE!

Two thermocouples are placed in boiling water, and the output voltages are measured five times. Calculate the standard deviations for each thermocouple to see which is giving the most reliable output. Is the voltage data presented here a sample or a population? Why?

TC_A (mV)	TC_B (mV)
3.029	2.999
3.179	3.002
3.170	3.007
3.022	3.004
2.928	3.013

4 ERRORS, DEVIATIONS, AND DISTRIBUTIONS

A *deviation* is the difference between a measured value in a sample and the sample mean:

$$\text{dev}_i = x_i - \bar{x}. \tag{4}$$

A related quantity, *error*, is computed for populations:

$$\text{error}_i = x_i - \mu. \tag{5}$$

A *deviation plot* is sometimes used to look at the distribution of deviation (or error) values around the mean. In a quality-control setting, for example, patterns in a deviation plot can offer hints that something is wrong.

Example: Tools made by two machines are supposed to be identical, and tolerances are measured on each tool as it comes off the line. When the deviations were plotted against time (or sample number if the samples were taken at regular intervals), the following graph was obtained:

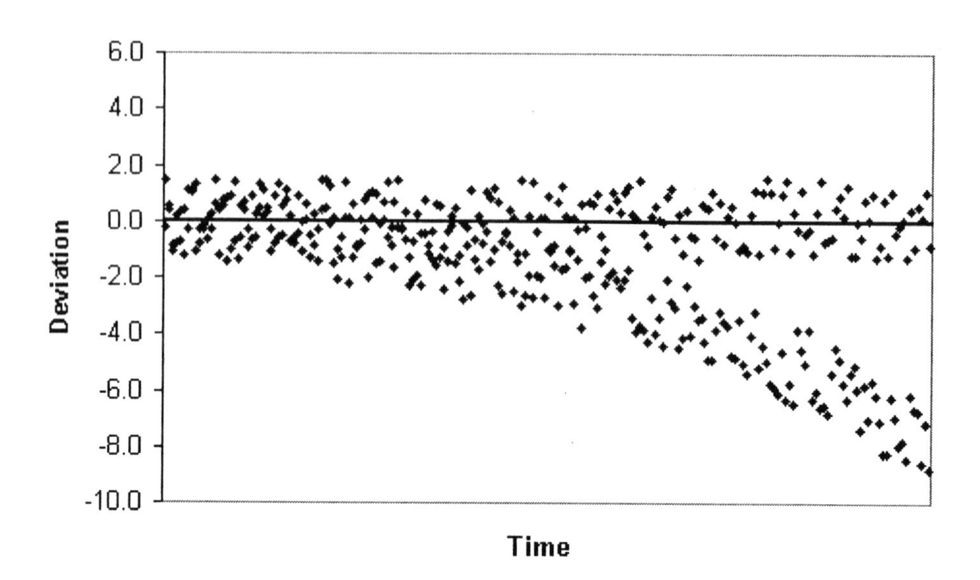

It looks as if something is going wrong with one of the machines. This type of trend could be seen in the tolerance measurements directly, but problems can often be hidden in the scale used to graph the original measurements, as in the following graph:

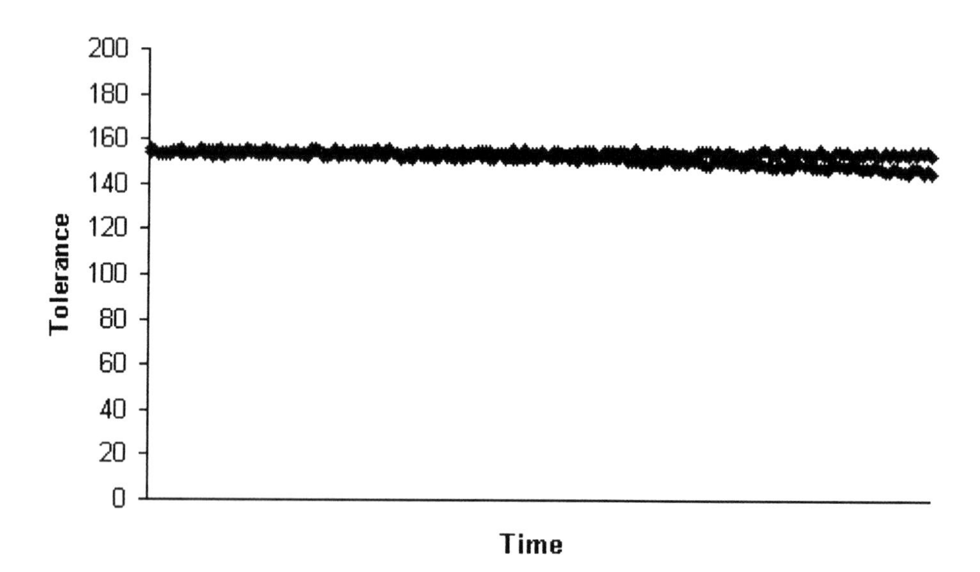

4.1 Frequency Distributions

Producing a *frequency distribution,* or *histogram,* can help you understand how the error in your data is distributed. Excel's Data Analysis package will automatically create frequency distributions (and perform several other statistical analyses, such as t-tests and ANOVA).

EXAMPLE 1

On a good day, when the tools made by the two machines are nearly identical, the deviation plot looks as follows:

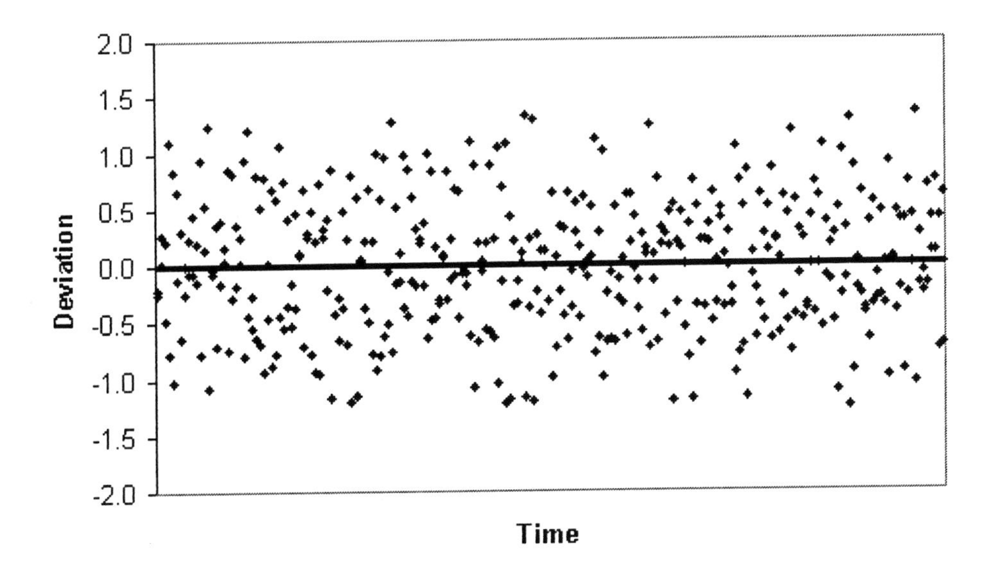

Notice that the magnitudes of the deviations are generally smaller than in the previous deviation plot. The machines are working better.

The basic idea of a frequency distribution is to separate the values into bins and then plot how many values fall into each bin. For deviations, if the bins near zero contain more values than the bins far from zero, then your deviations (sample) or errors (population) might follow a *normal distribution* (the classic bell curve). If all of the bins contain approximately the same number of values, then you might have a *uniform distribution*. Frequency distributions can be created by using deviations, as shown here, or directly from the original data values.

To create a frequency distribution in Excel, use the following steps:

1. Decide how many bins you want to use. The number of bins is arbitrary, but the following list is workable for the deviations just plotted:

BIN 1	FROM −1.4	TO −1.0
2	−1.0	−0.6
3	−0.6	−0.2
4	−0.2	0.2
5	0.2	0.6
6	0.6	1.0
7	1.0	1.4

2. Create a column of bin limits (cells C2:C9 in this example):

	A	B	C	D	E
1	Value	Deviation	Bins		
2	155.77	0.27	-1.4		
3	155.72	0.22	-1.0		
4	156.60	1.10	-0.6		
5	156.33	0.83	-0.2		
6	156.15	0.65	0.2		
7	155.80	0.30	0.6		
8	155.51	0.01	1.0		
9	155.42	-0.08	1.4		
10	155.94	0.44			
11	155.69	0.19			
12	156.43	0.93	Hidden Rows		
398	155.60	0.10			
399	155.61	0.11			
400	154.75	-0.75			
401	154.79	-0.71			
402					

Note the following:

a. *If you do not create a column of bin limits and do not indicate any bin limits in Step 6, Excel will automatically create them for you.*

b. *To hide one or more rows, first select the rows to be hidden and then right click on the selected rows and choose Hide from the pop-up menu. When you select a cell range across hidden rows, the hidden rows will be included in the selected cell range by default.*

3. Activate Excel's histogram analysis procedure by using Tools / Data Analysis . . . .

   Note: The data-analysis package is installed, but not as an activated part of Excel, by default. If the Data Analysis menu option does not appear under the Tools menu, it has not been activated. Use Tools/Add-Ins . . . , and activate the Analysis option. This has to be done only once.

4. Excel offers a wide variety of analysis options. Choose "Histogram" from the selection list:

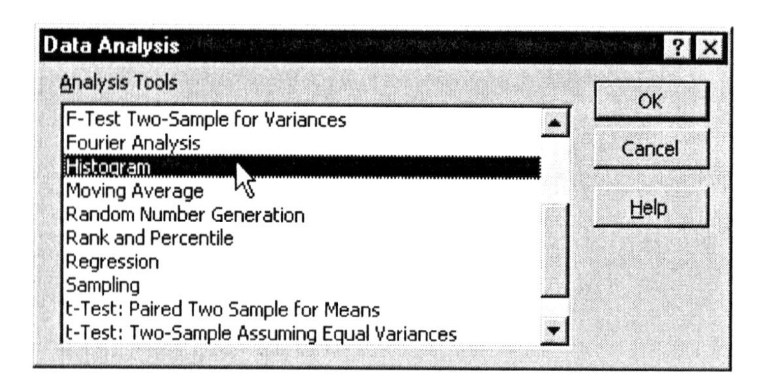

5. The Histogram dialog box will be displayed. You need to first indicate the range containing the deviations. You can either type in the range or click on the spreadsheet icon (as shown next) to go to the spreadsheet and indicate the range by using the mouse:

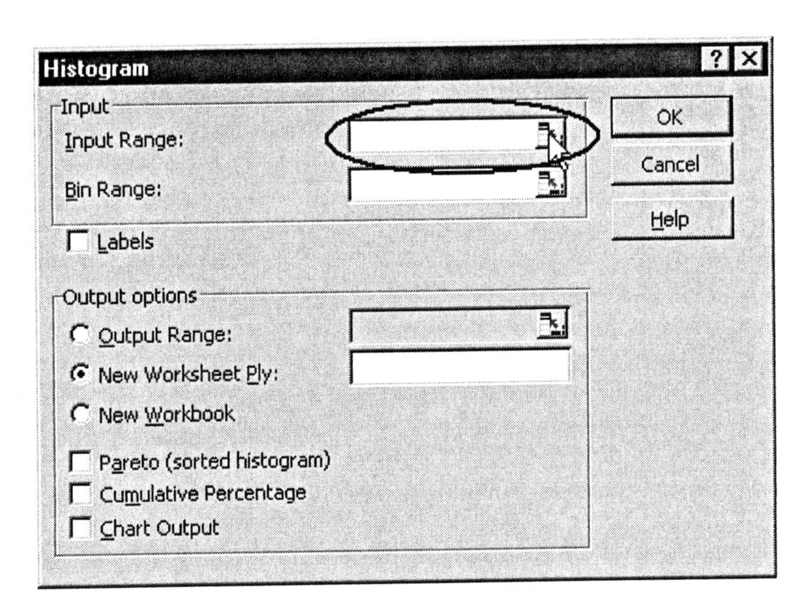

Back at the spreadsheet, indicate the range of cells that contains the deviation values (part of the range has been hidden to save space, but all of the deviation values were used in the analysis):

	A	B	C	D	E	F
1	Value	Deviation	Bins			
2	155.77	0.27	-1.4			
3	155.72	0.22	-1.0			
4	156.60	1.10	-0.6			
5	156.33	0.83	-0.2			
6	156.15	0.65	0.2			
7	155.80	0.30	0.6			
8	155.51	0.01	1.0			
9	155.42	-0.08	1.4			
10	155.94	0.44				
11	155.69	0.19				
12	156.43	0.93				
398	155.60	0.10				
399	155.61	0.11				
400	154.75	-0.75				
401	154.79	-0.71				
402						

Histogram
$B$2:$B$401

Once you have indicated the range containing the deviations, either click on the dialog box icon (right side of the data entry field in the Histogram window) or just press [Enter] to return to the Histogram dialog box.

6. In the same manner, indicate the cell range containing the bin limit values:

	A	B	C	D	E	F
1	Value	Deviation	Bins			
2	155.77	0.27	-1.4			
3	155.72	0.22	-1.0			
4	156.60	1.10	-0.6			
5	156.33	0.83	-0.2			
6	156.15	0.65	0.2			
7	155.80	0.30	0.6			
8	155.51	0.01	1.0			
9	155.42	-0.08	1.4			
10	155.94	0.44				
11	155.69	0.19				
12	156.43	0.93				
398	155.60	0.10				
399	155.61	0.11				
400	154.75	-0.75				
401	154.79	-0.71				
402						

Histogram
$C$2:$C$9

7. Now tell Excel how to handle the output data. Typically, you will want to put the results on a "New Worksheet Ply," and you will want "Chart Output." Both of these options have been indicated on the dialog box shown here:

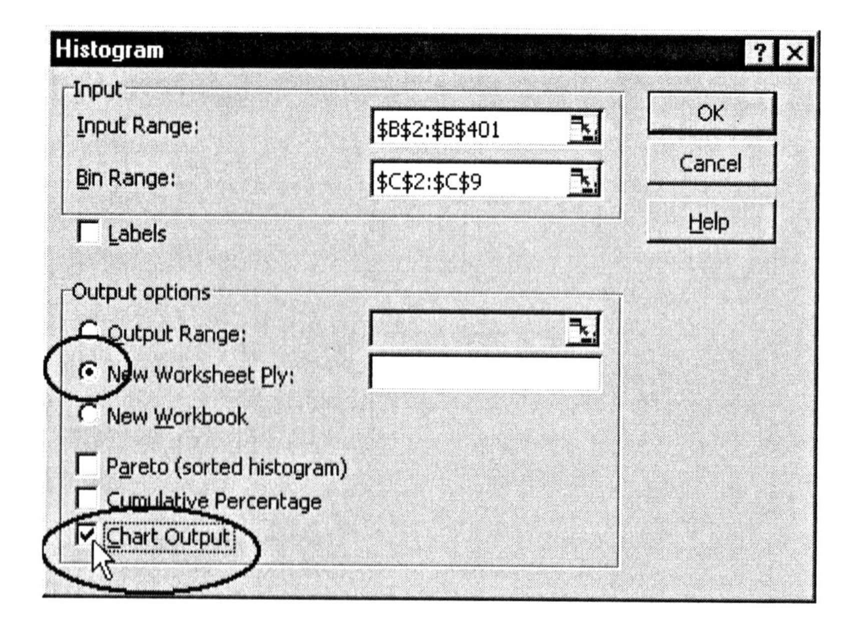

8. Click OK to create the histogram plot. The new histogram looks like this:

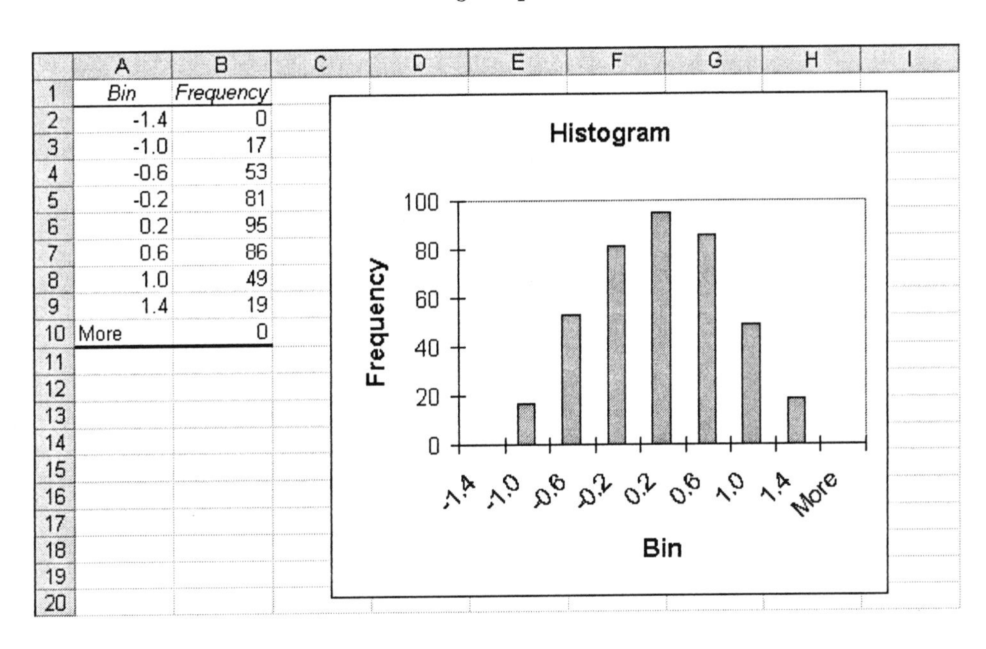

Bin	Frequency
-1.4	0
-1.0	17
-0.6	53
-0.2	81
0.2	95
0.6	86
1.0	49
1.4	19
More	0

This data set shows the "bell curve" shape suggesting a normal distribution.

5 CONFIDENCE INTERVALS

The public-opinion polls used by the news media usually are attempts to find out how the general population is thinking about issues by asking a small sample—typically only a few hundred people are actually polled. With such a small sample, there is always a possibility that the sample results do not accurately reflect the opinions of the entire population, so the poll results usually indicate an uncertainty in the result (plus or minus four percentage points is very common). There is also the question of how the sample was obtained. If you choose random telephone listings, your sample will exclude people whose names aren't in telephone directories. If you use voting records, you exclude non-voters. Coming up with a representative sample is sometimes difficult.

The public opinion polls point out a couple of things you should keep in mind:

- We often use sample information to predict something about the population.
- Any time you use a sample, you introduce some uncertainty into the result.
- If you use a sample, you need to take care how you choose the sample.

A pollster who wants to be 100% confident (zero uncertainty) would have to poll everyone in the population. If you are not going to poll everyone, you have to accept a level of uncertainty in your result—you choose a *confidence level*.

5.1 Confidence Levels and the Level of Significance

When you cannot be 100% confident, you must decide how much uncertainty you are willing to accept, or—put another way—how often you are willing to be wrong. It is very common to use a confidence level of 95%, implying that you are willing to be wrong 5% of the time, or one time out of every 20. There are other times when 95% confidence is totally unrealistic. No one would design a pitched curve on a highway, for example, such that 19 out of every 20 cars would successfully negotiate the curve, with one out of 20 going over the edge.

A confidence level of 95% will be used for the remainder of this chapter, but remember that the choice of confidence level is up to you and should be chosen to suit the accuracy required in your result.

The *level of significance*, α, is computed from the confidence level. The level of significance, α, corresponding to a confidence level of 95% is

$$\alpha = 1 - 0.95 = 0.05. \tag{6}$$

5.2 Confidence Intervals: Bounding the Extent of Uncertainty

The small data set (3, 9, 1, 3, 4, 6) was collected as a sample and has sample mean $\bar{x} = 4.33$; standard deviation, $s = 2.80$; and variance, $s^2 = 7.87$.

What is the population mean, μ?

Who knows? If the sample was well chosen, the population mean is probably close to 4.33. Sometimes "probably close to" is not good enough, and we need to say that the population mean will be between two limits, a *confidence interval*. In setting the limits, there are a couple of things to keep in mind:

- The most likely value of the population mean is the mean we calculated from the sample data, $\bar{x}$, so the range of possible population means will be centered on $\bar{x}$.
- The size of the range will depend on how willing you are to be wrong. If you want to avoid ever being wrong, then set the limits to $\pm\,\infty$. It's not a very useful result, but you can be sure the population mean will always fall in that range.
- The more uncertainty you are willing to accept (i.e., the lower your confidence level), the narrower the range of possible population mean values becomes. So lower confidence levels produce narrower confidence intervals.

The confidence interval uses sample information ($\bar{x}$, s) to say something about the population mean, μ. Specifically, the confidence interval indicates the range of likely population mean values.

With only six values in the small data set and a wide range of values in the set (ranging from 1 to 9), you should expect a pretty wide confidence interval (unless you are willing to be wrong a high percentage of the time). We'll calculate the 95% confidence interval ($\alpha = 0.05$) for this data set. The procedure is as follows:

1. Compute the mean and standard deviation of the sample (done).
2. Count the number of values in the sample. With the small data set used here, the number of values is obviously six. For larger data sets, it is convenient to have the spreadsheet count the number of values by using

   ```
   =COUNT(range)
   ```

3. Decide on a confidence level. A confidence level of 95%, or 0.95, will be used here.
4. Compute the level of significance from the confidence level:

   $$\alpha = 1 - 0.95 = 0.05. \tag{7}$$

5. Compute the *t-value*, using the number of values in the sample and the level of significance.

Note: The t-*value is usually obtained from tables, but the tables in various texts are not all set up the same. Some are based on confidence level (e.g., 95%), some are based on level of significance (e.g.,* $\alpha = 0.05$*). Some tables are one-tailed, some are two-tailed (this will be explained later). You need to be careful to match the equation for a confidence interval and the* t-*distribution table in the same text. Excel will compute* t-*values, and the equations shown in this text work with Excel. They will also work with the tables in some, but not all, texts.*

The *t*-value is computed in Excel by using the `TINV()` function, which returns the *t*-value for a two-tailed distribution. This function takes two parameters:

`=TINV(α, DOF)`

α level of significance

DOF *degrees of freedom* $= N_{\text{sample}} - 1$

One-Tailed and Two-Tailed *t* Tables A confidence level of 95% implies a 5% chance of being wrong. The t *distribution* is used as a probability map when calculating a confidence interval about a sample mean. Ninety-five percent of the area under the *t* distribution will be centered on the sample mean, with the remaining 5% divided in the two tails of the *t* distribution. When you are placing two *bounds* (upper and lower) on a mean, the likelihood of error (5% in this example) is divided between the two tails:

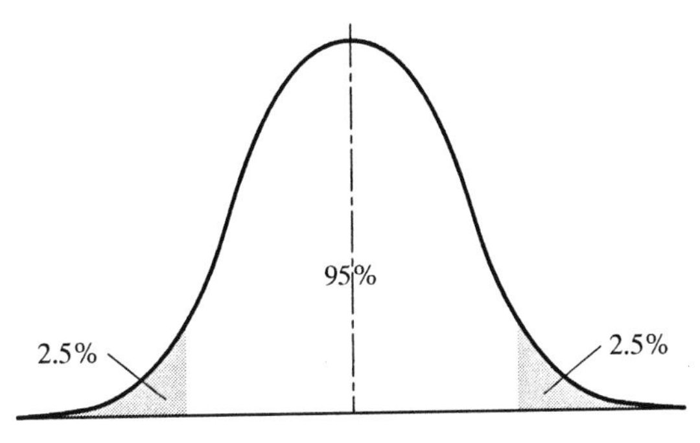

Excel's `TINV()` function returns *t*-values for a two-tailed *t* distribution—that is, the probability of error is divided between the tails on each side of the *t* distribution. For confidence intervals, that's exactly what we want.

Aside If the probability of error is all on one side of the distribution (illustrated in the accompanying figure), you want *t*-values from a one-tailed *t* distribution. One-tailed distributions are used (for example) when you want to see whether the mean value is less than a specified value.

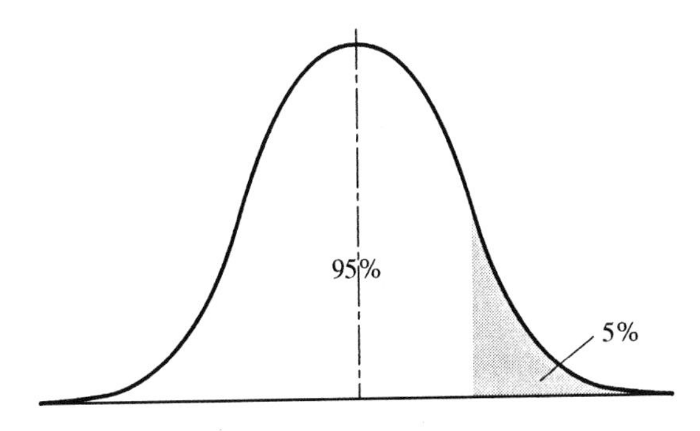

For this example, we need a t-value corresponding to a level of significance of 0.05 (spread between two tails) with five degrees of freedom. We can let Excel find the t-value by using `=TINV(0.05,5)`. The function returns the value $t = 2.571$, as is seen in the following spreadsheet:

B3 fx =TINV(0.05,5)

	A	B	C	D
1	't' Statistic			
2				
3		2.571		
4				
5				

6. The upper and lower bounds on the confidence interval are found by using the formulas

$$B_L = \bar{x} - t\frac{s}{\sqrt{N_{\text{sample}}}},$$

and

$$B_U = \bar{x} + t\frac{s}{\sqrt{N_{\text{sample}}}}. \tag{8}$$

The quantity $\frac{s}{\sqrt{N_{\text{sample}}}}$ has a name: It is called the *standard error of the sample*, or *SES*. So the t-value multiplied by the standard error of the sample, $t \cdot \text{SES}$ is the quantity that is added to and subtracted from the sample mean to calculate the upper and lower bounds of the confidence interval. In this example, the t-value is 2.571, and SES is

$$\text{SES} = \frac{s}{\sqrt{N_{\text{sample}}}} = \frac{2.80}{\sqrt{6}} = 1.143.$$

Then $t \cdot \text{SES} = 2.571 \cdot 1.143 = 2.939$. This is the value that is added to and subtracted from the sample mean to determine the confidence interval.

7. The confidence interval can be written as

$$(\bar{x} - t \cdot \text{SES}) \leq \mu \leq (\bar{x} + t \cdot \text{SES}).$$

and

$$B_L \leq \mu \leq B_U. \tag{9}$$

which, for the small data set, results in the 95% confidence interval

$$1.39 \leq \mu \leq 7.28. \tag{10}$$

This says that, with 95% confidence, the mean value for the complete population (from which the small sample was taken) is between 1.39 and 7.28. This is a pretty large band, but that's not surprising because of the small number of values and the large range of values in the data set.

Notice that the confidence interval uses sample information ($\bar{x}$ and s) to infer something about the population. The size of the confidence interval can be reduced by

(1) taking more samples or (2) using a lower confidence level (i.e., if you have better data or are willing to be wrong more frequently).

The following spreadsheet illustrates how the upper and lower bounds are computed for the test data set:

	A	B	C	D	E	F	G	H
1	**Small Data Set: Confidence Interval**							
2								
3		3						
4		9		**Mean:**	4.33		=AVERAGE(B3:B8)	
5		1		**St. Dev.:**	2.80		=STDEV(B3:B8)	
6		3		**N_{sample}:**	6		=COUNT(B3:B8)	
7		4						
8		6		**α:**	0.05		0.05	
9				**DOF:**	5		=E6-1	
10				**t:**	2.57		=TINV(E8,E9)	
11								
12				**B_L:**	1.39		=E4-E10*(E5/SQRT(E6))	
13				**B_U:**	7.28		=E4+E10*(E5/SQRT(E6))	
14								

The formulas used in column E are shown in column G.

Using Excel's Descriptive Statistics Package

One of Excel's data-analysis packages is designed to calculate descriptive statistics for a data set. To use the Descriptive Statistics package, select Data Analysis... from the Tools menu, and then select Descriptive Statistics from the list of analysis tools:

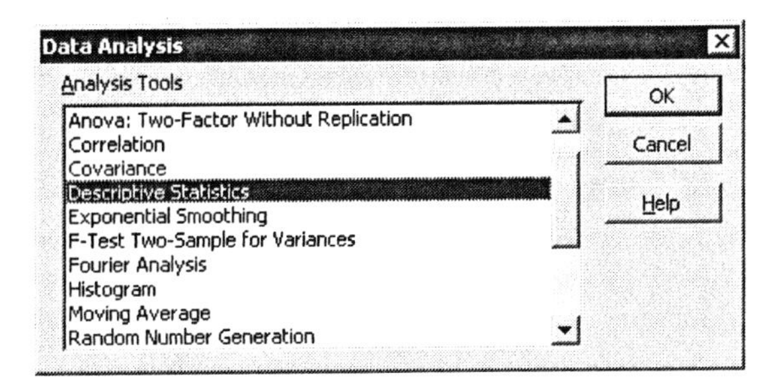

The Descriptive Statistics dialog will open. The required input is simply the range containing the data set (B3:B8), an indication of where you want the results placed and a selection of the type of results that should be calculated. Here, summary statistics (mean, standard deviation, variance, standard error of the sample, etc.) have been requested along with a confidence level of the mean, which has been set to 95% confidence:

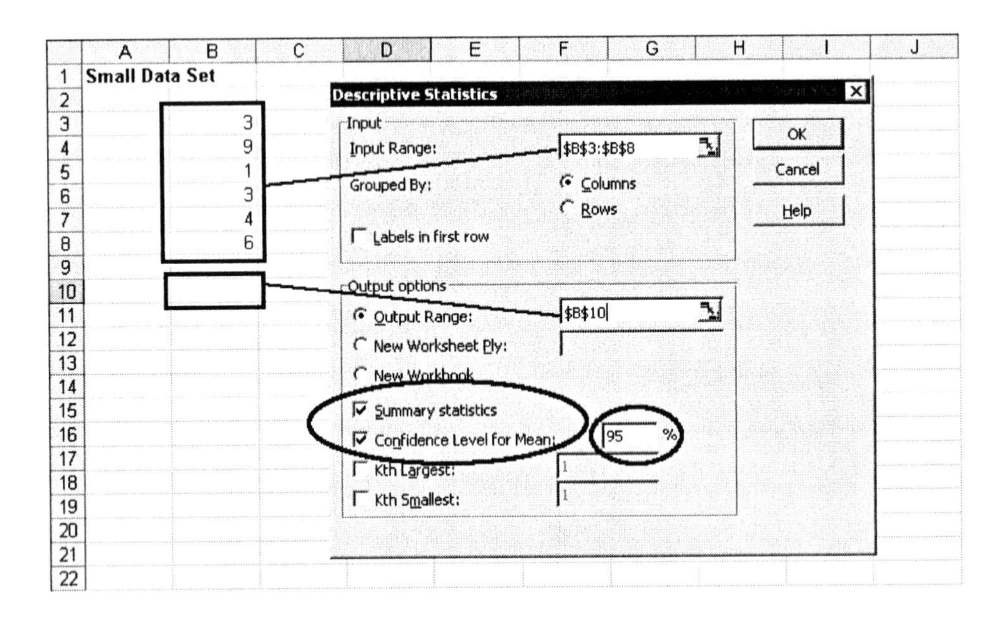

When the OK button is clicked, the results are calculated and presented on the spreadsheet:

	A	B	C	D
1	**Small Data Set**			
2				
3		3		
4		9		
5		1		
6		3		
7		4		
8		6		
9				
10		*Column1*		
11				
12		Mean	4.333333	
13		Standard Error	1.145038	
14		Median	3.5	
15		Mode	3	
16		Standard Deviation	2.804758	
17		Sample Variance	7.866667	
18		Kurtosis	0.670066	
19		Skewness	0.876235	
20		Range	8	
21		Minimum	1	
22		Maximum	9	
23		Sum	26	
24		Count	6	
25		Confidence Level(95.0%)	2.943413	
26				

The descriptive statistics are the same as those calculated earlier in the chapter by using Excel's functions, so the Descriptive Statistics package is simply an alternative method for calculating these quantities. But notice the value 2.94 in cell C25. The label is "Confidence

Level (95%)", but that value is actually $t \cdot \text{SES}$. This is a very handy way of calculating a confidence interval, because the confidence interval is simply

$$(\bar{x} - t \cdot \text{SES}) \leq \mu \leq (\bar{x} + t \cdot \text{SES}).$$

PRACTICE!

Two thermocouples are placed in boiling water and the output voltages are measured five times. Calculate the sample mean and standard deviation for each thermocouple. Then compute the confidence interval for the population mean for each thermocouple, assuming a 95% confidence level. The following table shows the measured values:

TC_A (mV)	TC_B (mV)
3.029	2.999
3.179	3.002
3.170	3.007
3.022	3.004
2.928	3.013

A More Realistic Example To generate a more realistic data set, I searched the lab for the oldest, most beat-up weight set I could find. Then I chose the worst looking weight in the set (the 2-gram weight) and weighed it 51 times on a very sensitive balance, but I left the scale doors open with air moving through the room to generate some noise. The results of the repeated sampling of the mass were a sample mean $\bar{x}$ of 1.9997 grams and a standard deviation s of 0.0044 grams, or

$$\bar{x} = 1.9997 \pm 0.0044 \text{ grams.} \tag{11}$$

A 95% confidence interval can be used to put bounds on the expected value of the true mass. The confidence interval for this example is computed as follows:

	A	B	C	D	E	F	G
1	Two-Gram Weight Data: Confidence Interval						
2							
3							
4		Mean:	1.9998	grams			
5		St. Dev.:	0.0044	grams			
6		N_{sample}:	51				
7							
8		α:	0.05				
9		DOF:	50			=C6-1	
10		t:	2.0086			=TINV(C8,C9)	
11							
12		B_L:	1.9986	grams		=C4-C10*(C5/SQRT(C6))	
13		B_U:	2.0010	grams		=C4+C10*(C5/SQRT(C6))	
14							

The formulas used in column C are shown in column F.

The 95% confidence interval for this example can be written as

$$1.9986\,g \leq \mu \leq 2.0010\,g. \tag{12}$$

For an old, beat-up weight, it's still pretty close to 2 grams (with 95% certainty).

KEY TERMS

Arithmetic average
Confidence interval
Confidence level
Degrees of freedom
Deviation
Deviation plot
Error
Frequency distribution
Histogram
Level of significance
Normal distribution
Population
Population mean
Random sample
Range
Representative sample
Sample
Sample mean
Sampling method
Standard deviation (sample, population)
Standard error of the sample (SES)
Statistics
t distribution (one-tailed, two-tailed)
Uniform distribution
Variance (sample, population)

SUMMARY

Population	When a data set includes information from each member of a group, or all possible measurements, it is said to represent the population.
Sample	When only a subset of the entire population is measured or only some of all possible measurements are taken, the data set is called a sample. Whenever a sample is used, care should be taken to ensure that the sample is representative of the population. This generally means that a random sample should be taken.
Random Sampling	Each member of a population should have an equal chance of being part of the sample.
Error	The difference between a value and the true value—typically, the population mean.
Deviation	The difference between a value and another value—typically, the sample mean.
Arithmetic Mean	The average value in the data set. Describes the central value in the data: `AVERAGE(range)`
Standard Deviation	A value that gives a sense of the range of scatter of the values in the data set around the mean: `STDEV(range)` sample `STDEVP(range)` population
Variance	The square of the standard deviation: `VAR(range)` sample `VARP(range)` population
Confidence Level	Statistical tests are based on probabilities. For each test you choose a confidence level—the percentage of the time you want to be right. A confidence level of 95%, or 0.95, is very common.
Level of Significance	One minus the (fractional) confidence level.
Confidence Interval	If you know the mean and standard deviation of your sample and choose a confidence level, you can calculate the range of values (centered on the sample mean) in which the population mean will probably lie. The range of possible values is called the confidence interval for the population mean.

Problems

Exam Scores

1. Calculate the average and standard deviation for the set of exam scores shown in the accompanying table. Using a 90% = A, 80% = B, and so on, grading scale, what is the average grade on the exam?

SCORES
92
81
72
67
93
89
82
98
75
84
66
90
55
90
91

Thermocouple Reliability I

2. Two thermocouples are supposed to be identical, but they don't seem to be giving the same results when they are both placed in a beaker of water at room temperature. Calculate the mean and standard deviation for each thermocouple. Which one would you use in an experiment?

TC_1 (mv)	TC_2 (mV)
0.3002	0.2345
0.2998	0.1991
0.3001	0.2905
0.2992	0.3006
0.2989	0.1559
0.2996	0.1605
0.2993	0.5106
0.3006	0.3637
0.2980	0.4526
0.3014	0.4458
0.2992	0.3666
0.3001	0.3663
0.2992	0.2648
0.2976	0.2202
0.2998	0.2889

Thermocouple Reliability II

3. The two thermocouples mentioned in the previous problem are supposed to be identical, but they don't seem to be giving the same results when they are both placed in a beaker of water at room temperature. What is the confidence interval for each set of readings ($\alpha = 0.05$)? Which thermocouple would you use in an experiment?

Sample Size and Confidence Interval

4. Some PRACTICE! Problems in this chapter have used five readings from a thermocouple. Those are actually the first five readings from a larger data set, which is reproduced here and available on the text's website, *http://www.coe.montana.edu/che/Excel*:

TC_A (mV)					
3.029	2.838	3.039	2.842	3.083	3.013
3.179	2.889	2.934	2.962	3.076	2.921
3.170	3.086	2.919	2.893	3.009	2.813
3.022	2.792	2.972	3.163	2.997	2.955
2.928	2.937	2.946	3.127	3.004	2.932

a. Calculate the confidence interval for the population mean (95% confidence), using the 5 data points in the left column, the 10 points in the left two columns, and all 30 data points.

b. How significant is the number of data points for the size of the confidence interval?

Thermocouple Calibration Curve

5. A thermocouple was calibrated by using the system illustrated. The thermocouple and a thermometer were dipped in a beaker of water on a hot plate. The power was set at a preset level (known only as 1, 2, 3 . . . , on the dial) and the thermocouple readings were monitored on the computer screen. When steady state had been reached, the thermometer was read, and 10 thermocouple readings were recorded. Then the power level was increased and the process repeated.

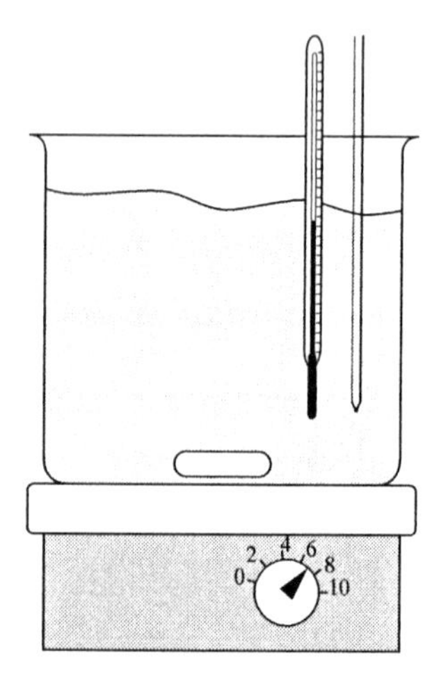

The accumulated calibration data (steady-state data only) is tabulated as follows and is available electronically at *http://www.coe.montana.edu/che/Excel.*

POWER SETTING	THERMO-METER	THERMOCOUPLE READINGS									
	(°C)	(mV)									
0	24.6	1.253	1.175	1.460	1.306	1.117	1.243	1.272	1.371	1.271	1.173
1	38.2	1.969	1.904	2.041	1.804	2.010	1.841	1.657	1.711	1.805	1.670
2	50.1	2.601	2.506	2.684	2.872	3.013	2.832	2.644	2.399	2.276	2.355
3	60.2	3.141	2.920	2.931	2.795	2.858	2.640	2.870	2.753	2.911	3.180
4	69.7	3.651	3.767	3.596	3.386	3.624	3.511	3.243	3.027	3.181	3.084
5	79.1	4.157	4.322	4.424	4.361	4.115	4.065	4.169	4.376	4.538	4.809
6	86.3	4.546	4.384	4.376	4.548	4.654	4.808	4.786	4.535	4.270	4.156
7	96.3	5.087	5.197	5.390	5.624	5.634	5.335	5.525	5.264	4.993	5.267
8	99.8	5.277	5.177	4.991	5.190	5.228	5.274	4.990	5.010	4.916	4.784

Note: This is very noisy thermocouple data, so that the error bars will be visible when graphed. Actual thermocouples are much more precise than the values reported here.

a. Calculate the average and standard deviation of the thermocouple readings at each power setting.

b. Plot the thermocouple calibration curve with temperature on the x-axis and average thermocouple reading on the y-axis.

c. Add a linear trendline to the graph, and have Excel display the equation for the trendline and the R^2 value.

d. Use the standard deviation values to add error bars (±1 std. dev.) to the graph.

Bottling Plant Recalibration

6. A bottling plant tries to put just a bit over 2 liters in each bottle. If the filling equipment is delivering less than 2.00 liters per bottle, it must be shut down and recalibrated.

   The last 10 sample volumes are listed here:

VOLUME
(LITERS)
1.92
2.07
2.03
2.04
2.11
1.94
2.01
2.03
2.13
1.99

a. Design a random-sampling protocol for a bottling plant filling 20,000 bottles per day. How many samples should you take? How often? How would you choose which bottles to sample?

b. Calculate the mean and standard deviation of the last 10 sample volumes.

c. Should the plant be shut down for recalibration?

Extracting Vanilla

7. When you want to extract vanilla from vanilla beans, you usually grind the bean to speed the extraction process, but you want very uniformly sized particles so that the vanilla is extracted from all of the particles at the same rate. If you have a lot of different-sized particles, the small particles extract faster (removing the vanilla *and* some poorer flavored components), while the larger particles could leave the process incompletely extracted.

A sample was collected from the vanilla-bean grinder and split into 50 parts. The average particle size of each part was determined. The following data were collected, and they are available on the text's website:

AVERAGE PARTICLE SIZE (μm)				
91	147	150	165	130
157	117	114	139	131
105	64	137	115	97
116	94	99	163	144
135	112	116	138	129
138	115	106	139	76
147	116	115	101	107
129	122	120	131	104
88	98	157	110	138
152	113	128	130	125

a. Calculate the standard deviation of the particle sizes in the sample. Is the standard deviation less than 15 μm? (If not, the grinder should be repaired.)

b. How would you determine the average particle size of the ground vanilla beans?

8

Matrix Operations in Excel

SECTIONS

OBJECTIVES

After reading this chapter, you will know

- How Excel handles matrix math
- How to use basic cell arithmetic to multiply matrices by a scalar
- How to understand matrix addition
- How to use Excel's array function `MMULT()` to multiply matrices
- How to transpose matrices, using two methods: menu commands Edit/Paste Special/Transpose, and array function `TRANSPOSE()`
- How to invert a matrix, using array function `MINVERSE()`
- How to find the determinant of a matrix, using array function `MDETERM()`
- How to solve systems of simultaneous linear equations, using matrix math

1 INTRODUCTION

Matrix manipulations are a natural for spreadsheets: The spreadsheet grid provides a natural home for the columns and rows of a matrix. All standard spreadsheets provide the standard matrix operations. Excel goes a step further and allows many matrix operations to be performed by using array functions rather than menu commands. This makes the matrix operations "live"; they will automatically be recalculated if any of the data is changed.

2 MATRICES, VECTORS, AND ARRAYS

Excel uses the term *array* to refer to a collection of values organized in rows and columns that should be kept together. For example, mathematical operations performed on any element of the array are performed on each element of the array, and Excel will not allow you to delete a portion of an array; the entire array must be deleted or converted to values using Edit/Paste Special/Values. Functions designed to operate on or return arrays are called *array functions*.

Standard mathematics nomenclature calls a collection of related values organized in rows and columns a *matrix*. A matrix with a single row or column is called a *vector*. In Excel, both would be considered arrays.

Defining and Naming Arrays

You define an array in Excel simply by filling a range of cells with the contents of the array. For example, the 3×2 matrix

$$A = \begin{bmatrix} 1 & 3 \\ 7 & 2 \\ 8 & 11 \end{bmatrix}$$

can be entered into a 3×2 range of cells:

	A	B	C	D
1				
2				
3				
4	[A], 3x2	1	3	
5		7	2	
6		8	1	
7				
8				
9				

Naming a range of cells allows you to use the name (e.g., A) in place of the cell range (e.g., B4:C6) in array formulas. Excel's matrix math functions do not require named arrays, but naming the cell ranges that contain the arrays is commonly done. Using named arrays not only expedites entering array formulas, it also makes your spreadsheets easier to read and understand.

To give a name to the range of cells that hold an array, first select the array:

B4 ▾ fx 1

Name box shows top-left cell address

	A	B	C	D
1				
2				
3				
4	[A], 3x2	1	3	
5		7	2	
6		8	1	
7				
8				
9				

Then, enter the desired name in the Name box at the left side of the Formula Bar. Here, the array has been called "A".

A ▾ fx 1

Selected range has been named "A"

	A	B	C	D
1				
2				
3				
4	[A], 3x2	1	3	
5		7	2	
6		8	1	
7				
8				
9				

Alternatively, a selected range can be assigned a name by using Insert/Name/Define.

3 HOW EXCEL HANDLES MATRIX MATH

Excel provides mechanisms for performing each of the standard matrix operations, but they are accessed in differing ways:

- Addition and *scalar* multiplication are handled through either basic cell arithmetic or array math operations.
- Matrix transposition, multiplication, and inversion are handled by array functions.

The various spreadsheet programs handle matrix operations, such as transposition, multiplication, and inversion, in different ways. Some programs treat a matrix as a range of values, and matrix operations (from menus, not functions) produce a new range of values. Excel provides many standard matrix operations using menu functions, but also provides array functions for matrix operations such as transposition, multiplication, and inversion. There are pros and cons to each approach. Excel's array functions require more effort on the user's part to perform matrix transposition, multiplication, and inversion, but, by using array functions, Excel can recalculate the resulting matrices if any of the input data change. When spreadsheet programs do not use functions for matrix transposition, multiplication, and inversion, they cannot automatically recalculate your matrix results when your spreadsheet changes.

4 BASIC MATRIX OPERATIONS

4.1 Adding Two Matrices

The two matrices to be added must be the same size. Begin by entering the two matrices to be added:

	A	B	C	D
1	**ADDITION**			
2	Matrices must be the same size			
3				
4	[A], 3x2	1	3	
5		7	2	
6		8	11	
7				
8	[B], 3x2	4	8	
9		6	1	
10		0	5	
11				

The matrices are added element by element. For example, the top left cell of the resultant matrix will hold the formula required to add 1 + 4 (cell B4 plus cell B8). The formula would be written as `=B4+B8`. When this formula is placed in cell B12, the result is displayed:

B12 | f_x =B4+B8

	A	B	C	D
1	**ADDITION**			
2	Matrices must be the same size			
3				
4	[A], 3x2	1	3	
5		7	2	
6		8	11	
7				
8	[B], 3x2	4	8	
9		6	1	
10		0	5	
11				
12	[A] + [B]	5		
13				

If the contents of cell B12 are now copied to cells B12:C14, Excel will add the [A] matrix and the [B] matrix element by element:

C13 | f_x =C5+C9

	A	B	C	D
1	**ADDITION**			
2	Matrices must be the same size			
3				
4	[A], 3x2	1	3	
5		7	2	
6		8	11	
7				
8	[B], 3x2	4	8	
9		6	1	
10		0	5	
11				
12	[A] + [B]	5	11	
13		13	3	
14		8	16	
15				

Matrix Addition Using Array Math

If the cell ranges holding matrices [A] and [B] are named, then the array names can be used to perform the addition. Here, the name "A" was applied to cell range B4:C6, and cells B8:C10 were named "B".

In Excel, any time array math is used, the size of the resulting array must be indicated before the entering of the array formula. The result of adding matrices [A] and [B] will be a 3×2 matrix, so a 3×2 region of cells (B16:C18) is selected:

	A	B	C	D	E	F	G
1	**ADDITION**						
2	Matrices must be the same size.						
3							
4	[A], 3x2	1	3				
5		7	2				
6		8	1				
7							
8	[B], 3x2	4	8				
9		6	1				
10		0	5				
11							
12	[A] + [B]	5	11		<< Using cell arithmetic		
13		13	3				
14		8	16				
15							
16	{[A] + [B]}				<< Using array math		
17							
18							
19							

Then the formula =A + B is entered in the top left cell of the selected range:

WEEKDAY ▾ ✕ ✓ fx =A+B

	A	B	C	D	E	F	G
1	**ADDITION**						
2	Matrices must be the same size.						
3							
4	[A], 3x2	1	3				
5		7	2				
6		8	11				
7							
8	[B], 3x2	4	8				
9		6	1				
10		0	5				
11							
12	[A] + [B]	5	11		<< Using cell arithmetic		
13		13	3				
14		8	16				
15							
16	{[A] + [B]}	=A+B			<< Using array math		
17							
18							
19							

Notice that, when the named arrays were entered in the formula, Excel put a box around the named arrays. This allows you to quickly see that the correct matrices are being added.

Excel requires a special character sequence when entering array formulas: [Ctrl–Shift–Enter], not just the [Enter] key. The [Ctrl–Shift–Enter] key combination tells Excel to fill the entire array (i.e., the selected region) with the results of the formula, not just one cell. After the pressing of [Ctrl–Shift–Enter], the spreadsheet will look like this:

B16 | fx {=A+B}

	A	B	C	D	E	F	G
1	**ADDITION**						
2	Matrices must be the same size.						
3					**Each cell in the new**		
4	[A], 3x2	1	3		**array contains {=A+B}**		
5		7	2				
6		8	11				
7							
8	[B], 3x2	4	8				
9		6	1				
10		0	5				
11							
12	[A] + [B]	5	11		<< Using cell arithmetic		
13		13	3				
14		8	16				
15							
16	{[A] + [B]}	5	11		<< Using array math		
17		13	3				
18		8	16				
19							

Each cell in the new array (B16:C18) contains the same formula, `{=A + B}`. The braces { } indicate that array math was used and that the result is an array. This means that the six cells in B16:C18 are considered a collection, and individual elements of the new array cannot be edited or deleted. However, if either matrix [A] or matrix [B] is changed, the new array will automatically be updated.

Note: Named arrays are not required for array math in Excel; the same result could have been obtained by selecting the B16:C18 range, then typing in the array formula `=B4:C6 + B8:C10` *and pressing [Ctrl–Shift–Enter]. The array formula* `{=B4:C6 + B8:C10}` *would have been entered into every cell of the new array, and matrices [A] and [B] would have been added.*

4.2 Multiplying a Matrix by a Scalar

Begin by entering the *scalar* (constant value) and the matrix that it is to multiply:

	A	B	C	D
1	SCALAR MULTIPLICATION			
2				
3	Scalar:	10		
4				
5	[A], 3x2	1	3	
6		7	2	
7		8	11	
8				

Multiplying a matrix by a scalar simply requires you to multiply each element of the matrix by the scalar:

B9 fx =$B$3*B5

	A	B	C	D
1	SCALAR MULTIPLICATION			
2				
3	Scalar:	10		
4				
5	[A], 3x2	1	3	
6		7	2	
7		8	11	
8				
9	10 [A]	10		
10				

By placing the formula `=$B$3*B5` in cell B9, you instruct Excel to multiply the contents of cell B3 (the scalar) and the contents of cell B5 (the top left element of the matrix). The dollar signs before the 'B' and '3' in `$B$3` are in preparation for copying the formula to other cells. When copied, the new formulas will continue to reference the scalar in cell B3; the dollar signs tell Excel not to increment either the column letter (`$B`) or row number (`$3`) during the copy process. You can type the dollar signs as you enter the formula, or just type the B3 and press [F4] to insert the dollar signs:

C11 fx =$B$3*C7

	A	B	C	D	E
1	SCALAR MULTIPLICATION				
2					
3	Scalar:	10			
4					
5	[A], 3x2	1	3		
6		7	2		
7		8	11		
8					
9	10 [A]	10	30		
10		70	20	Fill Handle	
11		80	110		
12					

Copying the formula in cell B9 to the range B9:C11 completes the process of multiplying the matrix [A] by the scalar, 10. The results are shown in cells B9:C11. The *fill handle* (small square at bottom right corner of indicator box) is pointed out in the figure. If, after entering the first formula in cell B9, you grab the fill handle with the mouse and drag the cell indicator down to cell B11, the contents of cell B9 will automatically be copied to cells B10:B11. Then, you can use the fill handle again to copy the contents of cells B9:B11 to C9:C11. (Alternatively, you can copy and paste.)

Scalar Multiplication Using Array Math

The same result can be obtained using array math and a named array. If the cells holding the [A] matrix (B5:B7 in this example) are given the name "A", then the array name can be used to perform the scalar multiplication.

First, the size of the result matrix is indicated by selecting a 3×2 range of cells (B13:C15), and the array formula `=B3 * A` is entered in the top-left cell of the new array:

WEEKDAY ▾ ✕ ✓ fx =B3*A

	A	B	C	D	E	F	G
1	SCALAR MULTIPLICATION						
2							
3	Scalar:	10					
4							
5	[A], 3x2	1	3				
6		7	2				
7		8	11				
8							
9	10 [A]	10	30		<< Using cell arithmetic		
10		70	20				
11		80	110				
12							
13	10 [A]	=B3*A			<< Using array math		
14							
15							
16							

The formula is concluded by pressing [Ctrl–Shift–Enter] to tell Excel to fill the entire selected region with the array formula. Excel places the array formula {`=B3 * A`} in each cell in the result array:

B13 fx {=B3*A}

	A	B	C	D	E	F	G
1	**SCALAR MULTIPLICATION**						
2							
3	Scalar:	10					
4							
5	[A], 3x2	1	3				
6		7	2				
7		8	11				
8							
9	10 [A]	10	30		<< Using cell arithmetic		
10		70	20				
11		80	110				
12							
13	10 [A]	10	30		<< Using array math		
14		70	20				
15		80	110				
16							

4.3 Multiplying Two Matrices

In order to multiply two matrices, the number of columns in the first matrix must equal the number of rows in the second matrix. Again, begin by entering the two matrices to be multiplied:

	A	B	C	D	E	F
1	**MULTIPLICATION**					
2	Inside dimensions must match (2, 2)					
3	Dimensions of resulting matrix from outside dimensions (3 x 1)					
4						
5	[A], 3x2	1	3			
6		7	2			
7		8	11			
8						
9	[e], 2x1	4				
10		8				
11						

Begin the matrix multiplication process by indicating where the product matrix will go.

Note: You should determine the actual size of the product matrix (from the outside dimensions of the matrices being multiplied) and indicate the correct number of cells—but too big is better than too small if you want to guess.

In this example the product matrix will be 3 rows by 1 column, as shown here:

	A	B	C	D	E	F
1	**MULTIPLICATION**					
2	Inside dimensions must match (2, 2)					
3	Dimensions of resulting matrix from outside dimensions (3 x 1)					
4						
5	[A], 3x2	1	3			
6		7	2			
7		8	11			
8						
9	[e], 2x1	4				
10		8				
11						
12	[A][e], 3x1					
13						
14						
15						

Once you have indicated where the new matrix is to go, begin entering the matrix multiplication array function, MMULT(first matrix, second matrix). After entering the equal sign, function name, and the opening parenthesis, use the mouse to indicate the cells that contain the first matrix:

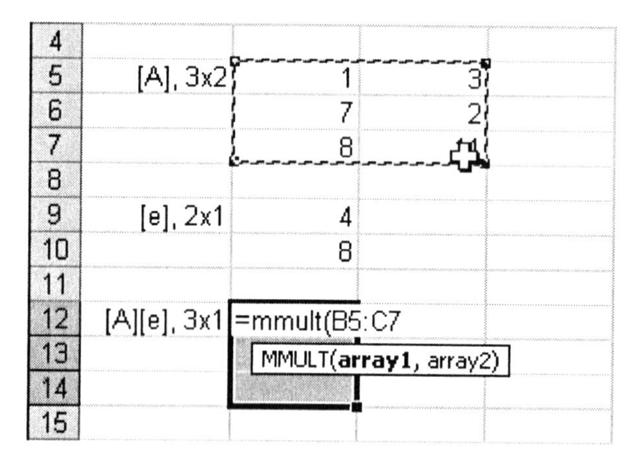

4			
5	[A], 3x2	1	3
6		7	2
7		8	
8			
9	[e], 2x1	4	
10		8	
11			
12	[A][e], 3x1	=mmult(B5:C7	
13		MMULT(**array1**, array2)	
14			
15			

After the first matrix has been indicated, enter comma, and indicate the cells containing the second matrix:

4			
5	[A], 3x2	1	3
6		7	2
7		8	11
8			
9	[e], 2x1	4	
10			
11			
12	[A][e], 3x1	=mmult(B5:C7,B9:B10	
13		MMULT(array1, **array2**)	
14			
15			

Finish entering the matrix multiplication formula by entering the final parenthesis and pressing [Ctrl-Shift-Enter], not just the [Enter] key. The `MMULT()` function is an array function, and the [Ctrl-Shift-Enter] is used to enter the function into *all* of the cells from B12 to B14:

	A	B	C
4			
5	[A], 3x2	1	3
6		7	2
7		8	11
8			
9	[e], 2x1	4	
10		8	
11			
12	[A][e], 3x1	=mmult(B5:C7,B9:B10)	
13			then [Ctrl-Shift-Enter]
14			
15			

Pressing [Enter] alone would enter the formula only in cell B12, and only one element of the product matrix would be displayed.

If the indicated size of the product matrix is incorrect, one of the following things will happen:

- If you indicated too few cells to hold the entire product matrix, only part of your result matrix will be displayed.
- If you indicated more cells than are needed to hold the product matrix, Excel will put "#N/A" in the extra cells, indicating that no formula was placed in the extra cells.

After pressing [Ctrl-Shift-Enter], you will find the result displayed in the indicated cells:

B12 fx {=MMULT(B5:C7,B9:B10)}

	A	B	C	D	E	F
1	**MULTIPLICATION**					
2	Inside dimensions must match (2, 2)					
3	Dimensions of resulting matrix from outside dimensions (3 x 1)					
4						
5	[A], 3x2	1	3			
6		7	2			
7		8	11			
8						
9	[e], 2x1	4				
10		8				
11						
12	[A][e], 3x1	28				
13		44				
14		120				
15						

Note: Excel places the formulas for multiplying the matrices in the result cells, not just the final values. Because of this, any changes in the first two matrices will automatically cause the product matrix to be updated.

PRACTICE!

Can the following matrices be multiplied, and, if so, what size will the resulting matrices be?

$$[A]_{3\times2}[B]_{2\times2} \qquad [C]_{3\times3}[D]_{1\times3} \qquad [D]_{1\times3}[C]_{3\times3} \qquad (1)$$

EXAMPLE 1

Multiplication of $[A]_{3\times2}$ and $[G]_{2\times4}$ matrix produces matrix $[H]_{3\times4}$. Skipping a lot of the details, we see that the multiplication process is summarized as

1. Enter the [A] and [G] matrices.
2. Indicate the size (3 × 4) and location of the result matrix.
3. Begin entering the `MMULT()` array function, and indicate the cells containing the first matrix, [A]: B36:C38
4. Indicate the cells containing the second matrix, [G]: B40:E41, and add the final parenthesis.

	A	B	C	D	E	F
1	**MULTIPLICATION**					
2	Inside dimensions must match (2, 2)					
3	Dimensions of resulting matrix from outside dimensions (3 x 4)					
4						
5	[A], 3x2	1	3			
6		7	2			
7		8	11			
8						
9	[G], 2x4	1	2	3	4	
10		5	6	7	8	
11						
12	[H], 3x4	=mmult(B5:C7,B9:E10)				
13						
14						
15						

5. Press [Ctrl-Shift-Enter] to create the product matrix, [H]: B43. The result of the multiplication is the 3 × 4 matrix called [H]:

B12 fx {=MMULT(B5:C7,B9:E10)}

	A	B	C	D	E	F
1	**MULTIPLICATION**					
2	Inside dimensions must match (2, 2)					
3	Dimensions of resulting matrix from outside dimensions (3 x 4)					
4						
5	[A], 3x2	1	3			
6		7	2			
7		8	11			
8						
9	[G], 2x4	1	2	3	4	
10		5	6	7	8	
11						
12	[H], 3x4	16	20	24	28	
13		17	26	35	44	
14		63	82	101	120	
15						

4.4 Transposing a Matrix

Any matrix can be transposed. To *transpose* a matrix, simply interchange the rows and columns. You can transpose a matrix in two ways: as values or by using array function `TRANSPOSE()`. Using values is simpler, but the result will not be automatically recalculated if the input data change. Both methods are described here.

Using PASTE SPECIAL to Transpose as Values The process in Excel can be summarized as follows:

1. Enter the original matrix.
2. Begin the transposition process by selecting the cells containing the matrix and copying the matrix to the Windows clipboard by selecting Edit/Copy.
3. Indicate the cell that will contain the top left corner of the result matrix.
4. Select Edit/Paste Special.
5. The Paste Special Dialog box is displayed.
6. Select Values from the Paste section of the dialog box, and check the Transpose check box at the bottom of the dialog box.
7. Click on OK to close the dialog box and create the transposed matrix (as values, not array functions).

Using a Matrix Function to Transpose a Matrix Using the `TRANSPOSE()` array function, the process is as follows:

1. Enter the original matrix.
2. Indicate where the result should be placed, showing the exact size of the transposed matrix:

	A	B	C	D	E
1	**TRANSPOSE**				
2	Interchange rows and columns				
3	Any size matrix				
4					
5	[A], 3x2	1	3		
6		7	2		
7		8	11		
8					
9	[A-trans], 2x3				
10					
11					

3. Enter the first portion of the TRANSPOSE(`matrix`) array function, and use the mouse to indicate the cells containing the matrix to be transposed:

	A	B	C	D	E
1	**TRANSPOSE**				
2	Interchange rows and columns				
3	Any size matrix				
4					
5	[A], 3x2	1	3		
6		7	2		
7		8			
8					
9	[A-trans], 2x3	=transpose(B5:C7			
10		TRANSPOSE(**array**)			
11					

4. Finish typing the function by adding the final parenthesis and press [Ctrl-Shift-Enter] to transpose the matrix:

B9 fx {=TRANSPOSE(B5:C7)}

	A	B	C	D	E
1	**TRANSPOSE**				
2	Interchange rows and columns				
3	Any size matrix				
4					
5	[A], 3x2	1	3		
6		7	2		
7		8	11		
8					
9	[A-trans], 2x3	1	7	8	
10		3	2	11	
11					

PRACTICE!

Transpose the following matrices.

$$[6\ 1\ 4]$$

$$\begin{bmatrix} 1 & 1.2 \\ 3 & 6.1 \\ 4 & 2.3 \end{bmatrix} \quad (2)$$

$$\begin{bmatrix} 1 & 0 & 0 \\ 0 & 1 & 0 \\ 0 & 0 & 1 \end{bmatrix}$$

4.5 Inverting a Matrix

Only square matrices (number of rows equal to number of columns) can possibly be inverted, and not even all square matrices can actually be inverted. (They must be *nonsingular* to be inverted.)

The procedure to *invert* a nonsingular, square matrix in Excel, using the MINVERSE() array function, is as follows:

1. Enter the matrix to be inverted.
2. Indicate where the inverted matrix should be placed and the correct size (same size as original matrix).
3. Enter the first portion of the MINVERSE(`matrix`) array function, and use the mouse to indicate the cells containing the matrix to be inverted. Finish the function by typing the final parenthesis:

	A	B	C	D	E
1	**INVERT**				
2	Matrix must be square and non-singular				
3					
4	[J], 3x3	2	3	5	
5		7	2	4	
6		8	11	6	
7					
8	[J-inv], 3x3	=minverse(B4:D6)			
9					
10					
11					

4. Press [Ctrl-Shift-Enter] to enter the array function in all the cells making up the result matrix:

B8 ▾ fx {=MINVERSE(B4:D6)}

	A	B	C	D	E
1	**INVERT**				
2	Matrix must be square and non-singular				
3					
4	[J], 3x3	2	3	5	
5		7	2	4	
6		8	11	6	
7					
8	[J-inv], 3x3	-0.1517	0.1754	0.0095	
9		-0.0474	-0.1327	0.1280	
10		0.2891	0.0095	-0.0806	
11					

4.6 Matrix Determinant

The *determinant* of a matrix is a single value, calculated from a matrix, that is often used in solving systems of equations. One of the most straightforward ways to use the determinant is to see whether a matrix can be inverted. If the determinant is zero, the matrix is *singular* and cannot be inverted. You can calculate a determinant only for square matrices.

Note: Calculating a determinant for a large matrix requires a lot of calculations and can result in round-off errors on digital computers. A very small, nonzero determinant (e.g., 1×10^{-14}) is probably a round-off error, and the matrix most likely cannot be inverted.

Excel's `MDETERM(matrix)` array function is used to compute determinant values. In the previous section, the [J] matrix was inverted, so it must have had a nonzero determinant.

B8 ▾ fx =MDETERM(B4:D6)

	A	B	C	D	E
1	**DETERMINANT**				
2	Matrix must be square				
3					
4	[J], 3x3	2	3	5	
5		7	2	4	
6		8	11	6	
7					
8	Det(J)	211			
9					

If the matrix is singular (and so cannot be inverted), the determinant will be zero. In the [K] matrix below, the second row is the same as the first row. Whenever a matrix contains two identical rows the matrix cannot be inverted, and the determinant will be zero:

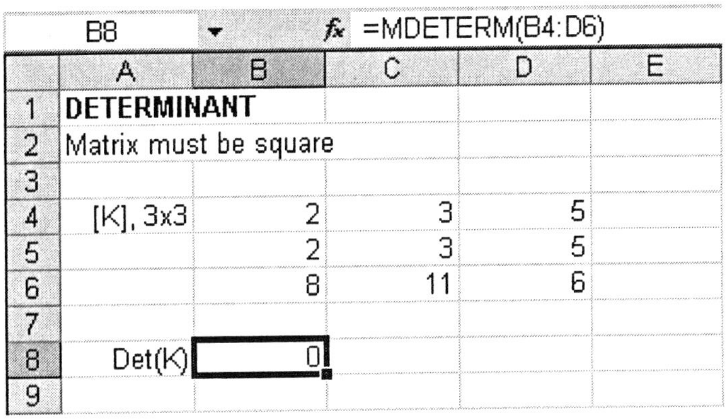

	A	B	C	D	E
1	**DETERMINANT**				
2	Matrix must be square				
3					
4	[K], 3x3	2	3	5	
5		2	3	5	
6		8	11	6	
7					
8	Det(K)	0			
9					

B8 =MDETERM(B4:D6)

A matrix is singular (and cannot be inverted) if

- any row (or column) contains all zeros;
- any two rows (or columns) are identical;
- any row (or column) is equal to a linear combination of other rows (or columns). (When two or more rows are multiplied by constants and then added, the result is a *linear combination* of the rows. When a linear combination of two or more rows is equal to another row in the matrix, the matrix is singular.)

5 SOLVING SYSTEMS OF LINEAR EQUATIONS

One of the most common uses of matrix operations is to solve *systems of linear algebraic equations*. The process of solving simultaneous equations by using matrices works as follows:

1. Write the equations in matrix form (*coefficient matrix* multiplying an *unknown vector*, equal to a *right-hand-side vector*).
2. Invert the coefficient matrix.
3. Multiply both sides of the equation by the inverted coefficient matrix.

The result of step 3 is a solution matrix containing the answers to the problem.

In order for inverting the coefficient matrix to be possible, it must be nonsingular. In terms of solving simultaneous equations, this means that you will be able to invert the coefficient matrix only if there is a solution to the set of equations. If there is no solution, the coefficient matrix will be singular.

Consider the following three equations in three unknowns:

$$\begin{aligned} 3x_1 + 2x_2 + 4x_3 &= 5, \\ 2x_1 + 5x_2 + 3x_3 &= 17, \\ 7x_1 + 2x_2 + 2x_2 &= 11. \end{aligned} \tag{3}$$

Step 1. Write the Equations in Matrix Form

The unknowns are x_1, x_2, and x_3, which can be written as the vector of unknown, $[x]$:

$$[x] = \begin{bmatrix} x_1 \\ x_2 \\ x_3 \end{bmatrix}.$$

The coefficients multiplying the various x's can be collected in a coefficient matrix [C]:

$$[C] = \begin{bmatrix} 3 & 2 & 4 \\ 2 & 5 & 3 \\ 7 & 2 & 2 \end{bmatrix}.$$

PRACTICE!

Try multiplying [C] times [x] (symbolically) to see that you do indeed get back the left side of the preceding equation.

The constants on the right side of the equations can be written as a right-hand-side vector [r]:

$$[r] = \begin{bmatrix} 5 \\ 17 \\ 11 \end{bmatrix}.$$

The three equations in three unknowns can now be written as

$$[C][x] = [r].$$

In a spreadsheet, they might resemble this:

	A	B	C	D	E	F	G	H
1	**Simultaneous Equations**							
2								
3	[C]	3	2	4		[r]	5	
4		2	5	3			17	
5		7	2	2			11	
6								

Step 2. Invert the Coefficient Matrix

Use the array function `MINVERSE()` to invert the [C] matrix:

B7 f_x {=MINVERSE(B3:D5)}

	A	B	C	D	E	F	G	H
1	**Simultaneous Equations**							
2								
3	[C]	3	2	4		[r]	5	
4		2	5	3			17	
5		7	2	2			11	
6								
7	[C-inv]	-0.05	-0.05	0.18				
8		-0.22	0.28	0.01				
9		0.40	-0.10	-0.14				
10								

Step 3. Multiply Both Sides of the Equation by the Inverted [C] Matrix:

$$\begin{aligned}[C_{\text{inv}}][C][x] &= [C_{\text{inv}}][r]\\ [I][x] &= [C_{\text{inv}}][r]\\ [x] &= [C_{\text{inv}}][r]. \end{aligned} \tag{4}$$

Multiplying the inverted [C] matrix and the original [C] matrix returns an identity matrix. (Try it!)

Multiplying the [x] vector by an identity matrix returns the [x] vector unchanged.

So multiplying the inverted [C] matrix and the [r] vector returns the [x] values and gives the solution:

G7 | fx {=MMULT(B7:D9,G3:G5)}

	A	B	C	D	E	F	G	H
1	**Simultaneous Equations**							
2								
3	[C]	3	2	4		[r]	5	
4		2	5	3			17	
5		7	2	2			11	
6								
7	[C-inv]	-0.05	-0.05	0.18	[x] = [C-inv][r]		0.846	
8		-0.22	0.28	0.01			3.846	
9		0.40	-0.10	-0.14			-1.31	
10								

The solutions to the original three equations in three unknowns are

$$\begin{aligned} x_1 &= 0.846,\\ x_2 &= 3.846,\\ x_3 &= -1.31. \end{aligned}$$

APPLICATIONS: MULTILOOP CIRCUITS I

Multiloop circuits are analyzed by using Kirchhoff's laws of voltage and current:

Kirchhoff's voltage law says that

for a closed circuit (a loop), the algebraic sum of all changes in voltage must be zero.

Kirchhoff's current law says that

at any junction in a circuit, the input current(s) must equal the output current(s).

We will use these laws, with the following circuit, to compute the three unknown currents, i_1 through i_3:

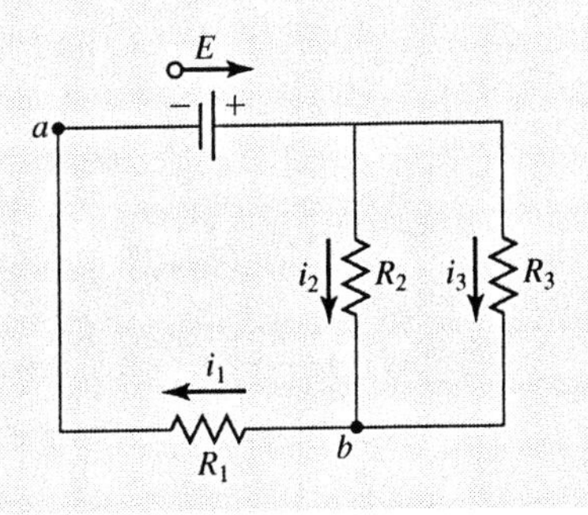

The voltage from the battery and the three resistances are as follows:

Known Values	
E	12 volts
R_1	30 ohms
R_2	40 ohms
R_3	50 ohms

Applying the current law at point b gives one equation:

$$i_1 = i_2 + i_3 \tag{5}$$

Applying the voltage law to the left loop and the overall loop provides two more equations:

$$E - V_2 - V_1 = 0,$$
$$E - V_3 - V_1 = 0.$$

In terms of current and resistance, these are

$$E - i_2 R_2 - i_1 R_1 = 0,$$
$$E - i_3 R_3 - i_1 R_1 = 0.$$

We now have three equations for i_1, i_2, and i_3. Writing them in matrix form with constants on the right side of the equal sign yields

$$1i_1 - 1i_2 - 1i_3 = 0,$$
$$R_1 i_1 + R_2 i_2 + 0i_3 = E,$$
$$R_1 i_1 + 0i_2 + R_3 i_3 = E.$$

The coefficients one and zero have been included in the equations as a reminder to include them in the coefficient matrix:

$$C = \begin{bmatrix} 1 & -1 & -1 \\ R_1 & R_2 & 0 \\ R_1 & 0 & R_3 \end{bmatrix} \qquad r = \begin{bmatrix} 0 \\ E \\ E \end{bmatrix}.$$

Substituting the known values, we get

$$C = \begin{bmatrix} 1 & -1 & -1 \\ 30 & 40 & 0 \\ 30 & 0 & 50 \end{bmatrix} \qquad r = \begin{bmatrix} 0 \\ 12 \\ 12 \end{bmatrix}.$$

In Excel, the coefficient matrix and right-hand-side vector are entered as

	A	B	C	D	E	F	G	H	I
1	**Multiloop Circuits I**								
2									
3		[C]	1	-1	-1		[r]	0	
4			30	40	0			12	
5			30	0	50			12	
6									

A quick check with Excel's `MDETERM()` array function shows that a solution is possible:

C7 | f_x =MDETERM(C3:E5)

	A	B	C	D	E	F	G	H	I
1	**Multiloop Circuits I**								
2									
3		[C]	1	-1	-1		[r]	0	
4			30	40	0			12	
5			30	0	50			12	
6									
7	**Determinant:**		4700						
8									

So the coefficient matrix is inverted by using the `MINVERSE()` array function:

C9 | f_x {=MINVERSE(C3:E5)}

	A	B	C	D	E	F	G	H	I
1	**Multiloop Circuits I**								
2									
3		[C]	1	-1	-1		[r]	0	
4			30	40	0			12	
5			30	0	50			12	
6									
7	**Determinant:**		4700						
8									
9		[Cinv]	0.43	0.01	0.01				
10			-0.32	0.02	-0.01				
11			-0.26	-0.01	0.01				
12									

The currents are found by multiplying the inverted [C] matrix and the [r] vector, using Excel's `MMULT()` array function:

H9 | f_x {=MMULT(C9:E11,H3:H5)}

	A	B	C	D	E	F	G	H	I
1	**Multiloop Circuits I**								
2									
3		[C]	1	-1	-1		[r]	0	
4			30	40	0			12	
5			30	0	50			12	
6									
7	**Determinant:**		4700						
8									
9		[Cinv]	0.43	0.01	0.01		[i]	0.23	**amp**
10			-0.32	0.02	-0.01			0.13	
11			-0.26	-0.01	0.01			0.10	
12									

The unknown currents have been found to be $i_1 = 0.23$, $i_2 = 0.13$, and $i_3 = 0.10$ amp, respectively.

Wheatstone Bridge I

A fairly commonly used circuit in instrumentation applications is the *Wheatstone Bridge*, shown in the accompanying figure. The bridge contains two known resistances, R_1 and R_2, and an adjustable resistance (i.e., a potentiometer). In use, the setting on the potentiometer is adjusted until points a and b are at the same voltage. Then the known resistances can be used to calculate an unknown resistance, shown as R_3 in the diagram:

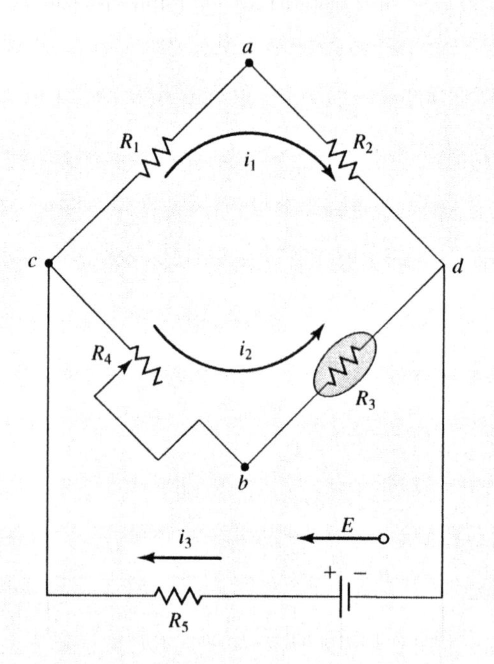

R_1 and the potentiometer, R_4, are connected at point c, and the circuit has been adjusted to have the same potential at points a and b, so the voltage drops across R_1 and R_4 must be equal:

$$V_1 = V_4. \tag{6}$$

But the voltages can be written in terms of current and resistance:

$$i_1 R_1 = i_2 R_4. \tag{7}$$

Similarly, the voltage drops across R_2 and R_3 must be equal, so

$$V_2 = V_3, \tag{8}$$

or

$$i_1 R_2 = i_2 R_3. \tag{9}$$

Solving one equation for i_1 and substituting into the other yields an equation for the unknown resistance, R_3, in terms of the known resistance values:

$$R_3 = R_4 \frac{R_2}{R_1}. \tag{10}$$

a. Given the known resistances and battery potential listed in the accompanying table, what is the resistance of R_3 when the potentiometer (R_4) has been adjusted to 24 ohms to balance the bridge?
b. Use Kirchhoff's laws to find currents i_1 through i_3.

Known Values	
E	12 volts
R_1	20 ohms
R_2	10 ohms
R_5	100 ohms

First, the known values are entered into the spreadsheet:

	A	B	C	D	E
1	**Wheatstone Bridge I**				
2					
3		E:	12	volts	
4		R1:	20	ohms	
5		R2:	10	ohms	
6		R4:	24	ohms	
7		R5:	100	ohms	
8					

Then the unknown resistance, R_3, is computed:

C9 =C6*(C5/C4)

	A	B	C	D	E
1	**Wheatstone Bridge I**				
2					
3		E:	12	volts	
4		R1:	20	ohms	
5		R2:	10	ohms	
6		R4:	24	ohms	
7		R5:	100	ohms	
8					
9		R3:	12	ohms	
10					

To find the currents, we need three equations to solve for the three unknowns. First, Kirchhoff's current law can be applied at point d:

$$i_1 + i_2 = i_3.$$

Then, the voltage law can be applied to the outer loop so that

$$E - V_5 - V_1 - V_2 = 0,$$

or, in terms of current and voltage,

$$E - i_3R_5 - i_1R_1 - i_1R_2 = 0.$$

Finally, the voltage law can be applied to the inner loop, so

$$E - V_5 - V_4 - V_3 = 0,$$

or

$$E - i_3R_5 - i_2R_4 - i_2R_3 = 0.$$

In matrix form, these equations become

$$C = \begin{bmatrix} 1 & 1 & -1 \\ R_1 + R_2 & 0 & R_5 \\ 0 & R_4 + R_3 & R_5 \end{bmatrix} \quad r = \begin{bmatrix} 0 \\ E \\ E \end{bmatrix}. \tag{11}$$

In Excel, the coefficient matrix and right-hand-side vector are

B13 fx =C4+C5

	A	B	C	D	E	F	G	H
11								
12	[C]	1	1	-1		[r]	0	
13		30	0	100			12	
14		0	36	100			12	
15								

The coefficient matrix is then inverted:

B16 fx {=MINVERSE(B12:D14)}

	A	B	C	D	E	F	G	H
11								
12	[C]	1	1	-1		[r]	0	
13		30	0	100			12	
14		0	36	100			12	
15								
16	[Cinv]	0.469	0.018	-0.013				
17		0.391	-0.013	0.017				
18		-0.141	0.005	0.004				
19								

It is next multiplied by the right-hand-side vector to find the currents:

G16 | f_x {=MMULT(B16:D18,G12:G14)}

	A	B	C	D	E	F	G	H
11								
12	[C]	1	1	-1		[r]	0	
13		30	0	100			12	
14		0	36	100			12	
15								
16	[Cinv]	0.469	0.018	-0.013		[i]	0.056	amp
17		0.391	-0.013	0.017			0.047	
18		-0.141	0.005	0.004			0.103	
19								

The results are

$$i_1 = 0.056 \text{ amp},$$
$$i_2 = 0.047 \text{ amp}, \quad (12)$$
$$i_3 = 0.103 \text{ amp}.$$

APPLICATION: CONDUCTION HEAT TRANSFER

The differential equation

$$\frac{\partial T}{\partial t} = \frac{k}{\rho\, C_p}\left[\frac{\partial^2 T}{\partial x^2} + \frac{\partial^2 T}{\partial y^2}\right]$$

describing energy conduction through a two-dimensional region can be applied to a surface exposed to various boundary temperatures. We might want to know the temperature distribution in a 50-cm- × -40-cm metal plate exposed to boiling water (100°C) along two edges, ice water (0°C) on one edge, and room temperature (25°C) along another, as represented in the following diagram:

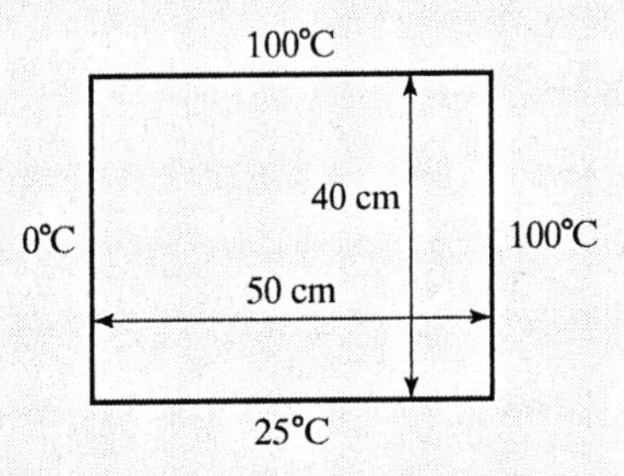

At steady state, $\frac{\partial T}{\partial t} = 0$, the equation simplifies considerably, to a form known as *Laplace's equation*:

$$0 = \frac{\partial^2 T}{\partial x^2} + \frac{\partial^2 T}{\partial y^2}$$

The partial derivatives can be approximated by using finite differences to produce the algebraic equation

$$0 = \left[\frac{T_{i+1,j} - 2T_{i,j} + T_{i-1,j}}{(\Delta x)^2}\right] + \left[\frac{T_{i,j+1} - 2T_{i,j} + T_{i,j-1}}{(\Delta y)^2}\right],$$

where subscript i,j represents a point on the plate at which the temperature is $T_{i,j}$; $T_{i-1,j}$ represents the temperature at a point to the left of i,j; and $T_{i,j-1}$ represents the temperature at a point above i,j, as indicated in the following diagram:

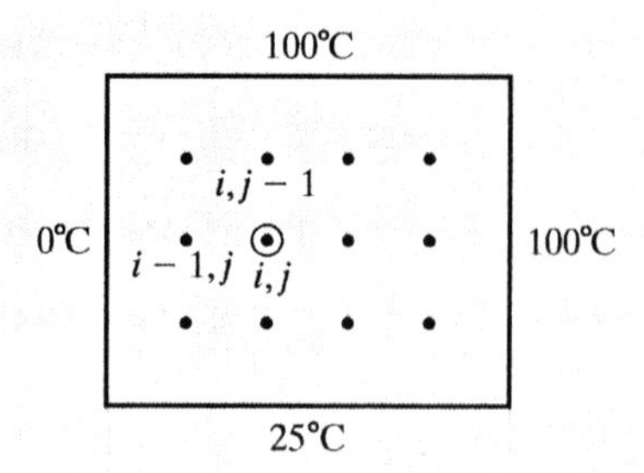

And, if we choose to make $\Delta x = \Delta y$, we get a particularly simple result:

$$0 = \lfloor T_{i+1,j} - 2T_{i,j} + T_{i-1,j} \rfloor + \lfloor T_{i,j+1} - 2T_{i,j} + T_{i,j-1} \rfloor,$$

or

$$4\,T_{i,j} = \lfloor T_{i+1,j} + T_{i-1,j} \rfloor + \lfloor T_{i,j+1} + T_{i,j-1} \rfloor \qquad \text{(general equation)}.$$

This equation says that the sum of the temperatures at the four points around any central point (i.e., any i,j) is equal to four times the temperature at the central point. (Remember, this is true only at steady state and only when $\Delta x = \Delta y$.) We can apply this equation at each interior point to develop a system of equations that, when solved simultaneously, will yield the temperatures at each point.

To help see how this is done, let's assign each interior point a letter designation and show the four points surrounding point A with a circle:

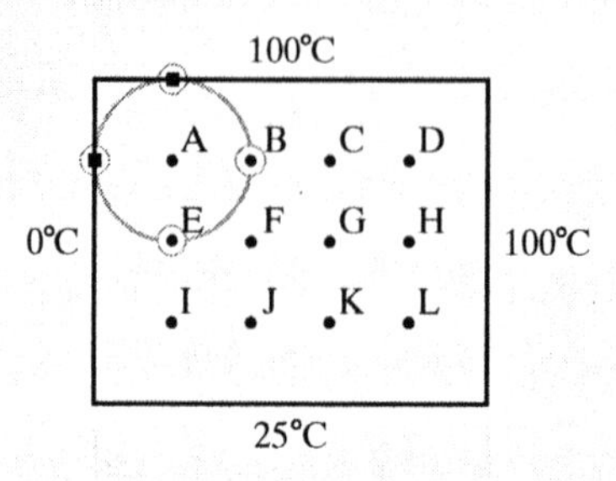

Applying the general equation at point A yields

$$4\,T_A = 0 + 100 + T_B + T_E$$

Then, we move the circle to point B:

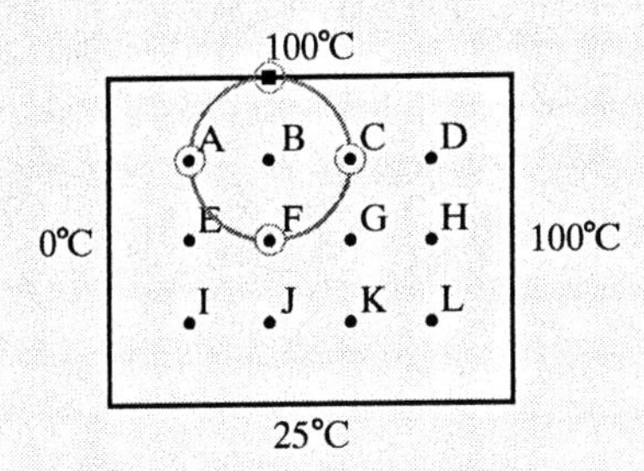

Applying the general equation at point B yields

$$4\,T_B = T_A + 100 + T_C + T_F$$

By continuing to apply the general equation at each interior point (points A through L), we generate 12 equations, one for each interior point:

$$\begin{aligned}
4\,T_A &= 0 + 100 + T_B + T_E\\
4\,T_B &= T_A + 100 + T_C + T_F\\
4\,T_C &= T_B + 100 + T_D + T_G\\
4\,T_D &= T_C + 100 + 100 + T_H\\
4\,T_E &= 0 + T_A + T_F + T_I\\
4\,T_F &= T_E + T_B + T_G + T_J\\
4\,T_G &= T_F + T_C + T_H + T_K\\
4\,T_H &= T_G + T_D + 100 + T_L\\
4\,T_I &= 0 + T_E + T_J + 25\\
4\,T_J &= T_I + T_F + T_K + 25\\
4\,T_K &= T_J + T_G + T_L + 25\\
4\,T_L &= T_K + T_H + 100 + 25
\end{aligned}$$

In matrix form, these equations can be written as

$$[C][T] = [r]$$

where

$$[C] = \begin{bmatrix}
-4 & 1 & 0 & 0 & 1 & 0 & 0 & 0 & 0 & 0 & 0 & 0\\
1 & -4 & 1 & 0 & 0 & 1 & 0 & 0 & 0 & 0 & 0 & 0\\
0 & 1 & -4 & 1 & 0 & 0 & 1 & 0 & 0 & 0 & 0 & 0\\
0 & 0 & 1 & -4 & 0 & 0 & 0 & 1 & 0 & 0 & 0 & 0\\
1 & 0 & 0 & 0 & -4 & 1 & 0 & 0 & 1 & 0 & 0 & 0\\
0 & 1 & 0 & 0 & 1 & -4 & 1 & 0 & 0 & 1 & 0 & 0\\
0 & 0 & 1 & 0 & 0 & 1 & -4 & 1 & 0 & 0 & 1 & 0\\
0 & 0 & 0 & 1 & 0 & 0 & 1 & -4 & 0 & 0 & 0 & 1\\
0 & 0 & 0 & 0 & 1 & 0 & 0 & 0 & -4 & 1 & 0 & 0\\
0 & 0 & 0 & 0 & 0 & 1 & 0 & 0 & 1 & -4 & 1 & 0\\
0 & 0 & 0 & 0 & 0 & 0 & 1 & 0 & 0 & 1 & -4 & 1\\
0 & 0 & 0 & 0 & 0 & 0 & 0 & 1 & 0 & 0 & 1 & -4
\end{bmatrix}
\quad [T] = \begin{bmatrix} T_A\\ T_B\\ T_C\\ T_D\\ T_E\\ T_F\\ T_G\\ T_H\\ T_I\\ T_J\\ T_K\\ T_L \end{bmatrix}
\quad [r] = \begin{bmatrix} -100\\ -100\\ -100\\ -200\\ 0\\ 0\\ 0\\ -100\\ -25\\ -25\\ -25\\ -125 \end{bmatrix}$$

The coefficient and right-hand-side (constant-value) matrices can be entered into Excel:

	A	B	C	D	E	F	G	H	I	J	K	L	M	N	O	P	Q	R
1	**Heat Conduction**																	
2																		
3			**A**	**B**	**C**	**D**	**E**	**F**	**G**	**H**	**I**	**J**	**K**	**L**				
4	**[C]**	**A**	-4	1	0	0	1	0	0	0	0	0	0	0		**[r]**	-100	
5		**B**	1	-4	1	0	0	1	0	0	0	0	0	0			-100	
6		**C**	0	1	-4	1	0	0	1	0	0	0	0	0			-100	
7		**D**	0	0	1	-4	0	0	0	1	0	0	0	0			-200	
8		**E**	1	0	0	0	-4	1	0	0	1	0	0	0			0	
9		**F**	0	1	0	0	1	-4	1	0	0	1	0	0			0	
10		**G**	0	0	1	0	0	1	-4	1	0	0	1	0			0	
11		**H**	0	0	0	1	0	0	1	-4	0	0	0	1			-100	
12		**I**	0	0	0	0	1	0	0	0	-4	1	0	0			-25	
13		**J**	0	0	0	0	0	1	0	0	1	-4	1	0			-25	
14		**K**	0	0	0	0	0	0	1	0	0	1	-4	1			-25	
15		**L**	0	0	0	0	0	0	0	1	0	0	1	-4			-125	
16																		

Now the coefficient matrix can be inverted and then multiplied by the [r] vector to find the temperatures at the interior points:

	A	B	C	D	E	F	G	H	I	J	K	L	M	N	O	P	Q	R
17																		
18	**[Cinv]**		-0.3	-0.1	-0	-0	-0.1	-0.1	-0	-0	-0	-0	-0	-0		**[T]**	50.4	$=T_A$
19			-0.1	-0.3	-0.1	-0	-0.1	-0.1	-0.1	-0	-0	-0	-0	-0		(°C)	70.6	$=T_B$
20			-0	-0.1	-0.3	-0.1	-0	-0.1	-0.1	-0.1	-0	-0	-0	-0			81.4	$=T_C$
21			-0	-0	-0.1	-0.3	-0	-0	-0.1	-0.1	-0	-0	-0	-0			90.2	$=T_D$
22			-0.1	-0.1	-0	-0	-0.3	-0.1	-0.1	-0	-0.1	-0.1	-0	-0			31.1	$=T_E$
23			-0.1	-0.1	-0.1	-0	-0.1	-0.4	-0.1	-0.1	-0.1	-0.1	-0.1	-0			50.8	$=T_F$
24			-0	-0.1	-0.1	-0.1	-0.1	-0.1	-0.4	-0.1	-0	-0.1	-0.1	-0.1			64.7	$=T_G$
25			-0	-0	-0.1	-0.1	-0	-0.1	-0.1	-0.3	-0	-0	-0.1	-0.1			79.5	$=T_H$
26			-0	-0	-0	-0	-0.1	-0.1	-0	-0	-0.3	-0.1	-0	-0			23.2	$=T_I$
27			-0	-0	-0	-0	-0.1	-0.1	-0.1	-0	-0.1	-0.3	-0.1	-0			36.6	$=T_J$
28			-0	-0	-0	-0	-0	-0.1	-0.1	-0.1	-0	-0.1	-0.3	-0.1			47.3	$=T_K$
29			-0	-0	-0	-0	-0	-0	-0.1	-0.1	-0	-0	-0.1	-0.3			62.9	$=T_L$
30																		

KEY TERMS

Array
Array function
Coefficient matrix
Determinant
Fill handle
Invert
Laplace's equation
Linear combination
Matrix
Nonsingular
Right-hand-side vector
Scalar
Singular
System of linear algebraic equations
Transpose
Unknown vector
Vector

SUMMARY

Basic Matrix Math Operations

Matrix Multiplication by a Scalar — Use basic cell arithmetic
Adding Two Matrices — Use basic cell arithmetic
Multiplying Two Matrices — Use array function `MMULT ( )`
Transposing a Matrix, two methods:

- Use Edit/Copy and then Edit/Paste Special/Transpose
- Use array function `TRANSPOSE ( )`

Invert a Matrix — Use array function `MINVERSE ( )`
Matrix Determinant — Use array function `MDETERM ( )`
Completing an Array Function — Use [Ctrl-Shift-Enter] to tell Excel to enter the matrix function into every cell of the result matrix.

Solving Simultaneous Linear Equations

1. Write the equations in the matrix form [C][x] = [r]:

$$3x_1 + 2x_2 = 7,$$
$$4x_1 + 6x_2 = 9, \tag{13}$$

becomes

$$\begin{bmatrix} 3 & 2 \\ 4 & 6 \end{bmatrix}\begin{bmatrix} x_1 \\ x_2 \end{bmatrix} = \begin{bmatrix} 7 \\ 9 \end{bmatrix} \tag{14}$$

2. Invert the coefficient matrix [C], using array function `MINVERSE()` to get the inverted coefficient matrix:

$$[C_{inv}] \tag{15}$$

3. Multiply the inverted coefficient matrix $[C_{inv}]$ and the right-hand-side vector [r] to get the solution vector

$$[x]. \tag{16}$$

That is,

$$[C_{inv}][C][x] = [C_{inv}][r],$$
$$[x] = [C_{inv}][r]. \tag{17}$$

Problems

Simultaneous Equations I

1. Use Excel's `MDETERM()` array function to see whether there is a solution to the simultaneous equations represented by each of the coefficient and right-hand-side matrices shown.

a. $C = \begin{bmatrix} 3 & 0 & 5 \\ 8 & 7 & 8 \\ 0 & 3 & 7 \end{bmatrix} \quad r = \begin{bmatrix} 3 \\ 8 \\ 2 \end{bmatrix},$

b. $C = \begin{bmatrix} 1 & 2 & 0 \\ 0 & 1 & 1 \\ 2 & 5 & 1 \end{bmatrix} \quad r = \begin{bmatrix} 4 \\ 3 \\ 3 \end{bmatrix},$

c. $C = \begin{bmatrix} 4 & 3 & 3 \\ 3 & 8 & 4 \\ 3 & 2 & 8 \end{bmatrix} \quad r = \begin{bmatrix} 7 \\ 3 \\ 2 \end{bmatrix}.$

If the solution exists, solve the equations by using matrix methods.

Simultaneous Equations II

2. Write the following sets of simultaneous equations in matrix form, and check the determinant to see whether there is a solution:

a.
$$\begin{aligned} 0x_1 + 7x_2 + 1x_3 &= 3, \\ 3x_1 + 6x_2 + 3x_3 &= 8, \\ -3x_1 + 8x_2 - 1x_3 &= 2. \end{aligned}$$

b.
$$\begin{aligned} 1x_1 + 8x_2 + 4x_3 &= 0, \\ -1x_1 + 1x_2 + 7x_3 &= 7, \\ 6x_1 + 7x_2 - 2x_3 &= 3. \end{aligned}$$

c.
$$\begin{aligned} 6x_1 + 5x_2 - 1x_3 + 6x_4 &= 0, \\ -2x_1 + 2x_2 + 2x_3 + 2x_4 &= 1, \\ 1x_1 - 1x_2 + 1x_3 - 2x_4 &= 1, \\ 7x_1 - 3x_2 + 8x_3 + 4x_4 &= 4. \end{aligned}$$

If a solutions exists, solve the equations using matrix methods.

Simultaneous Equations III

3. Write the following sets of simultaneous equations in matrix form and solve the new equations (if possible):

a.
$$\begin{aligned} 3x_1 + 1x_2 + 5x_3 &= 20, \\ 2x_1 + 3x_2 - 1x_3 &= 5, \\ -1x_1 + 4x_2 \quad &= 7. \end{aligned}$$

b.
$$\begin{aligned} 6x_1 + 2x_2 + 8x_3 &= 14, \\ x_1 + 3x_2 + 4x_3 &= 5, \\ 5x_1 + 6x_2 + 2x_3 &= 7. \end{aligned}$$

c.
$$\begin{aligned} 4y_1 + 2y_2 + y_3 + 5y_4 &= 52.9, \\ 3y_1 + y_2 + 4y_3 + 7y_4 &= 74.2, \\ 2y_1 + 3y_2 + y_3 + 6y_4 &= 58.3, \\ 3y_1 + y_2 + y_3 + 3y_4 &= 34.2. \end{aligned}$$

Multiloop Circuits II

4. Find the currents i_1 through i_3 in the following circuit (the battery potential and the resistances are tabulated):

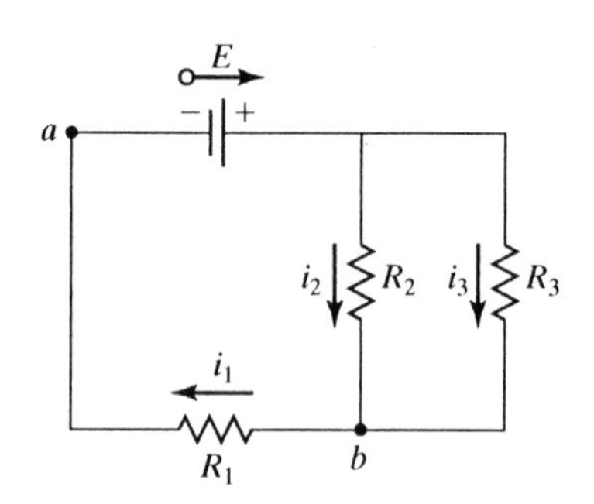

KNOWN VALUES	
E	12 volts
R_1	10 ohms
R_2	20 ohms
R_5	50 ohms

Material Balances on a Gas Absorber

5. The following equations are material balances for CO_2, SO_2, and N_2 around the gas absorber shown in the accompanying figure.

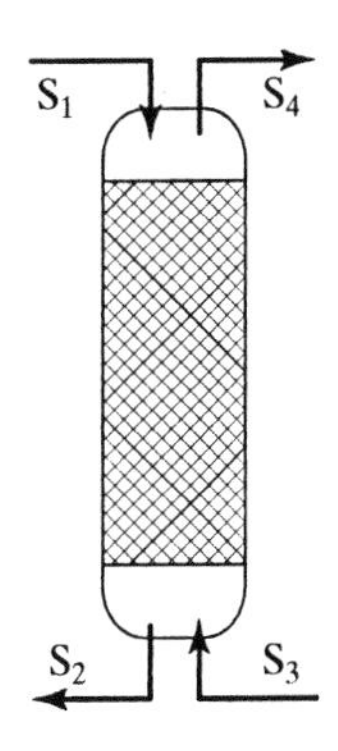

Stream S_1 is known to contain 99 mole % monoethanolamine (MEA) and 1 mole % CO_2. The flow rate in S_1 is 100 moles per minute. The compositions (mole fractions) used in the material balances are tabulated as

	S_1	S_2	S_3	S_4
CO_2	0.01000	0.07522	0.08000	0.00880
SO_2	0	0.01651	0.02000	0.00220
N_2	0	0	0.90000	0.98900
MEA	0.99000	0.90800	0	0

CO_2 Balance:	CO_2 in S_1 + CO_2 in S_3 = CO_2 in S_2 + CO_2 in S_4
	$1 \text{ mole} + 0.08000 \cdot S_3 = 0.07522 \cdot S_2 + 0.00880 \cdot S_4$
SO_2 Balance:	SO_2 in S_1 + SO_2 in S_3 = SO_2 in S_2 + SO_2 in S_4
	$0 + 0.02000 \cdot S_3 = 0.01651 \cdot S_2 + 0.00220 \cdot S_4$
N_2 Balance:	N_2 in S_1 + N_2 in S_3 = N_2 in S_2 + N_2 in S_4
	$0 + 0.90000 \cdot S_3 = 0 + 0.98900 \cdot S_4$

Solve the material balances for the unknown flow rates, S_2 through S_4.

Material Balances on an Extractor

6. This problem focuses on a low-cost, high-performance, chemical extraction unit: a drip coffee maker. The ingredients are water, coffee solubles (CS), and coffee grounds (CG). Stream S_1 is water only, and the coffee maker is designed to hold 1 liter of it. Stream S_2 is the dry coffee placed in the filter and contains 99% grounds and 1% soluble ingredients. The product coffee (S_3) contains 0.4% CS and 99.6% water. Finally, the waste product (S_4) contains 80% CG, 19.6% water, and 0.4% CS. (All percentages are on a volume basis.) The following is a diagram of the unit:

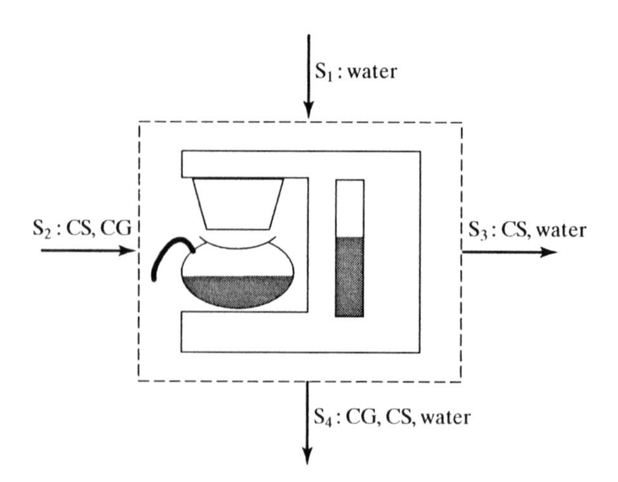

Write material balances on water, CS, and CG. Then solve the material balances for the volumes S_2 through S_4.

Flash Distillation

7. When a hot, pressurized liquid is pumped into a tank (flash unit) at a lower pressure, the liquid boils rapidly. This rapid boiling is called a flash. If the liquid contains a mixture of chemicals, the vapor and liquid leaving the flash unit will have different compositions, and the flash unit can be used as a separator. The physical principle involved is vapor–liquid equilibrium; the vapor and liquid leaving the flash unit are in equilibrium. This allows the composition of the outlet streams to be determined from the operating temperature and pressure of the flash unit. Multiple flash units can be used together to separate multicomponent mixtures.

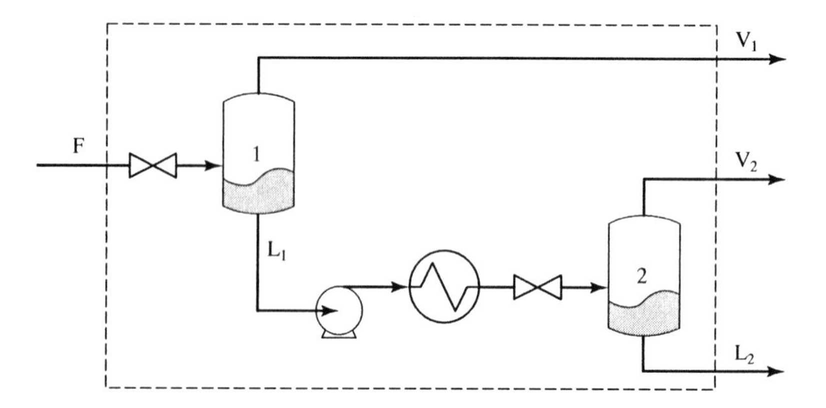

A mixture of methanol, butanol, and ethylene glycol is fed to a flash unit (Unit 1) operating at 165°C and 7 atm. The liquid from the first flash unit is recompressed, reheated, and sent to a second flash unit (Unit 2) operating at 105°C and 1 atm. The mixture is fed to the process at a rate of 10,000 kg/h. Write material balances for each chemical, and solve for the mass flow rate of each product stream (V_1, V_2, L_2). A material balance is simply a mathematical statement that all of the methanol (for example) going into the process has to come out again. (This assumes a steady state and no chemical reactions.) The following methanol balance is shown as an example:

$$\text{methanol in } F = \text{methanol in } V_1 + \text{methanol in } V_2 + \text{methanol in } L_2$$
$$0.300 \cdot (10{,}000 \text{ kg/h}) = 0.716 \cdot V_1 + 0.533 \cdot V_2 + 0.086 \cdot L_2$$

The compositions of the feed stream F and of the three product streams are listed here:

COMPONENT	MASS FRACTION IN STREAM			
	F	V_1	V_2	L_2
Methanol	0.300	0.716	0.533	0.086
Butanol	0.400	0.268	0.443	0.388
Ethylene Glycol	0.300	0.016	0.024	0.526

Wheatstone Bridge II

8. Because the resistances of metals vary with temperature, measuring the resistance of a metal sensor inserted in a material is one way to determine the temperature of the material. Resistance temperature detectors (RTDs) are devices commonly used to make temperature measurements.

   To compute the resistance of the RTD, it can be built into a Wheatstone bridge as the unknown resistance—R_3 in the following figure:

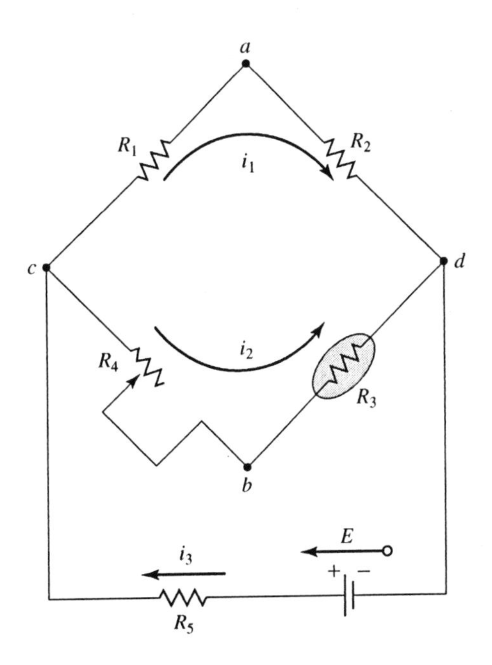

Once the bridge has been balanced, the unknown resistance can be computed from the known resistances, R_1 and R_2, and the setting on the potentiometer, R_4:

$$R_3 = R_4 \frac{R_2}{R_1} \tag{18}$$

The temperature can be determined from the resistance as

$$R_T = R_0[1 + \alpha T], \quad (19)$$

where

R_T is the resistance at the unknown temperature, T;
R_0 is the resistance at 0°C (known, one of the RTD specifications); and
α is the linear temperature coefficient (known, one of the RTD specifications).

a. For the known resistances and battery potential listed below, what is the resistance of the RTD when the potentiometer (R_4) has been adjusted to 24 ohms to balance the bridge?
b. Use Kirchhoff's laws to find currents i_1 through i_3.

KNOWN VALUES	
E	24 volts
R_1	15 ohms
R_2	15 ohms
R_5	40 ohms

9

Arrays and Matrix Operations

1 THE PRIMARY MATLAB DATA STRUCTURE

As we have previously stated, the basic data element in the MATLAB system is the array. A scalar is represented as a 1×1 array—that is, an array with one row and one column. Vectors are one-dimensional arrays. An $m \times 1$ array is called a *column vector*, where m is the number of rows in the single-column array. A $1 \times n$ array is called a *row vector*, where n is the number of columns in the single-row array. Array elements may be numbers, characters, strings, other arrays, or structures. Recall that the elements in an array must be uniform. A special type of array, called a cell array, allows nonuniform elements.

MATLAB supports multidimensional arrays. A *matrix* is a special case of an array. A matrix is a rectangular array containing elements of any specified algebraic system, usually real or complex numbers. The English mathematician Arthur Cayley first introduced the concept of a matrix in the mid-19th century. Matrices are employed to help solve systems of linear equations and to perform linear transformations. This chapter describes several applications of matrix algebra to scientific and engineering problems.

MATLAB arrays are, by default, self-dimensioning. That is, if we initialize an array with a set of values, MATLAB automatically allocates the correct amount of space for the array. If you append an element to an array, MATLAB automatically resizes the array to handle the new element. This is different from many programming languages, where memory allocation and array sizing takes a considerable amount of programming effort.

SECTION

OBJECTIVES

After reading this chapter, you should be able to

- Create arrays and matrices.
- Access elements in arrays and matrices.
- Add, modify, and delete elements from arrays.
- Perform element-by-element arithmetic operations on arrays.
- Perform vector and matrix multiplication.
- Perform matrix exponentiation.
- Compute the transpose, determinant, and inverse of a matrix.

Matrix A consisting of m rows and n columns is said to be of *order* $m \times n$. If $m = n$, then matrix A is called a *square matrix*. The following matrix A is a square matrix of order three:

$$A = \begin{bmatrix} 2 & 4 & 6 \\ 3 & 5 & 7 \\ 1 & 2 & 3 \end{bmatrix}$$

Recall that you can reference the cells in a matrix by subscripts, representing the row number and column number, respectively. Thus, A(2,3) = 7. We call the collection of cells in a matrix for which the row numbers equal the column numbers the *main diagonal*. The main diagonal of A is [2, 5, 3].

2 ENTERING ARRAYS AND MATRICES

You can create arrays and matrices several ways in MATLAB. You have already been shown how to enter arrays in the Command window by typing text commands. There are several other ways to enter arrays in MATLAB. You can enter arrays by loading a script file that creates the arrays. You can view and edit arrays and matrices by using a graphical user interface called the Array Editor. Finally, you can quickly enter several types of special matrices by using some of MATLAB's built-in matrix generators.

2.1 Command Line Entry

Let us review how to enter arrays in the Command window. The syntax includes brackets for the whole array and delimiters for rows and columns. Elements in the same row are separated by commas or spaces. A new row is created by using a semicolon or a new line. The whole array is bracketed by square braces. The array

$$\begin{bmatrix} 1 & 3 & 5 \\ 2 & 4 & 6 \\ 7 & 7 & 7 \end{bmatrix}$$

is entered as

```
>> [1, 3, 5; 2, 4, 6; 7, 7, 7]
ans =
     1     3     5
     2     4     6
     7     7     7
```

You can also create the same array by using spaces to separate the elements in the same row instead of commas:

```
>> [1 3 5; 2 4 6; 7 7 7];
```

You can also create the same array by moving to a new line every time you designate a new row:

```
>> [1 3 5
   2 4 6
   7 7 7]
```

Note that the continuation symbol (...) is not required.

Moreover, you can enter array elements in series more concisely by using the *colon operator*.

2.2 The Array Editor

The Array Editor is a graphical interface that displays the contents of workspace objects and allows you to edit them. If the Workspace window is not visible, select **View → Workspace** from the Menu bar. Enter the following command in the Command window:

```
>> A = 5 : 0.5 : 7
A =
     5.0000     5.5000     6.0000     6.5000     7.0000
```

The workspace contents will now include a 1×5 array named A as depicted in Figure 1.

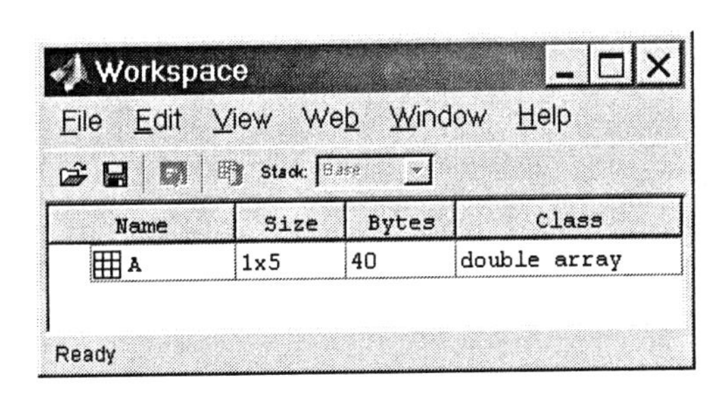

Figure 1. The Workspace window.

To see the Array Editor window, you should double-click anywhere on the line of the variable that you want to edit. In our example, click the mouse on the variable A in the Workspace window. The Array Editor will appear as depicted in Figure 2.

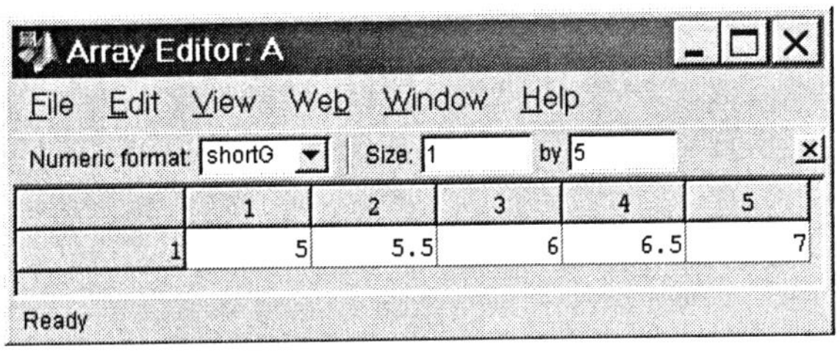

Figure 2. The Array Editor.

From the Array Editor, you can click on any cell in the array and edit the cell contents. You, can also change the array dimensions by changing the sizes in the window titled "Size". You can modify the display format by choosing a format from the drop-down menu titled "Numeric format".

2.3 Formatting Output

Numbers may be formatted several ways for display on the screen. The formatting does not affect the way the numbers are stored internally. Table 1 describes the MATLAB numeric formats. The numeric formats that you choose in the Array Editor window will return to the default of type "short" when you exit MATLAB. If you want to save your favorite format, then choose **File → Preferences → Array Editor** from the Menu bar. Preferences saved in this manner will persist when you exit and restart MATLAB.

TABLE 1. Numeric Formats.

Type	Format	Precision
short	fixed point, scaled	5 digits
short e	floating point	5 digits
short g	fixed or floating point (most accurate)	as many significant figures as possible with 5 digits
long	fixed point, scaled	15 digits
long e	floating point	15 digits
long g	fixed or floating point (most accurate)	as many significant figures as possible with 15 digits
rat	rational expression	approximates a rational fraction
hex	hexadecimal	base 16

You can also modify the display format by using the *format* command in the Command window. In addition, you can change the display format by choosing **File → Preferences → Command Window** from the Menu bar. The syntax of the *format* command is

```
format format-type
format ('format-type')
format
```

where *format-type* is one of the types listed in Table 1. Note that every MATLAB command may be represented in command form or functional form. The *command form* uses the command name followed by one or more spaces and then uses the command arguments—for example,

```
>> format long
```

The *functional form* uses the command named, followed by the arguments (if any) in parentheses. When using the functional form, you must place quotes around a string argument—for example,

```
>> format ('long')
```

We will not repeat the functional form in every example in the text, but it is understood that it may be used in place of the command form. The functional form is useful when programming because it allows you to manipulate the argument as a variable.

The *format* command without arguments resets the format to the default type. The default format is "short".

In addition to numeric formats, the *compact* and *loose formats* may be used to add or to delete extra line feeds in the display. Here are some examples:

```
>> format loose
>> log(2)

ans =

    0.6931

>> format compact
>> log(2)
ans =
    0.6931
```

If you forget what format you are utilizing, you can display the current format by using the *get* function. The *get* function gets an object attribute—in this case, the *format* attribute. The first argument is the number of the graphics object that contains the attribute. A graphics object in MATLAB is simply a named graphical structure (e.g., the Command window). The object number for the Command window screen is 0, as shown here:

```
>> get(0, 'format')
ans =
long
```

As an aside, you can see all of the attributes for an object by using the *get* function with the object number alone as an argument. The following command returns all of the attributes of the Command window:

```
>> get(0)
    CallbackObject = []
    Language = english
    CurrentFigure = []
    Diary = off
    DiaryFile = diary
    Echo = off
    ErrorMessage = Error: Expected a variable,
                   function, or constant, found ")".
    FixedWidthFontName = Courier
    Format = long
    ...
    (many more lines of output)
```

2.4 Built-In Matrix Generators

We use several types of arrays so frequently that MATLAB has provided special functions to support the generation of these arrays. We call a matrix in which all of the elements are zero a *zero matrix*. You can create a zero array or matrix by using the *zeros* function. The syntax of the *zeros* function is

```
zeros(dim1, dim2, dim3, ...)
```

If you specify a single, scalar parameter *dim1*, MATLAB returns a square zero matrix of order *dim1*. For example, the following command creates a 2 × 2 matrix of zeros:

```
>>A = zeros(2)
A =
     0     0
     0     0
```

If you specify multiple parameters, a multidimensional zero array of order *dim1* × *dim2* × *dim3*... is returned. The following command creates a 2 × 4 matrix of zeros:

```
>> A = zeros(2, 4)
A =
     0     0     0     0
     0     0     0     0
```

We call a matrix in which all of the elements are the number one a *ones matrix*. You can create a ones matrix by using the *ones* function. The syntax of the *ones* function is identical to the syntax of the *zeros* function. The following command creates a 3 × 2 matrix of ones:

```
>> A = ones(3, 2)
A =
      1     1
      1     1
      1     1
```

Similarly, you can generate an array of pseudorandom numbers by using one of MATLAB's several random array generator functions. One of these, the *rand* function, generates an array of random numbers whose elements are uniformly distributed in the range (0, 1). A uniform distribution is one in which there is an equal probability of occurrence for any value within the given range (0, 1)—for example,

```
>> A = rand(2,5)
A =
     0.9501    0.6068    0.8913    0.4565    0.8214
     0.2311    0.4860    0.7621    0.0185    0.4447
```

Another commonly used matrix form is the identity matrix. An *identity matrix* is a matrix in which every element of the main diagonal is one and every other element is zero. You can generate an $n \times n$ identity matrix by using the *eye* function with the syntax, as shown here:

```
eye(n)
```

Here is an example:

```
>> eye(3)
ans =
      1     0     0
      0     1     0
      0     0     1
```

You can use two arguments to specify both dimensions. An $m \times n$ identity matrix with ones on the diagonal and zeros elsewhere can be generated by using the syntax

```
eye(m,n)
```

For example, we might have

```
>> eye(4,3)
ans =
      1     0     0
      0     1     0
      0     0     1
      0     0     0
```

The *eye* function does not support more than two dimensions. Specifying more than two dimensions will result in a syntax error—for example,

```
>> A = eye(3,4,5)
??? Error using ==> eye
Too many input arguments.
```

3 ACCESSING AND MANIPULATING ARRAY ELEMENTS

3.1 Accessing Elements of an Array

You have already accessed array elements by using subscripts. Let us review what you have learned and cover a few more tricks for accessing array elements. We will use the following two-dimensional array *A* for the next few examples:

```
>> A = [1 3 5; 2 4 6; 3 5 7]
A =
      1     3     5
      2     4     6
      3     5     7
```

An element in a two-dimensional array can be accessed by using two subscripts, the first for the row and the second for the column; for example,

```
>> A(2,3)
ans =
      6
```

You can also access elements in a two-dimensional array by using a single subscript. In this case, imagine the columns lay end to end as follows:

```
A = [ 1
      2
      3
      3
      4
      5
      5
      6
      7 ]
```

This makes more sense if we look at how MATLAB stores arrays internally. Data are stored internally in a linear sequence of memory locations. MATLAB stretches out an array into a single sequence for storage.

We think of array *A* as a two-dimensional array. If *A* were stored one row at a time in memory, it might look like this:

```
1 3 5 2 4 6 3 5 7
```

This is called *row-major order*. However, if *A* were stored one column at a time in memory, it would look like the following:

```
1 2 3 3 4 5 5 6 7
```

This is called *column-major order*. MATLAB stores arrays in column-major order. MATLAB functions are written to take advantage of the underlying storage mechanism to speed up array operations.

The following examples demonstrate how to access an array element by using a single subscript:

```
>> A(1)
ans =
      1
>> A(4)
```

```
ans =
      3
>> A(8)
ans =
      6
```

We have already used the colon operator to generate arrays. You can also use the colon operator to access multiple array elements simultaneously. You do this by using the colon operator to define a subscript range. For example, the use of 1:2:9 as a subscript returns the first, third, fifth, seventh, and ninth elements of *A*:

```
>> A(1:2:9)
ans =
      1      3      4      5      7
```

When used alone, the colon denotes all rows or columns. The following command returns all columns of row two from array *A*:

```
>> A(2,:)
ans =
      2      4      6
```

The following command returns the second and third rows of the first and second columns from array *A*:

```
>> A(2:3, 1:2)
ans =
      2      4
      3      5
```

3.2 Expanding the Size of an Array

You can dynamically expand an array simply by adding more elements—for example,

```
>> A = [3 5 7]
A =
      3      5      7
>> A = [A 9]
A =
      3      5      7      9
```

When appending arrays to multidimensional arrays, the newly appended parts must conform to the dimensions of the original array. For example, if adding a new row to a two-dimensional array, the row must have the same number of columns as the original array:

```
>> A = [3 5 7];
>> B = [1 3 5];
>> C = [A; B]
C =
      3      5      7
      1      3      5
```

If you try to append to an array and the appended part does not conform dimensionally, an error will result. Here's an example:

```
>> A = [3 5 7];
>> B = [2 4];
```

```
>> C = [A; B]
??? Error using ==> vertcat
All rows in the bracketed expression must have the same
number of columns.
```

PROGRAMMING TIP 11

MATLAB supports preallocation of arrays by allowing the creation of an array that is filled with all zeros or ones. If you are using very large arrays in your programs, preallocation is more efficient than slowly growing an array.

If you know the size of your array ahead of time (e.g., 20,000), create a zero-filled array by using

```
zero(20000);
```

which is much faster than extending the size of the array one element at a time.

3.3 Deleting Array Elements

You can delete array elements by replacing them with the empty array, which we designate as []. In the following example, the second element of vector *A* is removed:

```
>> A = [3 5 7];
>> A(2) = []
A =
       3     7
```

You cannot remove a single element from a multidimensional array, since the array would no longer be conformant. This results in an error, as shown in this example:

```
>> A = [1 3 5; 2 4 6]
A =
       1     3     5
       2     4     6
>> A(2,3) = []
???  Indexed empty matrix assignment is not allowed.
```

You can use the colon operator in deletion operations. The colon operator allows deletion of whole rows or columns. In the next example, the second row of the 2×3 array *A* is removed:

```
>> A = [1 3 5; 2 4 6]
A =
       1     3     5
       2     4     6
>> A(2,:) = []
A =
       1     3     5
```

The following example removes the first, third, and fifth columns from array *A*:

```
>> A = [1 2 3 4 5 6; 7 8 9 10 11 12]
A =
       1     2     3     4     5     6
       7     8     9    10    11    12
```

```
>> A(:, 1:2:5) = []
A =
     2     4     6
     8    10    12
```

PRACTICE 1!

Let array

```
>> A = [ 1 0 1 0
         0 2 0 2
         3 1 3 1 ]
```

Write commands that will perform each of the following operations on array A:

1. Return the second column of A.
2. Return the first and third rows of A.
3. Delete the first and second columns of A.
4. Append the column vector `[7; 8; 9]` to A.

Re-create array A again before each problem. Check your answers by using MATLAB.

4 ELEMENT-BY-ELEMENT ARRAY OPERATIONS

4.1 Array Addition

MATLAB performs addition or subtraction of two arrays of the same order by adding or subtracting each pair of respective elements. The result is an array of the same order. For example, given that

$$A = [1\ 3\ 5] \text{ and } B = [10\ 12\ 14]$$

$A + B$ is calculated as follows:

$$[A(1) + B(1)\ \ A(2) + B(2)\ \ A(3) + B(3)] = [11\ 15\ 19].$$

Here is another example, this time we are using two-dimensional arrays. Given that

$$A = \begin{bmatrix} 1 & 3 & 5 \\ 2 & 4 & 6 \\ 7 & 7 & 7 \end{bmatrix}$$

and

$$B = \begin{bmatrix} -5 & 6 & 14 \\ 0 & -2 & 4 \\ 2 & 8 & 3 \end{bmatrix}$$

the sum of A and B is

$$A + B = \begin{bmatrix} -4 & 9 & 19 \\ 2 & 2 & 10 \\ 9 & 15 & 10 \end{bmatrix}$$

If two arrays are not of the same order, we say they are not *conformable* for addition or subtraction. For example, the following matrices C and D are not conformable for addition or subtraction because C's dimensions are 1×3 and D's dimensions are 2×3:

```
>> C = [1,3,5]
C =
      1     3     5

>> D = [2,4,6;3,5,7]
D =
      2     4     6
      3     5     7

>> C + D
??? Error using ==> +
Matrix dimensions must agree.
```

As you see, attempting to add them will result in an error.

The addition of arrays is commutative—that is,

$$A + B = B + A.$$

The addition and subtraction of arrays is associative—that is,

$$A + (B + C) = (A + B) + C.$$

4.2 Array Multiplication

MATLAB performs array multiplication by multiplying each pair of respective elements in two arrays of the same order. The symbol for array multiplication is a period followed by an asterisk (.*). The following example demonstrates array multiplication:

```
>> A = [1, 3, 5; 2, 4, 6]
A =
      1     3     5
      2     4     6

>> B = [2, 3, 4; -1, -2, -3]
B =
      2     3     4
     -1    -2    -3

>> A .* B
ans =
      2     9    20
     -2    -8   -18
```

To be conformable for array multiplication, the two arrays must be of the same order, unless one array is a scalar, in which case, each element of the other array is multiplied by the scalar—for example,

```
>> A = [5]
A =
      5

>> B = [2, 4, 6]
B =
      2     4     6

>> A .* B
ans =
     10    20    30
```

In this case (where at least one operand is a scalar), the period before the multiplication symbol is not required. The "*" alone will produce the same result. (See Section 5.2, titled "Matrix Multiplication" for details.) Here's an example:

```
>> A*B
ans =
     10     20     30
```

4.3 Array Right Division

MATLAB performs array right division of arrays *A* and *B* by dividing each element in array *A* by the respective element in array *B*. The symbol for array right division is a period followed by a forward slash (./). To be conformable for array right division, the two arrays must be of the same order, unless one array is a scalar. The following example demonstrates array right division:

```
>> A = [2, 4, 6]
A =
     2     4     6

>> B = [2, 2, 2]
B =
     2     2     2

>> A./B
ans =
     1     2     3
```

4.4 Array Left Division

MATLAB performs array left division of arrays *A* and *B* by dividing each element in array *B* by the respective element in array *A*. The symbol for array left division is a period followed by a back slash (.\). To be conformable for array left division, the two arrays must be of the same order, unless one array is a scalar. The following example demonstrates array left division, using the arrays *A* and *B* from the previous example:

```
>> A.\B
ans =
    1.0000    0.5000    0.3333
```

4.5 Array Exponentiation

MATLAB performs array exponentiation of arrays *A* and *B* by raising each element in array *A* to the power of its respective element in array *B*. The symbol for array exponentiation is a period followed by the caret symbol (.^). To be conformable for array exponentiation, the two arrays must be of the same order, unless one array is a scalar. The following example demonstrates array exponentiation:

```
>> A = [2, 3, 4]
A =
     2     3     4

>> B = [3, 2, 0.5]
B =
    3.0000    2.0000    0.5000
```

```
>> A.^B
ans =
     8     9     2
```

PRACTICE 2!

Given

```
A = [2 0 2; 1 0 1]
```

and

```
B = [4 4 4; 9 9 9]
```

calculate the following by hand:

```
1. A + B
2. A * 3
3. A .* 3
4. A .^ 3
5. (A + B) ./ B
6. (A + B) ./ A
```

Use MATLAB to check your answers.

5 BINARY MATRIX OPERATIONS

A binary operation is a mathematical computation performed by using two matrices as inputs. Binary matrix operations are not as straightforward to compute as element-by-element operations. Binary matrix operations have many applications, such as the solution of systems of linear equations.

5.1 Vector Multiplication

We will first describe vector multiplication mathematically and then show you how to perform the operation by using MATLAB. Two vectors a and b are multiplied by computing their dot product. The *dot product*, sometimes called the *inner product*, is calculated by adding the products of each pair of respective elements in vectors a and b. To be conformable for vector multiplication a must be a row vector and b must be a column vector. In addition, the vectors must contain the same number of elements, unless one is a scalar. If row vector

$$\mathrm{a} = [a_1 \quad a_2 \quad \ldots \quad a_n],$$

and column vector

$$\mathrm{b} = \begin{bmatrix} b_1 \\ b_2 \\ \ldots \\ b_n \end{bmatrix}$$

the dot product

$$\mathrm{a} \cdot \mathrm{b} = a_1b_1 + a_2b_2 + \ldots + a_nb_n.$$

The MATLAB symbol for vector multiplication is the asterisk (*)—for example,

```
A = [1, 5, -6]
A =
     1  5  -6
B = [-2; -4; 0]
B =
    -2
    -4
     0
C = A * B
C = -22
```

The result was calculated as follows:

```
A*B = (1*-2) + (5*-4) + (-6*0) = -22
```

Note how this differs from array multiplication, which would fail, since A and B are not conformable for array multiplication.

If you attempt to use nonconformable vectors, MATLAB returns an error. Here's an example:

```
>> A = [1, 2, 3]
A =
      1      2      3

>> B = [2, 3, 4]
B =
      2      3      4

>> A * B
??? Error using ==> *
Inner matrix dimensions must agree.
```

5.2 Matrix Multiplication

MATLAB performs the multiplication of matrix A by a scalar by multiplying each element of A by the scalar. Any array or matrix can be multiplied by a scalar. The following is an example:

```
A = [1, 3; -2, 0]
A =
     1   3
    -2   0
B = A * 5
B =
     5  15
   -10   0
```

MATLAB performs multiplication of nonscalar A and B by computing the dot products of each row in A with each column in B. Each result becomes a row in the resulting matrix. We will try to make this clearer by walking through an example:

```
>> A = [1 3 5; 2 4 6]
A =
     1      3      5
     2      4      6
```

```
>> B = [-2 4; 3 8; 12 -2]
B =
      -2     4
       3     8
      12    -2
```

Note that the number of rows in $A(m_A = 2)$ equals the number of columns in $B(n_B = 2)$. To be conformable for matrix multiplication, the number of rows in A must equal the number of columns in B. The result will be an $m_A \times n_B$ matrix. In the example, the result will be a 2×2 matrix.

The first step is to compute the dot product of row one of A and column one of B:

```
(1 * -2) + (3 * 3) + (5 * 12)= 67
```

Place the result in cell (1, 1) of the result matrix. Next, compute the dot product of row one of A and column two of B:

```
(1 * 4) + (3 * 8) + (5 * -2)= 18
```

Place the result in cell (1, 2) of the result matrix. Next, compute the dot product of row two of A and column one of B:

```
(2 * -2) + (4 * 3) + (6 * 12)= 80
```

Place the result in cell (2, 1) of the result matrix. Finally, compute the dot product of row two of A and column two of B:

```
(2 * 4) + (4 * 8) + (6 * -2)= 28
```

Place the result in cell (2, 2) of the result matrix. The resulting product is

```
>> A*B
ans =
      67    18
      80    28
```

For most cases of A and B, matrix multiplication is not commutative; that is,

$$AB \neq BA.$$

5.3 Matrix Division

The operations for left and right matrix division are not straightforward. We will not walk through the underlying algorithm for their computation in this text. However, we will show you an application of the left matrix division operator.

A common and useful application of matrices is the representation of systems of linear equations. The linear system

$$\begin{aligned} 3x_1 + 2x_2 + x_3 &= 5 \\ x_1 + 2x_2 + 3x_3 &= 13 \\ -5x_1 - 10x_2 - 5x_3 &= 0 \end{aligned}$$

can be represented compactly as the matrix product $AX = B$:

$$\begin{bmatrix} 3 & 2 & 1 \\ 1 & 2 & 3 \\ -5 & -10 & -5 \end{bmatrix} \begin{bmatrix} x_1 \\ x_2 \\ x_3 \end{bmatrix} = \begin{bmatrix} 5 \\ 13 \\ 0 \end{bmatrix}$$

MATLAB uses a complex algorithm to compute the solution to a linear system of the form $AX = B$. The operation is denoted by the matrix left division operator (the backslash) $X = A \backslash B$.

The solution to the preceding linear system can be determined as follows:

```
>> A = [3 2 1; 1 2 3; -5 -10 -5];
>> B = [5; 13; 0];
>> X = A\B
X =
     2.5000
    -4.5000
     6.5000
```

Verify that MATLAB produced a correct answer by substituting the results into the original three equations. You will learn more about solutions to linear systems when you take a course in linear algebra.

PRACTICE 3!

Given vectors

```
A = [ 2 -3 4 0]
B = [ 4; -12; 4; -12]
C = [ 2 12 0 0]
```

compute the following operations by hand and then check your answers by using MATLAB:

```
1. A * B
2. A * C
3. B * C
4. C * B
```

Given the matrices

```
A = [ 12 4; 3 -5]
B = [ 2 12; 0 0]
```

compute the following operations by hand and then check your answers by using MATLAB:

```
5. A * B
6. B * A
```

6 UNARY MATRIX OPERATIONS

Unary matrix operations are mathematical computations that are performed by using a single matrix as an input.

6.1 Transpose

We call the matrix that is created by exchanging the rows and columns of matrix A the *transpose* of A. For example, given

$$A = \begin{bmatrix} 1 & 2 & 3 \\ 4 & 5 & 6 \\ 7 & 8 & 9 \end{bmatrix}$$

the transpose of A, denoted in mathematics as A^T, is

$$A^T = \begin{bmatrix} 1 & 4 & 7 \\ 2 & 5 & 8 \\ 3 & 6 & 9 \end{bmatrix}$$

The MATLAB prime operator (') returns the transpose of its argument—for example,

```
>> A = [1, 2, 3; 4, 5, 6; 7, 8, 9]
A =
        1        2        3
        4        5        6
        7        8        9
>> A'
ans =
        1        4        7
        2        5        8
        3        6        9
```

6.2 Determinant

The *determinant* of a matrix is a transformation of a square matrix that results in a scalar. We denote the determinant of a matrix A mathematically as $|A|$ or $\det A$. In this text, we will use the second notation, since it resembles the MATLAB function for computing a determinant.

If a matrix has a single entry, then the determinant of the matrix is the value of the entry. For example, if $A = [3]$, the determinant of $A = 3$. We write this as

$$\det A = 3.$$

If a square matrix A has order 2, then the determinant of A is calculated as follows:

$$\det\begin{bmatrix} a_{11} & a_{12} \\ a_{21} & a_{22} \end{bmatrix} = a_{11} \cdot a_{22} - a_{21} \cdot a_{12}$$

MATLAB has a function that computes the determinant named *det*. The syntax for the *det* function is

```
det (A)
```

where A must be a square matrix—for example,

```
A =
        2        3
        6        4
>> det(A)
ans =
    -10
```

First, we will show you how to calculate mathematically the determinant of a matrix with order $n > 2$. Then we will show you how to use MATLAB to perform the same computation.

The strategy for calculating the determinant of a matrix with order $n > 2$ involves subdividing the matrix into smaller sections called *minors* and *cofactors*. If row i and column j of a square matrix A are deleted, the determinant of the resulting matrix is called the minor of a_{ij}. We denote the minor as M_{ij}. For example, given

$$A = \begin{bmatrix} 1 & 2 & 3 \\ 4 & 5 & 6 \\ 7 & 8 & 9 \end{bmatrix}$$

then the minor of a_{12} (deleting row 1 and column 2) is

$$M_{12} = \det\begin{bmatrix} 4 & 6 \\ 7 & 9 \end{bmatrix}.$$

The cofactor of a_{ij} is denoted as A_{ij} and is calculated as follows:

$$A_{ij} = (-1)^{i+j} M_{ij}.$$

In our example, the cofactor of a_{12} is

$$A_{12} = (-1)^{1+2}((4 \cdot 9) - (6 \cdot 7)) = 6.$$

The general form for the calculation of a determinant is

$$\det A = a_{i1}A_{i1} + a_{i2}A_{i2} + \cdots + a_{in}A_{in}$$

where i is any row in square matrix A of order n. The answer is the same no matter which row is chosen. A similar formula works by choosing any column in A. Let us follow the example and expand A around row 2:

$$\begin{aligned} \det A &= 4 \cdot (-1)^{2+1} \cdot \det\begin{bmatrix} 2 & 3 \\ 8 & 9 \end{bmatrix} + 5 \cdot (-1)^{2+2} \cdot \det\begin{bmatrix} 1 & 3 \\ 7 & 9 \end{bmatrix} \\ &\quad + 6 \cdot (-1)^{2+3} \cdot \det\begin{bmatrix} 1 & 2 \\ 7 & 8 \end{bmatrix} \\ &= (-4 \cdot -6) + (5 \cdot -12) + (-6 \cdot -6) \\ &= 0. \end{aligned}$$

We find that by using MATLAB to compute the determinant of A results in

```
A =
        1      2      3
        4      5      6
        7      8      9

>> det(A)
ans =
        0
```

As you can see, the determinant of a high order matrix is tedious to calculate by hand. Moreover, because the calculation of a higher order determinant is computationally intensive and involves a series of recursive steps, the rounding error can be significant.

6.3 Inverse

The *inverse* of a square matrix A, if it exists, is defined to be a square matrix such that

$$AA^{-1} = I,$$

where I is the identity matrix of the same order as A. The matrix inverse operation is denoted mathematically by using a negative one exponent, A^{-1}.

There is a method for determining if and when the inverse of a matrix exists. It depends on understanding the concept of matrix *singularity*. A square matrix is singular if and only if its determinant is equal to zero. Otherwise, a matrix is nonsingular. Furthermore, a square matrix has an inverse if and only if it is nonsingular. So, a square matrix A has an inverse if and only if $det(A) \neq 0$.

However, on a computer, zero is not always zero. Computer representations of real numbers are usually approximations. Thus, calculations can result in highly accurate, but approximate results. If the determinant of a matrix is close to zero, MATLAB will give a warning that the inverse of A may not be correct.

The syntax for MATLAB's inverse function *inv* is

```
inv(square-matrix)
```

Recall from the previous example that the determinant of the matrix

```
A =
      1     2     3
      4     5     6
      7     8     9
```

is singular (i.e., $det(A) = 0$) and should not have an inverse. MATLAB returns a warning noting this:

```
>> inv(A)
Warning: Matrix is close to singular or badly scaled.
         Results may be inaccurate. RCOND = 1.541976e-
         018.

ans =
   1.0e+016 *
    -0.4504     0.9007    -0.4504
     0.9007    -1.8014     0.9007
    -0.4504     0.9007    -0.4504
```

6.4 Matrix Exponentiation

MATLAB computes the positive integer power of a square matrix A by multiplying A times itself the requisite number of times. The multiplication operation that is performed is matrix multiplication, not element-by-element multiplication—for example,

```
>> A = [1, 2; 3, 4]
A =
      1     2
      3     4

>> A^2
ans =
      7    10
     15    22

>> A^3
ans =
     37    54
     81   118
```

The negative integer power of a square matrix A is computed by performing matrix multiplication of the inverse of A the requisite number of times. For example, to compute the second negative root of A, we type

```
>> A^-2
ans =
     5.5000   -2.5000
    -3.7500    1.7500
```

This only works if the matrix is nonsingular. MATLAB issues a warning if the computed determinant of A is equal or very close to zero. Here's an example:

```
>> A = [1,1; 0,0]
A =
     1     1
     0     0

>> det(A)
ans =
     0

>> A^-2
Warning: Matrix is singular to working precision.
ans =
   Inf   Inf
   Inf   Inf
```

PRACTICE 4!

Given the square matrices

```
A = [ 2 0; 1 -5]
B = [ 3 -2 0; 4 1 5; 0 -3 4]
```

compute the following operations by hand and then check your answers by using MATLAB:

```
1. A'
2. det(A)
3. B'
4. det(B)
```

`Compute the following with MATLAB:`

```
5. A^2
6. inv(A)
7. inv(B)
8. A^-2
```

7 MULTIDIMENSIONAL ARRAYS

We have previously used examples of two-dimensional arrays. Many of MATLAB's array operations can be extended to more than two dimensions.

The following command creates a three-dimensional array of order $2 \times 3 \times 2$. Since MATLAB cannot display the whole array at once, it displays the array a page at a time. There are two pages in the following example, as the third dimension takes two levels:

```
>> A = ones(2,3,2)
A(:,:,1) =
     1     1     1
     1     1     1
```

```
A(:,:,2) =
     1     1     1
     1     1     1
```

8 USEFUL ARRAY FUNCTIONS

MATLAB contains scores of useful functions for manipulating and extracting information from arrays. This section presents a few of the most commonly used array functions.

ndims

The *ndims* function returns the number of dimensions of its argument—for example,

```
>> A = ones(2,3,2);
>> ndims(A)
ans =
     3
```

size

The *size* function returns the length of each dimension, or the order of the array. The result is a vector that contains the size of dimension 1, dimension 2, dimension 3, etc. Here's an example,

```
>> A = zeros(2,3,2,4);
>> size(A)
ans =
     2     3     2     4
```

You can also use the size function to return the size of each dimension to a separate variable—for example,

```
>> [m, n, s, t] = size(A)
m =
     2
n =
     3
s =
     2
t =
     4
```

diag

The *diag* function returns the elements of the main diagonal. For a matrix, *diag* returns the elements with equal row and column indices (i.e., elements (1,1), (2,2), (3,3), etc.):

```
>> A = [1 3 5; 2 4 6; 0 2 4]
A =
     1     3     5
     2     4     6
     0     2     4
```

```
>> diag(A)
ans =
     1
     4
     4
```

The main diagonal is also called the *zero diagonal*. A second argument may be passed to *diag* that specifies the nth diagonal above or below zero. If the second argument is positive, the nth diagonal above the zero diagonal is returned, as in this example:

```
>> diag(A,1)
ans =
     3
     6
```

If the second argument is negative, the nth diagonal below the zero diagonal is returned. Here's an example:

```
>> diag(A,-1)
ans =
     2
     2
```

length

The *length* function returns the length of the largest dimension of an array. For a one-dimensional array (vector), this equals the number of elements in the vector. The length of A in the following example is three, which is the size of the largest dimension:

```
>> A = [1 3; 2 4; 0 2];
>> length(A)
ans =
     3
```

reshape

The *reshape* function reshapes an array. It has the syntax

```
reshape(A, m, n, p, ...)
```

where A is the array to be reshaped, and $m, n, p, \ldots$ are the new dimensions. The number of elements in the old array must equal the number of elements in the new array. Consider the array

```
>> A = ones(2,6,2);
```

Since the number of elements in $A = 2 \times 6 \times 2 = 24$, we should be able to reshape A into any order in which the product of the dimensions equals 24—for example,

```
>> reshape(A,2,12)
ans =
     1  1  1  1  1  1  1  1  1  1  1  1
     1  1  1  1  1  1  1  1  1  1  1  1
```

An attempt to reshape an array into a nonconforming array results in an error. Here's an example:

```
>> reshape(A,3,5)
??? Error using ==> reshape
To RESHAPE the number of elements must not change.
```

We shall consider another example. The following transformation makes sense, since you know that MATLAB stores arrays in column-major order:

```
>> A = [ 1 2 3; 4 5 6; 7 8 9; 10 11 12]
A =
     1     2     3
     4     5     6
     7     8     9
    10    11    12
>> reshape(A, 2, 6)
ans =
     1     7     2     8     3     9
     4    10     5    11     6    12
```

sort

The *sort* function sorts arrays. When used on a vector, the sort is in ascending order:

```
>> A = [4 2 3 9 1 2];
>> sort(A)
ans =
     1     2     2     3     4     9
```

When used on a two-dimensional array, MATLAB performs the sort on each column:

```
>> A = [5 0 4; 2 2 1]
A =
     5     0     4
     2     2     1
>> sort(A)
ans =
     2     0     1
     5     2     4
```

For more than two dimensions, MATLAB performs the sort on the first dimension with the size greater than one. We call a dimension of size one a *singleton dimension*. Another way of stating this rule is that the sort is performed on the first nonsingleton dimension.

You can specify the dimension on which to sort as a second argument. For example, if we want to sort the two-dimensional array *A* across rows instead of down columns, we could use the following command:

```
>> A = [5 0 4; 2 2 1]
A =
     5     0     4
     2     2     1
>> sort(A,2)
ans =
     0     4     5
     1     2     2
```

You can perform descending sorts by using the colon operator.

max, min, mean, median

The *max*, *min*, *mean*, and *median* functions each work in a similar fashion to the *sort* function. Given a vector argument, the functions return the maximum, minimum, mean, or median value, respectively. If given a two-dimensional array, each function returns a vector that contains the result of the operation on each column.

Because these functions each work in a similar fashion, we will demonstrate their use with the *min* function. First, we will use a vector as an example:

```
>> A = [ 3 2 -6 1 10];
>> min(A)
ans =
     -6
```

Next, we will show an example that uses a two-dimensional array:

```
>> A = [ 2 1 3; 4 2 2; 5 0 -2]
A =
       2      1      3
       4      2      2
       5      0     -2
>> min(A)
ans =
       2      0     -2
```

Note that *min* returns the minimum for each column.

PRACTICE 5!

Each of the five columns in matrix A represents the four exam grades for a student in a MATLAB programming class:

```
A = [ 89 97 55 72 95
     100 92 63 85 91
      82 96 71 91 82
      90 98 48 83 70 ]
```

1. Give a command that sorts each student's grades and returns a matrix with the sorted grades.
2. Give a command that computes the mean of each student's grades and returns a vector with the results.
3. Give a command that computes the median of each student's grades and returns a vector with the results.
4. Give a single command that returns the overall mean grade for all five students in the course.

   Now, change your view of matrix *A*. Assume that each of the four rows in matrix *A* represents the five exam grades of a student. *Note*: Each row represents a student.
5. Give a command that sorts each student's grades and returns a matrix with the sorted grades.
6. Give a command that computes the mean of each student's grades and returns a vector with the results.
7. Give a command that computes the median of each student's grades and returns a vector with the results.
8. Give a single command that returns the overall mean grade for all five students in the course.

APPLICATION! COMMUNICATION ROUTES

The calculation of the number of communication paths is important in a variety of fields, for example, the control of network router traffic. Scientists use the same theory to model behavior in fields such as human communication, political influence, and the flow of money through organizations.

A common example, used to demonstrate principles of communication routes, is the number of roads connecting cities. In this diagram we depict four cities along with the roads connecting them:

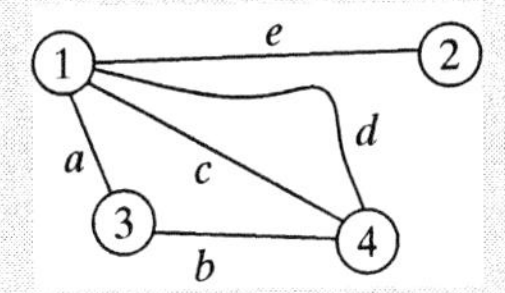

Table 2 shows the number of direct routes between each pair of cities. A direct route does not go through any intermediate city. For example, there are two direct routes between City 1 and City 4. The table expresses this information redundantly. You can see the routes between City 1 and City 4 by looking at either (row 1, column 4) or (row 4, column 1). We have presented the data in such a manner, so that it can be stored in a square matrix.

The square matrix A summarizes the connectivity between the cities. For example, $A(1,4) = 2$ indicates that there are two direct routes from City 1 to City 4:

```
A =
     0     1     1     2
     1     0     0     0
     1     0     0     1
     2     0     1     0
```

Note that A is symmetric. This means that the cells above the main diagonal are a mirror image of the cells below the diagonal when reflected along the diagonal. Symmetry is also defined as $A(n, m) = A(m, n)$ for any m and n.

It is known that the matrix A^2 represents the number of ways to travel between any two cities by passing through only one intermediate city.

```
>> B = A^2
B =
     6     0     2     1
     0     1     1     2
     2     1     2     2
     1     2     2     5
```

Matrix B summarizes the number routes between pairs of cities if the route contains one intermediate city: Note the six ways to travel from City 1 back to City 1 by passing through exactly one other city: *a–a*, *c–c*, *c–d*, *d–c*, *d–d*, and *e–e*. The two ways to travel from City 2 to City 4 by passing through exactly one other city are *e–c* and *e–d*.

We count traveling in one direction differently than traveling the same route in the opposite direction. Thus, there are two routes from City 1 to City 4, *c–d* and *d–c*.

TABLE 2. Number of routes among four cities.

	City 1	City 2	City 3	City 4
CITY 1	0	1	1	2
CITY 2	1	0	0	0
CITY 3	1	0	0	1
CITY 4	2	0	1	0

KEY TERMS

cofactor
colon operator
column-major order
column vector
command form
compact format
conformable
determinant
dot product
functional form
identity matrix
inner product
inverse
loose format
main diagonal
matrix
minor
ones matrix
order
row-major order
row vector

short format
singleton dimension
singularity
square matrix
transpose
zero diagonal
zero matrix

NEW MATLAB FUNCTIONS, COMMANDS, AND RESERVED WORDS

clock—returns current date and time
det—returns the determinant of a square matrix
diag—returns the diagonal of a matrix
etime—returns time elapsed between 2 times
eye—returns identity matrix
format—formats numeric output
get—returns the named properties of an object
inv—returns the inverse of a square matrix
length—returns the number of elements in a vector
max—returns the maximum element(s) along the first non-singleton dimension
mean—returns the mean element(s) along the first non-singleton dimension
median—returns the median element(s) along the first non-singleton dimension
min—returns the minimum element(s) along the first non-singleton dimension
ndims—returns the number of dimensions of an array
ones—returns an array of ones
rand—returns uniformly distributes pseudo-random numbers in [0,1]
reshape—reshapes an array
size—returns the order (size) of an array
sort—sorts an array in ascending order
zeros—creates an array of zeros

SOLUTIONS TO PRACTICE PROBLEMS

1.
```
1. A(:,2)
2. A(1:2:3,:)
3. A(:,1:2) = []
4. A = [A [7; 8; 9]]
```

2.
```
1. A+B = [6 4 6; 10 9 10]
2. A*3 = [6 0 6; 3 0 3]
3. A.*3 = [6 0 6; 3 0 3]
4. A.^3 = [8 0 8; 1 0 1]
5. (A + B)./B = [1.500 1.000 1.500;
                 1.1111 1.0000 1.1111]
6. (A + B)./A = Warning: Divide by zero.
                [ 3 Inf  3
                 10 Inf 10]
```

3.
```
1. A*B = 60
2. A*C = ??? Error using ==> *
         Inner matrix dimensions must agree.
3. B*C =  [ 8    48    0    0
          -24  -144    0    0
            8    48    0    0
          -24  -144    0    0]
4. C*B = -136
```

```
5. A*B = [ 24   144;    6 36 ]
6. B*A = [ 60   -52;    0   0 ]
```

4.

```
1. A'      = [ 2   1; 0 -5 ]
2. det(A)  = -10
3. B'      = [ 3       4       0
              -2       1      -3
               0       5       4 ]
4. det(B)  = 89
5. A^2 = [ 4   0; -3   25 ]
6. inv(A)  = [ 0.5000 0; 0.1000 -0.2000 ]
7. inv(B)  = [ 0.2135      0.0899     -0.1124
              -0.1798      0.1348     -0.1685
              -0.1348      0.1011      0.1236]
8. A^-2 = [ 0.2500     0; 0.0300     0.0400 ]
```

5.

```
1. sort(A)
2. mean(A)
3. median(A)
4. mean(mean(A))
5. sort(A,2)
6. mean(A,2)
7. median(A,2)
8. mean(mean(A,2))
```

Problems

Section 1.

What is the order and main diagonal of the following matrices?

1. `[3, 4; 5, 6; 7, 8]`
2. `[2 3 4 5; 6 7 8 9]`
3. `[2 1 0; 2 −3 1; 4 0 0; 3 2 1]`

Verify your answers by using appropriate MATLAB functions.

Section 2.

4. Create a vector *A* that contains the following fractions:

```
>> A
A =
    1/2 2/3 3/4 4/5 5/6
```

   What command changes your format so the vector displays rational fractions instead of decimals?

5. What command creates a `4 × 5` matrix that contains all zeros?

Section 3.

6. The loads in kilograms on the center points of five beams are
   400.3
   521.1

212.1
349.5
322.2

Create a row vector named "Loads" that contains the five values. What is a single command that replaces the second and fourth values of "Loads" with zero? What is a single command that deletes the third and fifth elements of "Loads"?

7. Re-create the original row vector "Loads" from the previous problem. The lengths in meters of the five beams are, respectively,

14.3
6.2
22.6
2.4
10.2

Create a row vector named "Lengths" that contains the five beam lengths in meters. In a single command, create a matrix named "Beams" by concatenating "Loads" and "Lengths". "Beams" should have two rows with the load values on the first row and the respective lengths on the second row. Your answer should look like the following:

```
>> Beams =
   400.3000   521.1000   212.1000   349.5000   322.2000
    14.3000     6.2000    22.6000     2.4000    10.2000
```

Section 4.

8. Assume that the loads for the five beams in Problem 6 are distributed evenly across the length of each beam. Using array arithmetic, and the original vectors "Loads" and "Lengths", create a vector that represents the average load in kg/m for each beam.

9. The command *rand*(1,*n*) produces a row vector of *n* uniformly distributed, pseudorandom numbers between 0.0 and 1.0. Use array arithmetic and the *rand* function to create 100 uniformly distributed pseudorandom numbers between 8.0 and 10.0.

Section 5.

10. Express the following linear system in matrix form as matrices A and B:

$$\begin{aligned} 3x_1 + 2x_2 &= 4 \\ -5x_1 + 10x_2 &= 0 \end{aligned}$$

11. Use the MATLAB left matrix division operator to find the solution of the linear system in the previous problem.

Section 6.

12. The transpose of the transpose of a matrix equals the original matrix. This can be stated as $(A^T)^T = A$. Using MATLAB, demonstrate that the theorem is true for the following matrix:

```
A = [1 2 4 6; 4 3 2 1].
```

13. Experiment with the transpose operator on a few example matrices. What conclusion do you reach about the main diagonal of a matrix and the main diagonal of its transpose?

14. Given a matrix representation of a system of linear equations $AX = B$, if the determinant of A equals zero, the system does not have a unique solution. Two possibilities are that the system has no solutions and that the system has an infinite number of solutions. Determine if the following system has a unique solution:

$$2x_1 + 3x_2 + 4x_3 = 10$$
$$-x_1 + 3x_2 - x_3 = 12$$
$$x_1 + \frac{3}{2}x_2 + 2x_3 = 0$$

15. The inverse of an array A multiplied by itself should equal the identity matrix of the same order as A. Show how you would test this assumption. Use matrix multiplication and the *inv*, *eye*, and *size* functions.

16. The following matrix represents the numbers of direct paths between four network routers:

	R1	R2	R3	R4
R1	0	2	1	3
R2	2	0	0	2
R3	1	0	0	2
R4	3	2	2	0

How many paths are there from router two to router four if each path passes through exactly one other router?

Section 7.

17. Create a $2 \times 4 \times 3$ array of random numbers. Replace the cell contents in the third page of the array with zeros.

18. Create a three-dimensional array of order $6 \times 2 \times 3$. Fill page one with 1's, page two with 2's, and page 3 with 3's. Can you solve the problem in a single command?

Section 8.

19. Create the following array:

$$A = [1{:}10;\ 11{:}20;\ 21{:}30].$$

Reshape A into a two-column array. What is the bottom number in each column?

Challenge Problem

20. Reread Programming Tip 1. Test the assertion in the tip by writing a program that creates a 1×20000 row vector of ones in a single command. Write another program that creates a 1×1 row vector and then builds a 1×20000 vector of ones a single cell at a time using a loop.

Time both programs and compare the efficiency of the two methods. *Hints*: The function *clock* returns a six-element vector containing the current date and time. The meaning of each element in the vector is [year, month, day, hour, minute, seconds].

The elapsed time function, *etime*(*t2*, *t1*), returns the elapsed time in seconds between time *t2* and time *t1*. The following code segment computes the time taken to execute the code between *t1* and *t2*:

```
t1 = clock
...
...
t2 = clock
ElapsedTime = etime(t2,t1)
```

10

Plotting and Graphing

SECTION

OBJECTIVES

After reading this chapter, you should be able to

- Create plots at the command line.
- Use MATLAB's graphical Plot Editor.
- Use line and marker styles.
- Label a plot.
- Create multiple plots in the same figure.
- Create log–log and semilog scaled plots.

1 INTRODUCTION

Creating plots of data sets and functions is very useful for engineers and scientists. You can use plots to present results for papers and presentations or to visually search for approximate solutions to problems. MATLAB has a rich set of plotting commands. In this chapter, we describe MATLAB's basic plotting operations.

2 THE *PLOT* COMMAND

The basic plotting command in MATLAB is *plot*. If you give the *plot* function a vector argument, MATLAB plots the contents of the vector against the indices of the vector.

The following command creates a vector Y, with 10 elements indexed from 1 to 10, that crudely approximates the sine function from zero to 4π:

```
>> Y = sin(0: 1.3: pi*4);
```

The command *plot*(Y) automatically opens the Plot Editor window and creates the plot depicted in Figure 1.

If you pass two vectors, X and Y, to the plot command, MATLAB plots the corresponding X_i, Y_i pairs and draws a single line connecting the points. The following example is a plot of two vectors—indeed, the same plot as that in the previous example (Figure 1):

```
>> X = 0 : 1.3 : pi*4;
>> Y = sin(X);
>> plot(X,Y)
```

Figure 2 shows another example, resulting from the following commands:

```
>> X = sin(0:0.1:10);
>> Y = cos(0:0.1:10);
>> plot(X,Y)
```

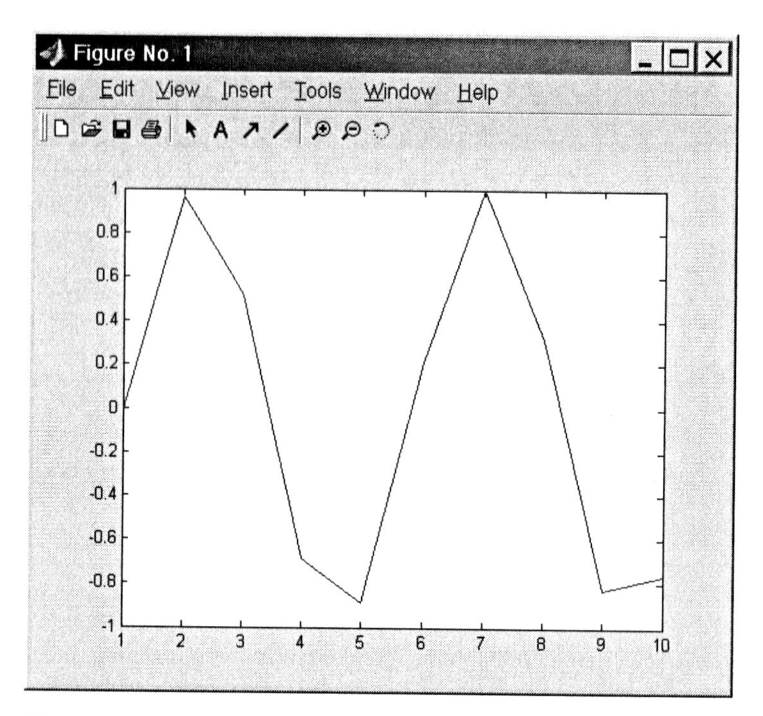

Figure 1. The Plot Editor and a plot of vector Y.

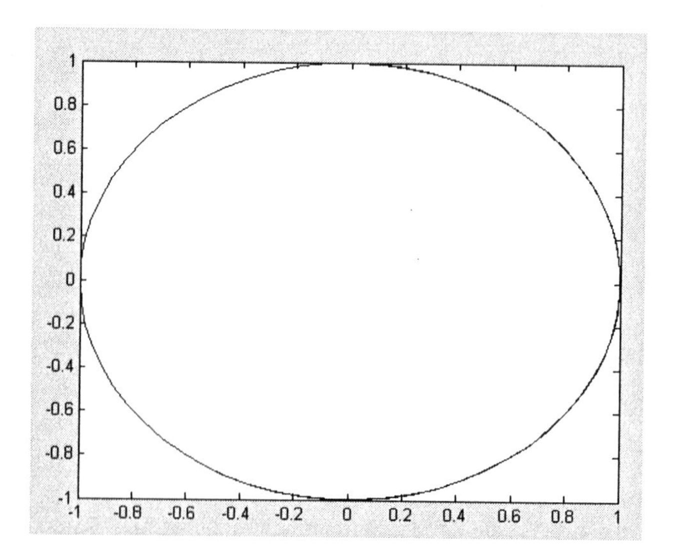

Figure 2. A plot of two vectors Y and X.

If one or both of the arguments to *plot* are matrices, then MATLAB plots the corresponding elements as before, but draws multiple connecting lines, for each column or row, depending on which is conformant. The following example plots matrix Y against vector X:

```
>> X = [9 8 7 6 5 4];
>> Y = [1 3 2 4 3 5; 12 13 14 15 16 17];
```

Since the columns of X and Y are of the same order, but the rows are not, the plot function creates two lines, one for each row. The first line is a plot of row one of Y against X. The second line is a plot of row two of Y against X. Figure 3 shows the resulting plot.

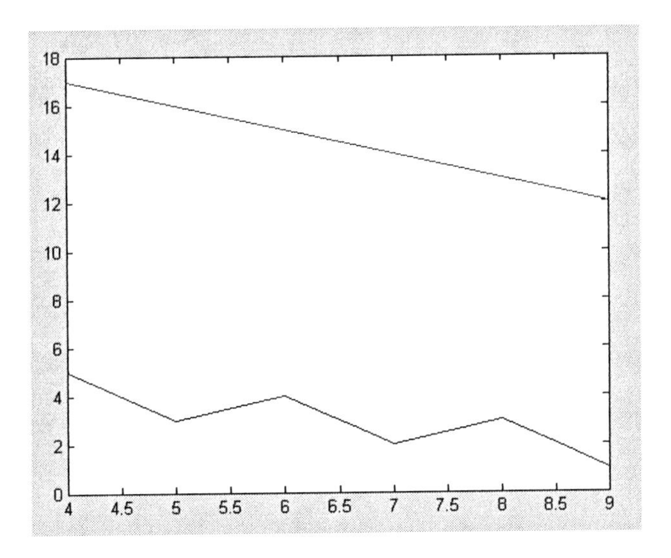

Figure 3. A plot of matrix Y versus vector X.

3 USING THE PLOT EDITOR

Choose **Insert** from the Menu bar of Plot Editor, and a drop-down menu will appear. Figure 4 shows the Insert drop-down menu of the Plot Editor. From this menu, you can insert and modify many plot elements.

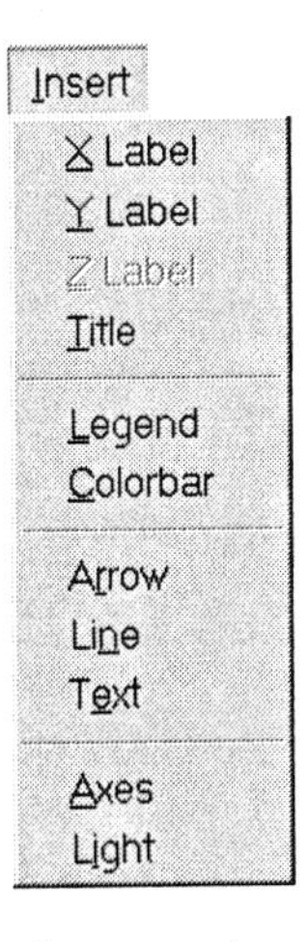

Figure 4. The Insert drop-down menu.

Click on the arrow in the Figure toolbar of the Plot Editor. (See Figure 5 for the location of the depressed arrow.) After you have clicked on the arrow, click on the plot line. The data points should appear as shown in Figure 5. Now, right click the mouse, and a drop-down menu will appear, as indicated in the figure. From this drop-down

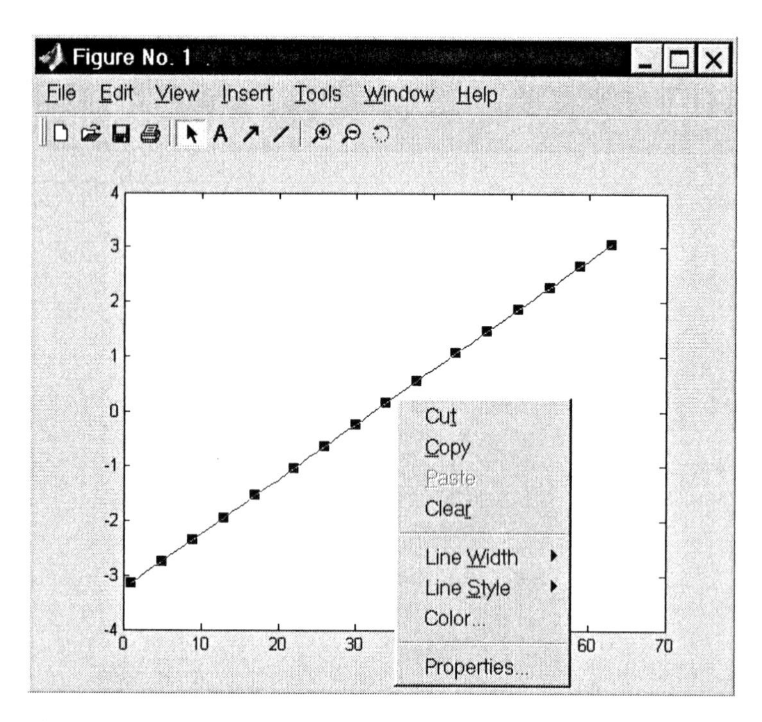

Figure 5. Changing attributes with the Plot Editor.

menu, you can change attributes of the plot line, such as the line width, line style, color, and other properties.

Oddly enough, now that we have shown you this technique, we are going to abandon it. The reason for doing so is that you can create and manipulate the same elements from the command line by using MATLAB function calls. Since this is a text on MATLAB programming, we will focus on the function calls. You should be able to figure out how to perform the same functions by using the Plot Editor on your own.

4 LINE AND MARKER STYLES

In this section, we will show you the command line options for adding and modifying the color and texture of the plot lines, as well as the command line options for changing the marker styles.

4.1 LineSpec Argument

You can control the color and texture of plot lines by using an additional argument of the *plot* command, called the line specification or *LineSpec*. This argument is a cryptic collection of characters that specifies the line character, the marker symbol, and the colors of both.

Let us look at three of these attributes as an example: the line character, the marker symbol, and the color. The available line characters are as follows:

- solid line (-)
- dashed line (- -)
- dotted line (:)
- dotted-dashed line (-.)

The default is a solid line. The marker symbol is one of 13, and the marker codes are as follows:

- point (.)
- circle (o)
- x-mark (×)
- plus (+)
- star (*)
- square (s)
- diamond (d)
- down triangle (v)
- up triangle (^)
- left triangle (<)
- right triangle (>)
- pentagram (p)
- hexagram (h)

The following are the color codes:

- r–red
- g–green
- b–blue
- c–cyan
- m–magenta
- y–yellow
- k–black
- w–white

Now we will create a plot of the sine function with a diamond-shaped marker, a dashed line, and the color red. The symbols for the dashed line, diamond marker shape, and red color are enclosed in quotes as an argument to the *plot* command. The arguments within the quotes can be placed in any order. Figure 6 displays the results, except that your results should be in color. The MATLAB code is

```
>> X = 0 : 0.4 : 4*pi;
>> Y = sin(X);
>> plot(X,Y, '- -dr')
```

4.2 Line Properties

You can control other line qualities by using property-value pairs as additional arguments to *plot*. Examples of line attributes are *LineWidth* and *MarkerSize*. You can find the complete list of line attributes by choosing **Help → Index**. Type *line* in the box labeled *Search index for*, and choose **Properties** from the resulting list. Do not forget that the Help Index feature is case sensitive: Typing *Line* will get different results than typing *line*.

Let us re-create the previous plot, but use a solid line with LineWidth = 2 and a circular marker with MarkerSize = 6. In the following command, the lowercase character *o* designates a circular marker:

```
>> plot(X,Y, '-o', 'LineWidth', 2, 'MarkerSize', 6)
```

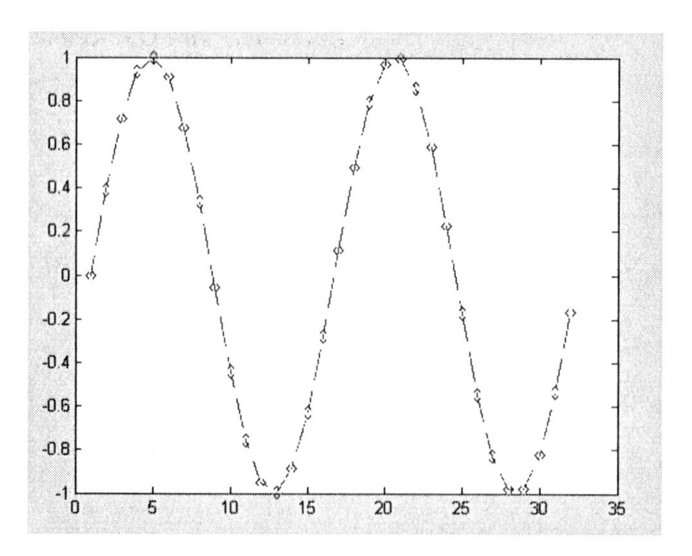

Figure 6. Sample use of the LineSpec argument.

Note that the property *names* are always placed in quotes, since they are always strings. If the property *values* are strings, place them in quotes, too. If the property *values* are numeric types, do not place them in quotes. Figure 7 shows the resulting plot.

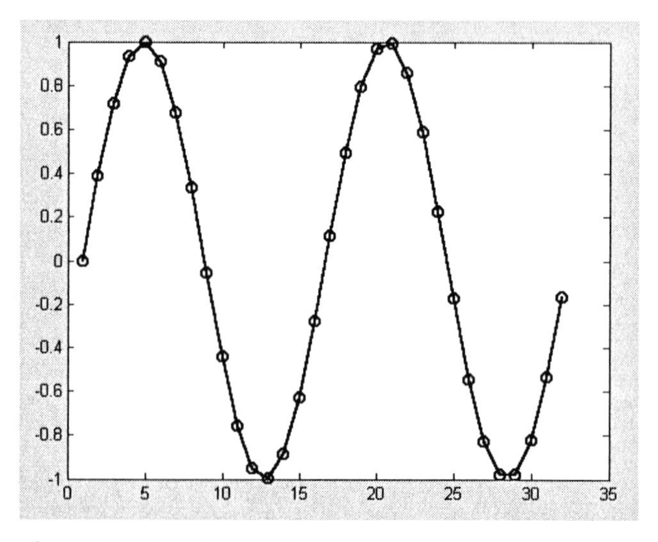

Figure 7. Sample use of line properties.

5 LABELING A PLOT

You should label a plot carefully. Plot labeling includes a title, axis labels, and if necessary, a legend. Labels, titles, legends, and other text can be created with the *xlabel, ylabel, legend, title,* and *text* commands.

5.1 Creating axis labels and titles

The *xlabel* command has several syntactic variants. The first variant takes a string argument and displays it as the X-axis label:

```
xlabel('string')
```

The second form takes a function as an argument:

```
xlabel(function)
```

The function must return a string.

You can use additional arguments to specify property-value pairs, in a manner similar to the way *Line* properties are specified in the *plot* statement. For *xlabel*, the properties are derived from the *Text* class, whereas the properties used in the *plot* statement are derived from the *Line* class. The term *class* refers to a group of characteristics shared by a group of objects.)

Some of the *Text* class properties are as follows:

- HorizontalAlignment
- FontName
- FontSize
- Color

You can see the full list of *Text* properties by choosing **Help → Index**. Type *text* in the box labeled *Search index for*, and choose **Properties** from the resulting list.

The *ylabel* command has the same syntactic variants and properties as *xlabel* and performs the same operations, but on the Y-axis instead of the X-axis.

The *title* command, too, has the same syntax and properties as *xlabel*, but creates a title for the graph. The *xlabel, ylabel,* and *title* commands share the same *Text* class properties.

5.2 Creating general text

The *text* command is the underlying function for the other labeling commands. By specifying its coordinates, text can be placed anywhere on the graph.

By default, text formatting for string objects uses a formatting language called *TeX*. MATLAB supports a subset of the TeX formatting commands. This subset is listed as properties of the *String* class. To see the available formatting commands, choose **Help → Index**. Type *string* in the box labeled *Search index for*, and choose **Text Property**. Table 1 displays a few of the most common TeX formatting codes.

The *text* command

```
>>text(0.5,0.5,'y \leq \pi * x^2')
```

will place the following in the Plot window, beginning at point (0.5, 0.5):

$$y \leq \pi * x^2$$

5.3 Creating a legend

The *legend* command creates a legend for the plot. You can pass the *legend* command either a list of strings that describe the legend's contents or a matrix of strings. In the

TABLE 1. A few of the TeX formatting codes.

Code	Character or Format
`\bf`	**bold font**
`\it`	*italics font*
`\rm`	normal font
`\pi`	π
`\theta`	θ
`\rightarrow`	$\rightarrow$
`\leftarrow`	$\leftarrow$
`\leq`	$\leq$
`\geq`	$\geq$
`^`	superscript
`_`	subscript

second case, each row of the string matrix becomes a line in the legend. The syntax for the legend command is

```
legend('str1','str2',...)
legend(string_matrix)
```

You can optionally supply an additional argument to *legend* that indicates the position of the legend in the graph:

```
legend('str1','str2',...,position)
```

Table 2 lists the codes for the position argument. The default position is the upper right corner of the plot. If position code is zero, MATLAB tries to obscure as few of the plotted points as possible.

TABLE 2. Position codes for the *legend* command.

Code	Placement
−1	outside the axes (on the right side of the chart)
0	inside the boundaries of the axes
1	at the upper right corner
2	at the upper left corner
3	at the lower left corner
4	at the lower right corner

The M-file in Figure 8 creates the labeled plot of the sine function displayed in Figure 9. Copy this file and execute it. Modify the plot formatting arguments until you feel comfortable using them.

6 MULTIPLE PLOTS

You can display multiple, simultaneous overlapping plots by using the *hold* command. The *hold* command is an example of a *toggle*. A toggle has two values: on or off.

The command

```
>>hold on
```

```
1   % Plots the sine function from 0 to 4 pi
2   % at intervals of 0.4 radians.
3
4   % create a vector containing the plot points
5   X = 0 : 0.4 : 4*pi;
6   Y = sin(X);
7
8   % create the plot with a solid line; use a circle as
9   % the marker, line width of 2, and marker size of 6
10  plot(X,Y, '-o', 'LineWidth', 2, 'MarkerSize', 6)
11
12  % create a title and axis labels
13  title('\bf Trigonometric Sine')
14  ylabel('\bf sin(x)')
15  xlabel('\bf 0 to 4\pi')
16
17  % create a legend
18  legend('sin(x)')
```

Figure 8. An M-file that demonstrates plot formatting commands.

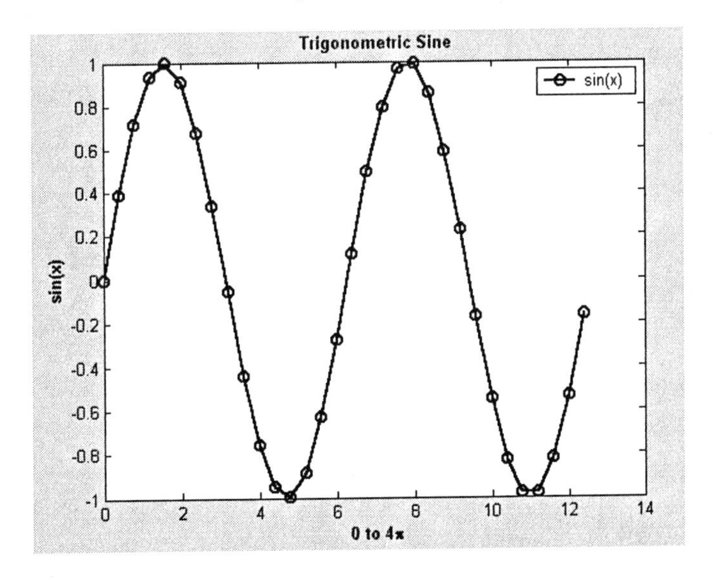

Figure 9. Example of labeled plot.

causes subsequent plot commands to superimpose new plots on the current plot. The command

```
>>hold off
```

causes the next plot command to refresh the Plot window.

You can display multiple nonoverlapping plots by using the *subplot* command, which divides the Plot window into $m \times n$ subwindows called *panes*. The syntax is

```
subplot(m, n, pane_number)
```

For example, the command

```
>> subplot(2,1,2)
```

results in the Plot window being divided into 2 rows by 1 column of panes. The *pane_number* argument 2 indicates that the next plot command will place the subplot in pane number 2.

7 SCALING A PLOT

By default, the axes in MATLAB plots are linear. To plot a function with a logarithmic scale on the X-axis, use the *semilogx* command. Similarly, the *semilogy* command creates a logarithmic (or log) scale on the Y-axis. To create log scales on both axes, use the *loglog* command. These three commands have the same syntax and arguments as the *plot* command.

You may want to superimpose a grid over the graph when using semilog and log–log plots. Such a grid visually emphasizes the nonlinear scaling. Use the *grid* command to toggle a grid over the graph.

The M-file in Figure 10 uses the *semilogx* command to demonstrate that a log function plotted on a log scale is a straight line. This M-file also demonstrates how to

```
 1  % Plots a log function on linear and log scales.
 2
 3  % create a vector containing the plot points
 4  X = 1 : 100;
 5  Y = log(X);
 6
 7  % create a subplot using linear scale
 8  subplot(2,1,1)
 9  plot(X,Y)
10  title('\bf Log Plot on Linear Scale')
11  ylabel('\bf log(x)')
12  grid on
13
14  % create a subplot using log scale on X axis
15  subplot(2,1,2)
16  semilogx(X,Y)
17  title('\bf Log Plot on Semilog Scale')
18  ylabel('\bf log(x)')
19  grid on
```

Figure 10. Example of *subplot* and *semilogx* commands.

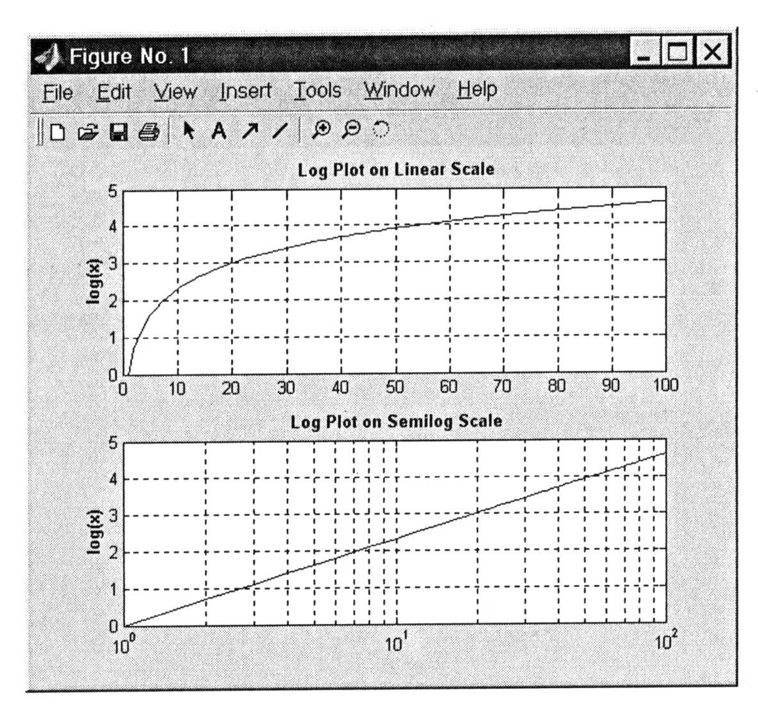

Figure 11. Log function plotted on linear and semilog scales.

use the *subplot* command to place two plots on the same graph. Figure 11 shows the results.

PRACTICE 1!

Write a script that performs the following tasks:

1. Create a vector *X* containing the values from -10 to 10 in increments of 0.5.
2. Create a vector *Y* that contains the square of each value in X.
3. Plot *X* and *Y*, using a dashed line and a pentagram marker.
4. Create a title in italics that reads $Y = X^2$.
5. Create appropriate labels for the X- and Y-axes.

KEY TERMS

panes TeX toggle

NEW MATLAB FUNCTIONS, COMMANDS, AND RESERVED WORDS

comet—plots an animated graph
grid—toggles plot grid on or off
hold—toggles multiplot on or off
legend—creates a plot legend
Line—the line graphics class, used in *plot* command
LineSpec—line type, property of the Line class
LineWidth—line width, property of the line class
loglog—creates a log–log scale plot
MarkerSize—marker size, property of the line class

plot—plots vectors and matrices
polar—plots polar coordinates
semilogx—creates a plot with log scale on the X-axis
semilogy—creates a plot with log scale on the Y-axis
String—the String graphics class, used in *text* command
subplot—creates a multiwindow plot
text—places text on named coordinates
Text—the text graphics class, used in *xlabel, ylabel, title* commands
title—creates a plot title
xlabel—creates a label on the X-axis of a plot
ylabel—creates a label on the Y-axis of a plot

SOLUTIONS TO PRACTICE PROBLEMS

1.

```
% Plot of x^2 in the range [-10, 10]
X = -10 : 0.5 : 10;
Y = X.^2;
plot(X,Y, '- -p');
title('\it Y=X^2');
xlabel('-10 to 10'); ylabel('X ^2');
```

Problems

Section 1.

1. Create a plot of the function $Y = 3X^2 + 5X - 3$ for $X =$ `[-5:0.1:5]`. Turn the grid on. Look at the graph. What is the approximate minimum of Y?

Section 2.

2. Create vector $X =$ `[-5:0.1:5]`. Create a matrix Y that consists of rows $sin(X)$, $sin(X + 1)$, $sin(X + 2)$, and $sin(X + 3)$. Plot matrix Y against vector X.

Section 4.

3. Write an M-file that creates a plot of the function $Y = 5X^2 - 2X - 50$ for $X = [-10:1:10]$. Use a pentagon-shaped marker of size 10 and a dotted line of width 2.

Section 5.

4. Create an appropriate legend, labels for the axes, and a title for the plot in Problem 2.
5. Create appropriate labels for the axes and a title for the plot in Problem 3. Create the title in bold font.

Section 6.

6. Write an M-file that creates multiple superimposed plots of $Y = nX^2$ for $n = [1:10]$ and $X = [-10:0.01:10]$. Label the plot appropriately.
7. Write an M-file that creates subplots (not superimposed) of $Y = X^n$ for $n = [1:5]$ and $X = [-10:0.01:10]$. Each subplot's Y axis should have an appropriate

bold face title. Use a *for* loop to minimize the size of your code. Your results should resemble Figure 12.

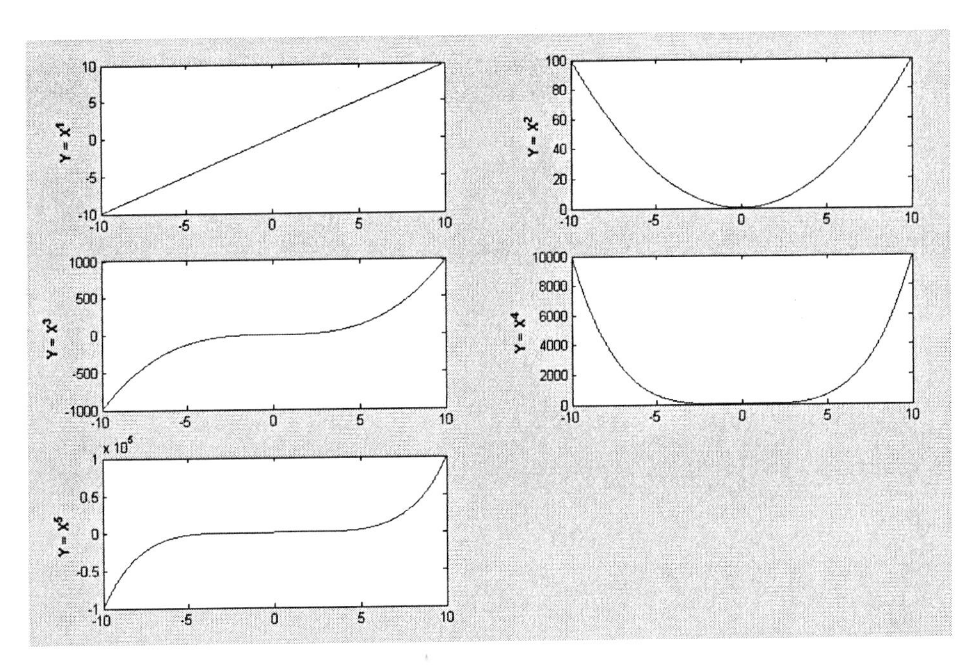

Figure 12. Subplots of $Y = X^n$ for $n = [1:5]$.

Section 7.

8. A graph that uses logarithmic scales on both axes is called a log–log graph. A log–log graph is useful for plotting power equations, which appear as straight lines on a log–log graph. A power equations has the form

$$y = bx^m$$

Plot the data in Table 3. Use a log–log plot. After viewing the plot, what can you infer about the relationship between the resistance and area of a conductor?

TABLE 3. Resistance vs. Area of a Conductor.

Area (mm²)	Resistance (milliohms/meter)
0.009	2000.0
0.021	1010.0
0.063	364.0
0.202	110.0
0.523	44.0
1.008	20.0
3.310	8.0
7.290	3.5
20.520	1.2

Challenge Problems.

9. The plots that have been shown so far use rectangular, or Cartesian, coordinates. Another method of plotting uses polar coordinates. In a polar coordinate system, the points are plotted as an angle and radius (theta, rho) instead of vertical (Y) and horizontal (X) components. The *polar* command creates a plot that uses polar coordinates. The syntax of the *polar* command is

```
polar(theta, Rho, LineSpec)
```

Plot the following function over the range 0 to π, using the polar command:

$$\rho = \cos(3\theta).$$

This function is known as the three-petal rose. Label the graph appropriately.

10. The *comet* command has the syntax

```
comet(X,Y)
```

and the effect is to trace a plot in slow motion with a tail. Use the *comet* command with $sin(X)$ for $X = [0:0.01:4\pi]$. Create a loop so that the sine function is plotted forwards and then backwards continuously.

11

Numerical Techniques

Grand Challenge: Enhanced Oil and Gas Recovery

The design and construction of the Alaska pipeline presented numerous engineering challenges. One of the most important problems that had to be addressed was how to protect the permafrost (the perennially frozen subsoil in arctic or subarctic regions) from the heat of the pipeline itself. The oil flowing in the pipeline is warmed by pumping stations and by friction from the walls of the pipe such that the supports holding the pipeline have to be insulated or even cooled to keep them from melting the permafrost at their bases.

Sections

Objectives

After reading this chapter, you should be able to

- perform linear and cubic-spline interpolation
- calculate the best-fit straight line and polynomial to a set of data points
- compute a numerical estimate for an integral
- apply the principles in this chapter to a problem in pipeline flow analysis, and
- compute a numerical estimate for a derivative.

1 INTERPOLATION

In this section, we present two types of interpolation: linear interpolation and cubic-spline interpolation. In both techniques, we assume that we have a set of data points that represents a set of xy-coordinates for which y is a function of x—that is, $y = f(x)$. We further assume that we need to estimate a value $f(b)$, which is not one of the original data points, but for which b is between two of the x values from the original set of data points. We want to approximate (or interpolate) a value for $f(b)$, using the information from the original set of data points. In Figure 1, we show a set of six data points that have been connected with straight-line segments and that have also been connected with cubic-degree polynomial segments. From this figure, we see that the values determined for the function between sample points depend on the type of interpolation that we select.

1.1 Linear Interpolation

Linear interpolation is one of the most common techniques for estimating data values between two given data points. If we assume that the function between the two points can be estimated by a straight line drawn between the points, we can compute the value of the function at any point between the two data values, using an equation derived from similar triangles.

1.2 Cubic-Spline Interpolation

A cubic spline is a smooth curve constructed to go through a set of points. The curve between each pair of points is a third-degree polynomial (which has the general form $a_0x^3 + a_1x^2 + a_2x + a_3$) that is computed so that it provides a smooth curve between the two points and a smooth transition from the third-degree polynomial between the previous pair of points. Refer to the cubic spline shown in Figure 1, which connects six points. A total of five different cubic equations are used to generate this smooth function that joins all six points.

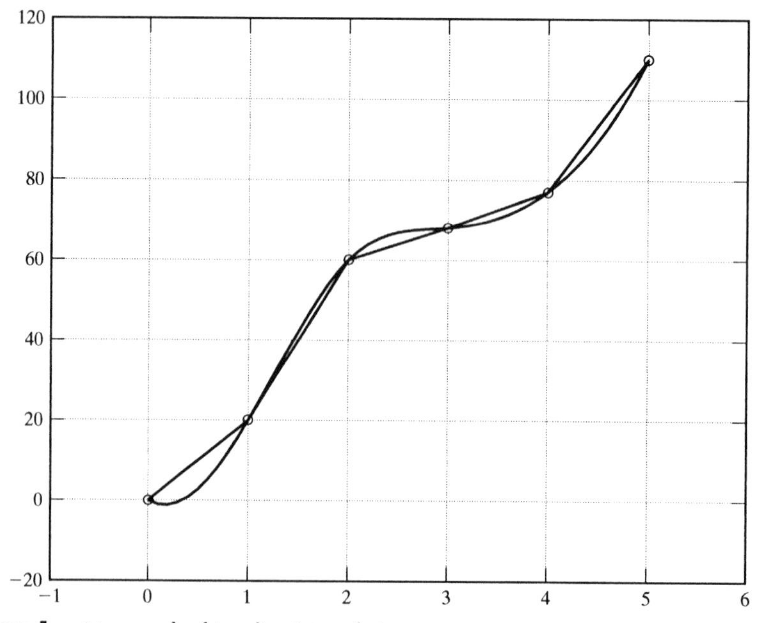

Figure 1. Linear and cubic-spline interpolation.

1.3 `interp1` Function

The MATLAB function that performs interpolation has three forms. Each form assumes that vectors **x** and **y** contain the original data values and that another vector **x_new** contains the new points for which we want to compute interpolated **y_new** values. (The **x** values should be in ascending order, and the **x_new** values should be within the range of the **x** values.) A summary of these forms is as follows:

interp1(x,y,x_new) Returns a vector the size of **x_new** that contains the interpolated **y** values that correspond to **x_new** using linear interpolation.

interp1(x,y,x_new,'linear') Returns a vector the size of **x_new** that contains the interpolated **y** values that correspond to **x_new** using linear interpolation.

interp1(x,y,x_new,'spline') Returns a vector the size of **x_new** that contains the interpolated **y** values that correspond to **x_new** using cubic-spline interpolation.

PRACTICE!

Use the following sets of data points for this example:

```
x = 0:5;
y = [0,20,60,68,77,110];
```

Define a finer grain of **x** values for the interpolation:

```
newx = 0:0.1:5;
```

Use the **interp1** function twice, once with linear interpolation and once with cubic–spline interpolation. Generate plots of each interpolation, as depicted in Figure 6.1. The MATLAB commands are as follows:

```
newy_1 = interp1(x,y,newx,'linear');
newy_2 = interp1(x,y,newx,'spline');
plot(newx,newy_1,newx,newy_2,x,y,'o'),
title('Linear and Cubic Spline Interpolation'),
   grid,axis([-1,6,-20,120]),pause
```

MATLAB provides other one-dimensional interpolation methods, including nearest neighbor interpolation and cubic interpolation. In addition, MATLAB provides two-dimensional **(interp2)** and three-dimensional **(interp3)** interpolation functions. These functions will not be discussed here. Type **help interp2** or **help interp3** to see a description and examples of each.

2 CURVE FITTING: LINEAR AND POLYNOMIAL REGRESSION

Assume that we have a set of data points collected from an experiment. After plotting the data points, we find that they generally fall in a straight line. However, if we were to try to draw a straight line through the points, only a couple of the points would probably fall exactly on the line. A **least-squares** curve-fitting method could be used to find the straight line that is the closest to the points by minimizing the distance from each point to the straight line. Although this line can be considered a "best fit" to the data points, it is possible that none of the points would actually fall on the line of best fit. (Note that this method is very different from interpolation, because the curves used in linear interpolation and cubic-spline interpolation actually contained all of the original data points.) In this section, we first discuss fitting a straight line to a set of data points, and then we discuss fitting a polynomial to a set of data points.

2.1 Linear Regression

Linear regression is the name given to the process that determines the linear equation which is the best fit to a set of data points, in terms of minimizing the sum of the squared distances between the line and the data points. To understand this process, we first consider the set of data values used in the discussion on interpolation from the previous section. If we plot these points, it appears that a good estimate of a line through the points is $y = 20x$, as shown in Figure 2. The following commands were used to generate this plot:

```
%  These statements compare a linear model
%  with a set of data points. (Figure 2)
%
x = 0:5;
y = [0,20,60,68,77,110];
y1 = 20*x;
plot(x,y1,x,y,'o'),title('Linear Estimate'),
xlabel('Time, s'),ylabel('Temperature, Degrees F'),grid,
axis([-1,6,-20,120]),pause
```

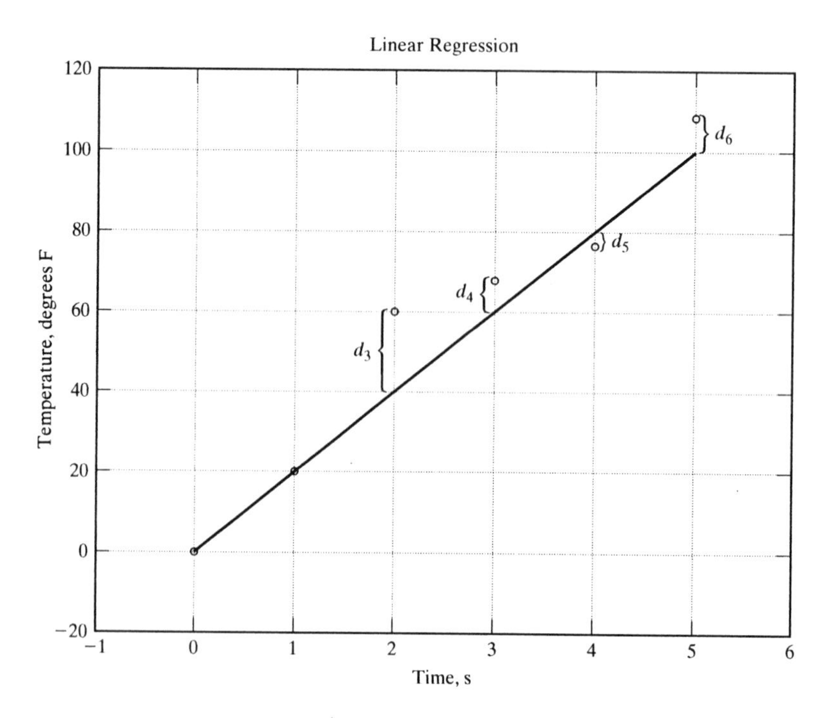

Figure 2. A linear estimate.

To measure the quality of the fit of this linear estimate to the data, we first determine the distance from each point to the linear estimate; these distances are also shown in Figure 2. The first two points fall exactly on the line, so d_1 and d_2 are zero. The value of d_3 is equal to 60 − 40, or 20; the rest of the distances can be computed in a similar way. If we compute the sum of the distances, some of the positive and negative values would cancel each other and give a sum that is smaller than it should be. To avoid this problem, we could add absolute values or squared values; linear regression uses squared values. Therefore, the measure of the quality of the fit of this linear estimate is the sum of the **squared distances** between the points and the linear estimates. This sum can be computed with the following command:

```
sum_sq = sum((y-y1).^2)
```

For this set of data, the value of **sum_sq** is 573.

If we drew another line through the points, we could compute the sum of squares that corresponds to this new line. Of the two lines, the better fit is provided by the line with the smaller sum of squared distances. To find the line with the smallest sum of squared distances, we can write an equation that computes the distances using a general linear equation, $y = mx + b$. We then write an equation that represents the sum of the squared distances; this equation will have m and b as its variables. Using techniques from calculus, we can compute the derivatives of the equation with respect to m and b and set the derivatives equal to zero. The values of m and b that are determined in this way represent the straight line with the minimum sum of squared distances. The MATLAB statement for computing this best-fit linear equation is discussed in the next section. For the data presented in this section, the best fit is shown in Figure 3; the corresponding sum of squares is 356.8190.

2.2 Polynomial Regression

In the previous discussion, we presented a technique for computing the linear equation that best fits a set of data. A similar technique can be developed using a single polynomial (not a set of polynomials, as in a cubic spline) to fit the data by minimizing the distance of the polynomial from the data points. First, recall that a polynomial with one variable can be written by using the following general formula:

$$f(x) = a_0x^n + a_1x^{n-1} + a_2x^{n-2} + \cdots + a_{n-1}x + a_n$$

The **degree of a polynomial** is equal to the largest value used as an exponent. Therefore, the general form of a cubic polynomial is

$$g(x) = a_0x^3 + a_1x^2 + a_2x + a_3$$

Note that a linear equation is also a polynomial of degree one.

In Figure 4 we plot the original set of data points that we used in the linear regression example, along with plots of the best-fit polynomials with degrees two through five. Note that as the degree of the polynomial increases, the number of points that fall on the curve also increases. If a set of n points is used to determine an nth-degree polynomial, all n points will fall on the polynomial.

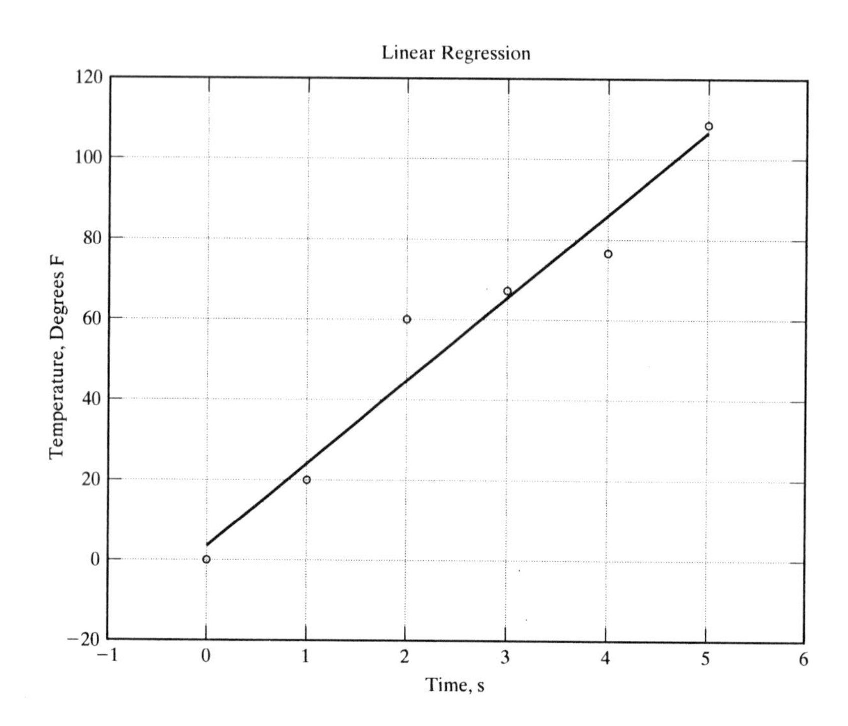

Figure 3. Data and best-fit line.

2.3 **polyfit** and **polyval** Functions

The MATLAB function for computing the best fit to a set of data with a polynomial with a specified degree is the **polyfit** function. This function has three arguments: the x and y coordinates of the data points and the degree n of the polynomial. The function returns the coefficients, in descending powers of x, of the nth-degree polynomial that fits the vectors **x** and **y**. (Note that an nth-degree polynomial has $n + 1$ coefficients.) A summary of this function is

> **polyfit(x,y,n)** Returns a vector of **n+1** coefficients that represents the best-fit polynomial of degree **n** for the **x** and **y** coordinates. The coefficient order corresponds to decreasing powers of **x**.

The best linear fit for a set of data can be found using the **polyfit** function with $n = 1$. The following example demonstrates how to find a best-fit linear estimate.

PRACTICE!

First, we define six data points:

```
x = 0:5;
y = [0,20,60,68,77,110];
```

The **polyfit** function (with $n = 1$) returns a vector containing the coefficients of a polynomial of degree one:

```
coef = polyfit(x,y,1)
coef = 20.8286   3.7619
```

The best y estimates are calculated using the coefficients:

```
ybest = coeff(1) * x + coeff(2)
ybest = 3.7619  24.5905  45.4190  66.2476  87.0762  107.9048
```

We can calculate the sum of squares using the following commands:

```
sum_sq = sum((y - ybest).^2)
sum_sq = 356.8190
```

The best-fit linear equation is plotted as follows:

```
plot(x,ybest,x,y,'o'),title('Linear Regression'),
xlabel('Time, s'),ylabel('Temperature, Degrees F'),grid,
axis([-1,6,-20,120]),pause
```

This plot is depicted in Figure 3.

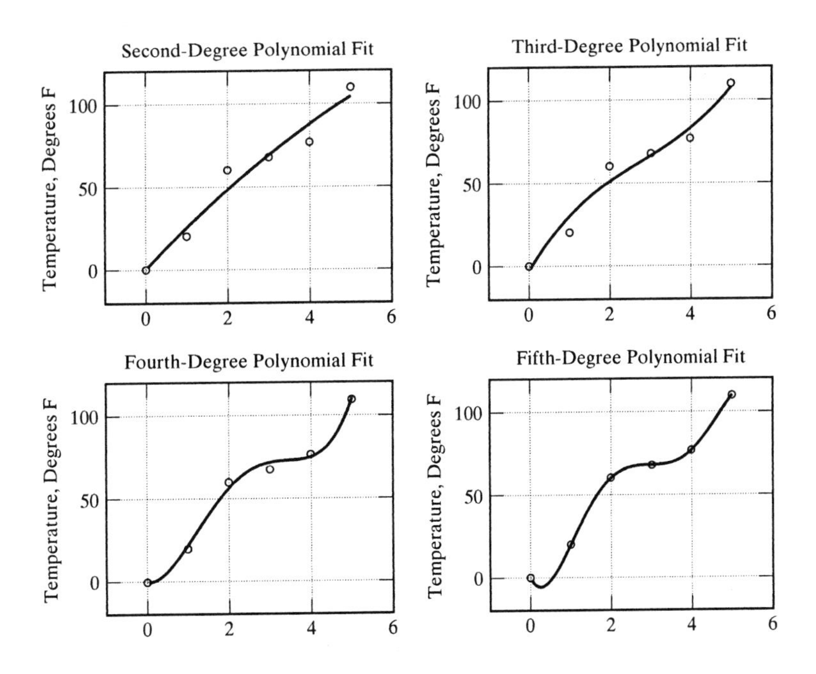

Figure 4. Polynomial fits.

The **polyval** function is used to evaluate a polynomial at a set of data points. The first argument of the **polyval** function is a vector containing the coefficients of the polynomial (in an order corresponding to decreasing powers of x), and the second argument is the vector of x values for which we want polynomial values. A summary of the function is

polyval(coef,x) Returns a vector of polynomial values $f(x)$ that correspond to the **x** vector values. The order of the coefficients corresponds to decreasing powers of x.

In the previous example, we computed the points of the linear regression using values from the coefficients. We could also have computed them using the **polyval** function:

```
ybest = polyval(coef,x);
```

The **polyfit** and **polyval** functions can be used in combination to write concise programs that find best-fit polynomials. This method is convenient if you are using higher order polynomials. For example, the following statement returns an evaluation of the best-fit fifth-order polynomial using the data in the previous example:

```
polyval(polyfit(x,y,5),0:0.05:5)
```

To plot the results in a single statement, use the following command:

```
plot(0:0.05:5, polyval(polyfit(x,y,5),0:0.05:5))
```

PRACTICE!

This example illustrates the computation of the best-fit polynomials of degree one through degree five. We will use the same data that were used for the linear regression example.

First, define the six data points:

```
x = 0:5;
y = [0, 20, 60, 68, 77, 110];
```

Define a finer grain of **x** values for the polynomial evaluation:

```
newx = 0:0.05:5;
```

The following loop generates a 5 × 101 matrix that contains the evaluation of the best-fit polynomials from order one to five.

```
for n=1:5
  f(:, n) = polyval( polyfit(x, y, n), newx)';
end
```

Then, for example, to plot the third-degree polynomial, we could use the following statement:

```
plot(newx, f(:,3), x, y, 'o')
```

Additional statements are necessary to define the subplot, label each plot, and set the limits of the axes. The results are depicted in Figure 4.

From the previous discussion on polynomial fits, we would expect that the lower degree polynomials would not contain all of the data points and that the fifth-degree polynomial would contain all six data points. The plots in Figure 4 verify these expectations.

PRACTICE!

The following set of data represents the flow of water through a culvert as a function of the water's height.

HEIGHT, FT	FLOW, CFS
1.70	2.60
1.95	3.60
2.60	4.03
2.92	6.45
4.04	11.22
5.24	30.61

1. Compute a best-fit linear equation for the data. Evaluate the resulting linear equation for x = 0:0.05:6. Plot the results.
2. Compute a third-order best-fit polynomial for the data. Evaluate the resulting polynomial for x = 0:0.05:6. Plot the results.

3 NUMERICAL INTEGRATION

The integral of a function $f(x)$ over the interval $[a,b]$ is defined to be the area under the curve of $f(x)$ between a and b, as shown in Figure 5. If the value of this integral is K, the notation to represent the integral of $f(x)$ between a and b is

$$K = \int_a^b f(x)dx$$

For many functions, this integral can be computed analytically. However, for a number of functions, the integral cannot easily be computed analytically and thus requires a numerical technique to estimate its value. The numerical evaluation of an integral is also called quadrature, a term that comes from an ancient geometrical problem.

The numerical integration techniques estimate the function $f(x)$ by another function $g(x)$, where $g(x)$ is chosen so that we can easily compute the area under $g(x)$. Then, the better the estimate of $g(x)$ to $f(x)$, the better will be the estimate of the integral of $f(x)$. Two of the most common numerical integration techniques estimate $f(x)$ with a set of piecewise linear functions or with a set of piecewise parabolic functions. If we estimate the function with piecewise linear functions, we can then compute the area of the trapezoids that compose the area under the piecewise linear functions; this technique is called the **trapezoidal rule**. If we estimate the function with piecewise quadratic functions, we can then compute and add the areas of these components; this technique is called **Simpson's rule**.

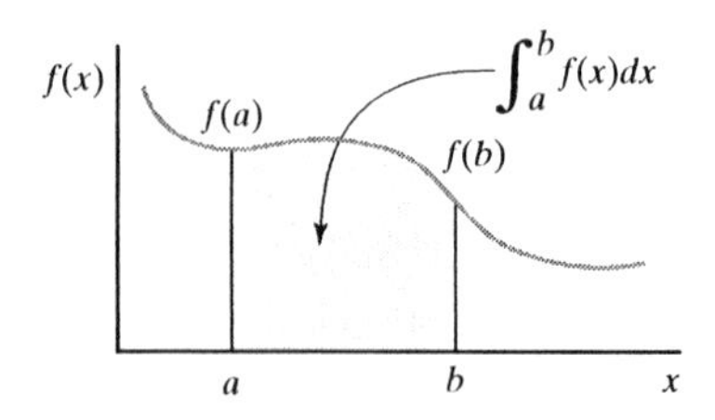

Figure 5. Integral of $f(x)$ from a to b.

3.1 Trapezoidal Rule and Simpson's Rule

If the area under a curve is represented by trapezoids and if the interval $[a,b]$ is divided into n equal sections, then the area can be approximated by the formula (trapezoidal rule)

$$K_T = \frac{b-a}{2n}(f(x_0) + 2f(x_1) + 2f(x_2) + \ldots + 2f(x_{n-1}) + f(x_n))$$

where the x_i values represent the end points of the trapezoids and where $x_0 = a$ and $x_n = b$.

If the area under a curve is represented by areas under quadratic sections of a curve and if the interval $[a,b]$ is divided into $2n$ equal sections, then the area can be approximated by the formula (Simpson's rule)

$$K_S = \frac{h}{3}(f(x_0) + 4f(x_1) + 2f(x_2) + 4f(x_3) + \ldots + 2f(x_{2n-2}) + 4f(x_{2n-1}) + f(x_{2n}))$$

where the x_i values represent the end points of the sections and where $x_0 = a$, $x_{2n} = b$, and $h = (b - a)/(2n)$.

If the piecewise components of the approximating function are higher degree functions (the trapezoidal rule uses linear functions, and Simpson's rule uses quadratic functions), the integration techniques are referred to as **Newton-Cotes integration techniques**.

The estimate of an integral improves as we use more components (such as trapezoids) to approximate the area under a curve. If we attempt to integrate a function with a singularity (a point at which the function or its derivatives are infinity or are not defined), we may not be able to get a satisfactory answer with a numerical integration technique.

3.2 MATLAB Quadrature Functions

MATLAB has two quadrature functions for performing numerical function integration. The **quad** function uses an adaptive form of Simpson's rule, whereas **quadl** uses an adaptive Lobatto quadrature. The **quadl** function is better at handling functions with certain types of singularities, such as $\int_0^1 \sqrt{x}\, dx$. Both functions print a warning message if they detect a singularity, but an estimate of the integral is still returned.

The simplest form of the **quad** and **quadl** functions requires three arguments. The first argument is the name (in quotes) of the MATLAB function that returns a vector of values of $f(x)$ when given a vector of input values **x**. This function name can be the name of another MATLAB function, such as **sin**, or it can be the name of a user-written

MATLAB function. The second and third arguments are the integral limits **a** and **b**. A summary of these functions is as follows:

> **quad('function',a,b)** Returns the area of the **'function'** between **a** and **b**, assuming that **'function'** is a MATLAB function.
>
> **quadl('function',a,b)** Returns the area of the **'function'** between **a** and **b**, assuming that **'function'** is a MATLAB function.

PRACTICE!

The script shown next can be used to compare the results of the **quad** and **quad8** functions with the analytically calculated results. The script prompts the user for a specified interval.

```
%  These statements compare the quad and quad8 functions
%  with the analytical results for the integration of the
%  square root of x over an interval [a,b], where a and b
%  are nonnegative.
%
a = input(' Enter left endpoint (nonnegative): ');
b = input('Enter right endpoint (nonnegative): ');
%
%  k is the computed analytical result
k = (2/3)*(b^(1.5) - a^(1.5));
%
%  The following two statements compute the quad and quad
%  functions from a to b
kquad=quad('sqrt',a,b);
kquadl=quadl('sqrt',a,b);
%
%  Display the results
fprintf('Analytical: %f \n',k);
fprintf('       Quad: %f \n',kquad);
fprintf('      Quadl: %f \n',kquadl);
```

These integration techniques can handle some singularities that occur at one or the other interval end points, but they cannot handle singularities that occur within the interval. For these cases, you should consider dividing the interval into subintervals and providing estimates of the singularities using other results, such as l'Hôpital's Rule.

To illustrate, assume that we want to determine the integral of the square-root function for nonnegative values of a and b:

$$K_Q = \int_a^b \sqrt{x}\, dx$$

The square-root function $f(x) = \sqrt{x}$ is plotted in Figure 6 for the interval [0, 5]; the values of the function are complex for $x < 0$. This function can be integrated analytically to yield the following for nonnegative values of a and b:

$$K = \frac{2}{3}(b^{3/2} - a^{3/2})$$

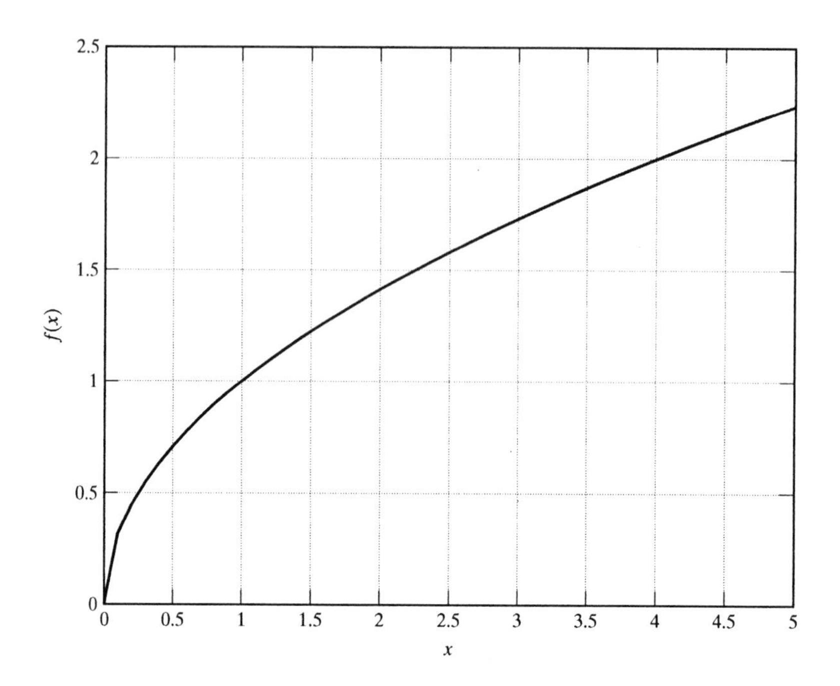

Figure 6. Square-root function.

PRACTICE!

You can cut and paste the script for this example into a file and test it. If you select an interval that contains a singularity you will see a message similar to the following:

```
Recursion level limit reached in quad.  Singularity likely.
```

The following examples demonstrate the script's use:

```
Enter left endpoint (nonnegative): 1.5
Enter right endpoint (nonnegative): 15
Analytical: 37.505089
     Quad: 37.504990
     Quadl: 37.505088
Enter left endpoint (nonnegative): 0.2
Enter right endpoint (nonnegative): 5
Analytical: 7.393931
     Quad: 7.393905
     Quadl: 7.393926
```

The **quad** and **quadl** functions can also include a fourth argument, which represents a tolerance. If the tolerance is omitted, a default value of 0.001 is assumed. The integration function continues to refine its estimate for the integration until the relative error is less than the tolerance, using the following iterative test:

$$\frac{\text{previous estimate} - \text{current estimate}}{\text{previous estimate}} < \text{tolerance}$$

PRACTICE!

Sketch the function $f(x) = x$, and indicate the areas specified by the given integrals. Then compute the integrals by hand, and compare your results with those generated by the **quad** function.

1. $\int_{0.5}^{0.6} |x| dx$
2. $\int_{-1}^{-0.5} |x| dx$
3. $\int_{0}^{1} |x| dx$
4. $\int_{-0.5}^{0.5} |x| dx$

4 PROBLEM SOLVING APPLIED: PIPELINE FLOW ANALYSIS

In this section, we perform computations in an application related to the enhanced oil recovery grand challenge. The friction in a circular pipeline causes a velocity profile to develop in the flowing oil. Oil that is in contact with the walls of the pipe does not move at all, whereas oil at the center of the flow moves the fastest. The diagram in Figure 7 shows how the velocity of the oil varies across the diameter of the pipe and defines the variables used in this analysis. The following equation describes this velocity profile:

$$v(r) = v_{max}\left(\bar{1} - \frac{r}{r^{0}}\right)^{\frac{1}{n}}$$

The variable v is an integer between 5 and 10 that defines the shape of the forward flow of the oil. In this case, the value of v for the diagram in Figure 7 is 8. The average flow velocity of the pipe can be computed by integrating the velocity profile from zero to the pipe's radius, r_0. Thus, we have

$$v_{ave} = \frac{\int_{0}^{r_0} v(r) 2\pi r dr}{\pi r_0^2} = \frac{2v_{max}}{r_0^2}\int_{0}^{r_0} r\bar{1} - \frac{r}{r_0}\sqrt{1/2}dr$$

The values of v_{max} and v can be measured experimentally, and the value of r_0 is the radius of the pipe. We will assume that v_{max} is 1.5 m, is 0.5 m, and v is 8.

First, we will plot the function $\bar{1} - \frac{r}{r_0}\sqrt{1/2}\,dr$ for r, varying from 0 to 0.5 meters, in increments of 0.01 meters. We can approximate the area under this function using a triangle and a trapezoid, as shown in Figure 8.

$$\text{area} = 0.1 \leftrightarrow 0.35 + \frac{0.4 \leftrightarrow 0.35}{2} = 0.105\,\text{m}^2$$

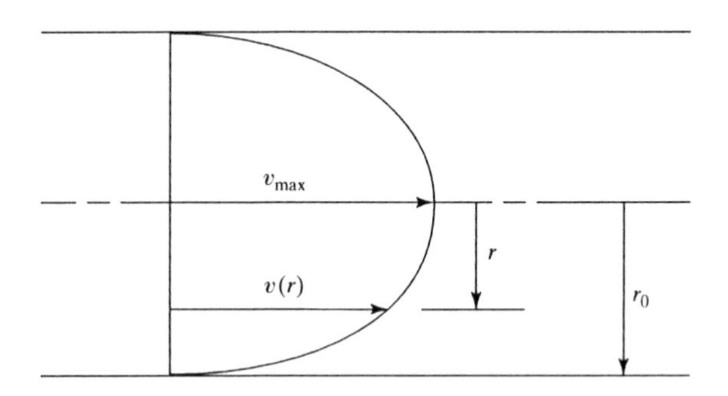

Figure 7. Velocity profile of flowing oil.

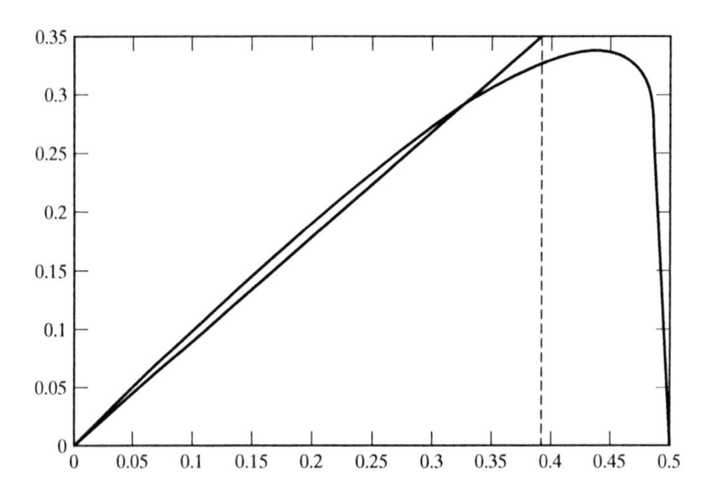

Figure 8. Function approximation using a triangle and rectangle.

Now we will compute the area, using the **quad** and **quad8** functions. In order to use the **quad** and **quads** functions, we first create a function that describes the velocity profile:

```
function s=vel(x)
%
% vel - describes the velocity profile
%
s = x.* (1-(x/0.5)).^(1/8);
```

Then we use this function as an argument to the **quad** and **quad8** functions:

```
% plot velocity profile, compare quad and quad8 solutions
r = [0.0:0.01:0.5];
plot(r, vel(r));
fprintf('Quad = %f\n',quad('vel',0.0,0.5));
fprintf('Quadl = %f\n',quadl('vel',0.0,0.5));
```

Compare the answers with the foregoing estimation:

```
Quad = 0.104563
Quadl = 0.104574
```

The average flow velocity for this pipe can now be calculated (using the **quadl** estimate):

$$\mathrm{v}_{max} = \frac{2v_{max}}{r_0^2}\int_0^{r_0} r\bar{1} - \frac{r}{r_0}\sqrt{1/(2dr)} = \left(\frac{2 \leftrightarrow 1.5}{(0.5)} \leftrightarrow 0.1045\right)$$

5 NUMERICAL DIFFERENTIATION

The derivative of a function $f(x)$ is defined to be a function $f'(x)$ that is equal to the rate of change of $f(x)$ with respect to x. The derivative can be expressed as a ratio, with the change in $f(x)$ indicated by $df(x)$ and the change in x indicated by dx, giving

$$f'(x) = \frac{df(x)}{dx}$$

There are many physical processes for which we want to measure the rate of change of a variable. For example, velocity is the rate of change of position (as in meters per second), and acceleration is the rate of change of velocity (as in meters per second squared). It can also be shown that the integral of acceleration is velocity and that the integral of velocity is position. Hence, integration and differentiation have a special relationship, in that they can be considered to be inverses of each other: The derivative of an integral returns the original function, and the integral of a derivative returns the original function, to within a constant value.

The derivative $f'(x)$ can be described graphically as the slope of the function $f(x)$, where the slope of $f(x)$ is defined to be the slope of the tangent line to the function at the specified point. Thus, the value of $f'(x)$ at the point a is $f'(a)$, and it is equal to the slope of the tangent line at the point a, as shown in Figure 9.

Because the derivative of a function at a point is the slope of the tangent line at the point, a value of zero for the derivative of a function at the point x_k indicates that the line is horizontal at that point. Points with derivatives of zero are called **critical points** and can represent either a horizontal region of the function or a local maximum or a local minimum of the function. (The point may also be the global maximum or global minimum, as shown in Figure 10, but more analysis of the entire function would be needed to determine this.) If we evaluate the derivative of a function at several points in an interval and we observe that the sign of the derivative changes, then a local maximum or a local minimum occurs in the interval. The second derivative (the derivative of $f'(x)$) can be used to determine whether or not the critical points represent local maxima or local minima. More specifically, if the second derivative of an **extrema point** is positive, then the value of the function at the extrema point is a local minimum; if the second derivative of an extrema point is negative, then the value of the function at the extrema point is a local maximum.

5.1 Difference Expressions

Numerical differentiation techniques estimate the derivative of a function at a point x_k by approximating the slope of the tangent line at x_k using values of the function at points near x_k. The approximation of the slope of the tangent line can be done in several ways, as shown in Figure 11.

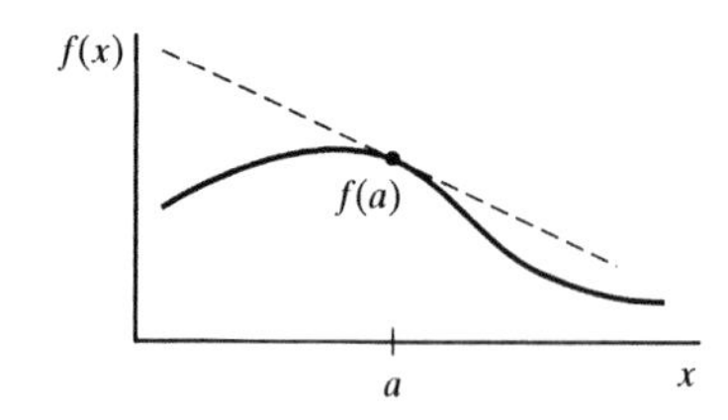

Figure 9. Derivative of $f(x)$ at $x = a$.

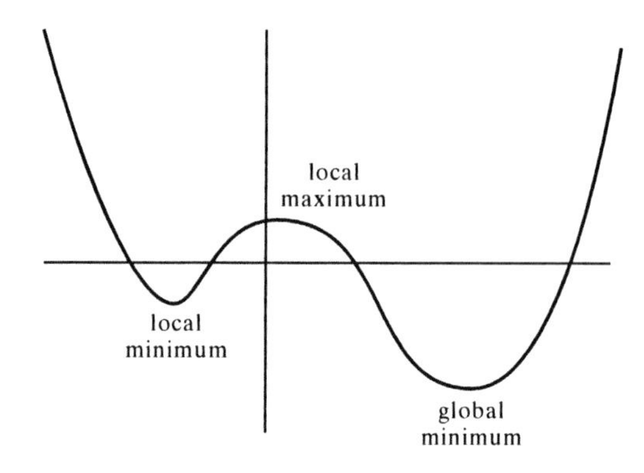

Figure 10. Example of function with critical points.

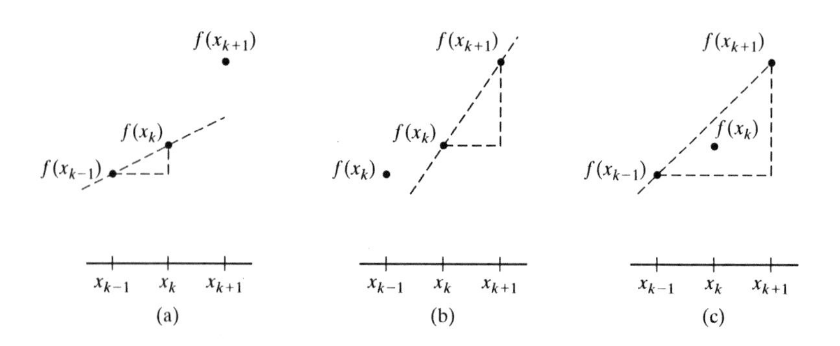

Figure 11. Techniques for computing $f'(x_k)$.

Figure 11(a) assumes that the derivative at x_k is estimated by computing the slope of the line between $f(x_{k-1})$ and $f(x_k)$, as in

$$f'(x_k) = \frac{f(x_k) - f(x_{k-1})}{x_k - x_{k-1}}$$

This type of derivative approximation is called a **backward difference approximation**.

Figure 11(b) assumes that the derivative at x_k is estimated by computing the slope of the line between $f(x_k)$ and $f(x_{k+1})$, as in

$$f'(x_k) = \frac{f(x_{k+1}) - f(x_k)}{x_{k+1} - x_k}$$

This type of derivative approximation is called a **forward difference approximation**.

Figure 11(c) assumes that the derivative at x_k is estimated by computing the slope of the line between $f(x_{k-1})$ and $f(x_{k+1})$, as in

$$f'(x_k) = \frac{f(x_{k+1}) - f(x_{k-1})}{x_{k+1} - x_{k-1}}$$

This type of derivative approximation is called a **central difference approximation**, and we usually assume that x_k is halfway between x_{k-1} and x_{k+1}. The quality of all of these types of derivative computations depends on the distance between the points used to estimate the derivative; the estimate of the derivative improves as the distance between the two points decreases.

The second derivative of a function $f(x)$ is the derivative of the first derivative of the function:

$$f''(x) = \frac{df'(x)}{dx}$$

This function can be evaluated using slopes of the first derivative. Thus, if we use backward differences, we have

$$f''(x_k) = \frac{f'(x_k) - f'(x_{k-1})}{x_k - x_{k-1}}$$

Similar expressions can be derived for computing estimates of higher derivatives.

5.2 `diff` Function

The **`diff`** function computes differences between adjacent values in a vector, generating a new vector with one fewer value. If the **`diff`** function is applied to a matrix, it operates on the columns of the matrix as if each column were a vector. A second, optional argument specifies the number of times to recursively apply **`diff`**. Each time **`diff`** is applied, the length of the vector is reduced in size. A third, optional argument specifies the dimensions in which to apply the function. The forms of **`diff`** are summarized as follows:

`diff(X)` For a vector **`X`**, **`diff`** returns
`[X(2)-X(1)  X(3)-X(2)  ...  X(n)-X(n-1)]`.

diff(X) For a matrix **X**, **diff** returns the matrix of column differences **[X(2:m,:) - X(1:m-1,:)]**

diff(X,n,dim) The general form of **diff** returns the **n**th difference function along dimension **dim** (a scalar). If n >= the length of **dim**, then **diff** returns an empty array.

PRACTICE!

To illustrate, define vectors **x**, **y**, and **z** as follows:

```
x = [0 1 2 3 4 5];
y = [2 3 1 5 8 10];
z = [1 3 5; 1 5 10];
```

Then the vector generated by **diff(x)** is

```
diff(x)
ans =
     1     1     1     1     1
```

The vector generated by **diff(y)** is

```
diff(y)
ans =
     1    -2     4     3     2
```

The next example recursively executes **diff** twice. Note that the length of the returned vector is 4:

```
diff(y,2)
ans =
    -3     6    -1    -1
```

The **diff** function can be applied to either dimension of matrix **z**:

```
diff(z,1,1)
ans =
     0     2     5
diff(z,1,2)
ans =
     2     2
     4     5
```

An approximate derivative dy can be computed by using **diff(y)./diff(x)**.

Note that these values of dy are correct for both the forward difference equation and the backward difference equation. The distinction between the two methods for computing the derivative is determined by the values of the vector **xd**, which correspond to the derivative dy. If the corresponding values of **xd** are [1,2,3,4,5], dy computes a backward difference. If the corresponding values of **xd** are [0,1,2,3,4], dy computes a forward difference.

PRACTICE!

As an example, consider the function given by the following polynomial:

$$f(x) = x^5 - 3x^4 - 11x^3 + 27x^2 + 10x - 24$$

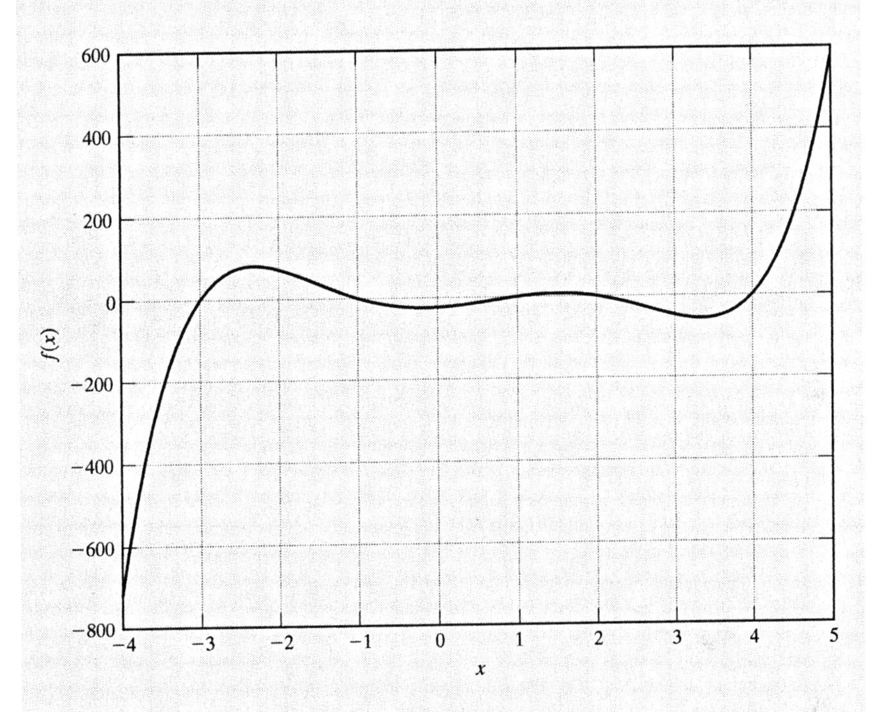

Figure 12. Fifth-degree polynomial.

A plot of this function is shown in Figure 13. Recall that the zeros of the derivative correspond to the points of local minima or local maxima of a function. The function in this example does not have a global minimum or global maximum, because the function ranges from $-\infty$ to ∞. The local minima and maxima (or critical points) of this function occur at -2.3, -0.2, 1.5, and 3.4. You can use the **find** function to identify the critical points of a function. Assume that we want to compute the derivative of this function over the interval [4,5]. We can perform this operation using the **diff** function as, shown in the following script, where *df* represents **df** and *xd* represents the x values corresponding to the derivative:

```
%  Evaluate f(x) and f'(x).
%
x = -4:0.1:5;
f = x.^5 - 3*x.^4 - 11*x.^3 + 27*x.^2 + 10*x - 24;
df = diff(f)./diff(x);
xd = x(2:length(x));
plot(xd, df);
```

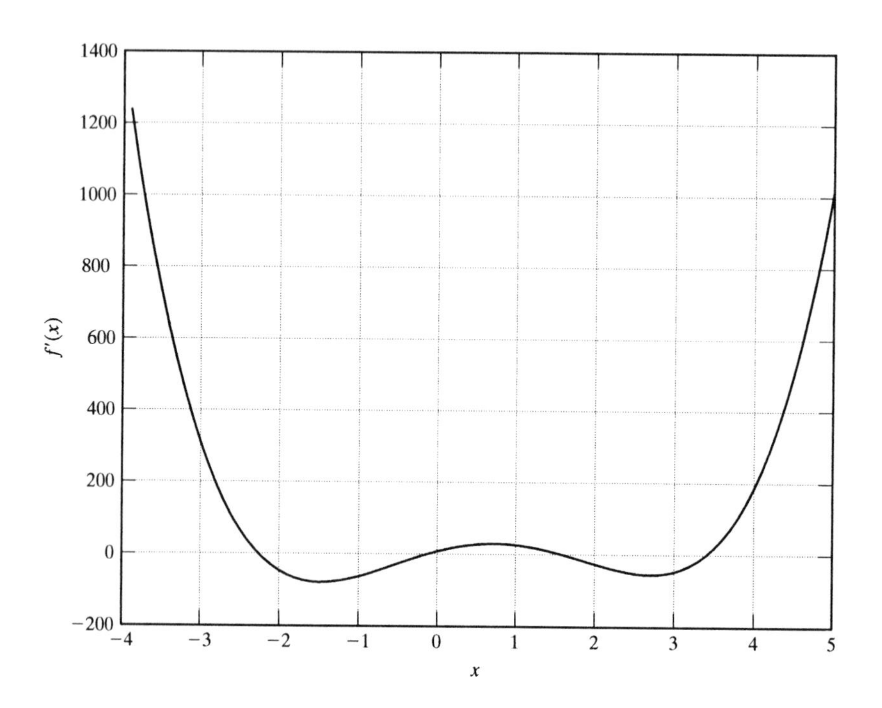

Figure 13. Derivative of fifth-degree polynomial.

PRACTICE!

In this example, we will use the values of **df** and **xd** from the previous example. The **find** function is used to determine the indices k of the locations in **product** for which **df(k)** is equal to 0. These indices are then used with the vector **xd** to print the approximation to the locations of the critical points.

```
% Find locations of critical points of f'(x).
%
product = df(1:length(df)-1).*df(2:length(df));
critical = xd(find(product<0))

critical =
-2.3000    -0.2000    1.5000    3.4000
```

PRACTICE!

This example shows the method for computing a central difference derivative using vectors **x** and **f**.

```
x = -4:0.1:5;
f = x.^5 - 3*x.^4 - 11*x.^3 + 27*x.^2 + 10*x - 24;
```

The following script evaluates $f(x)$ using central differences:

```
% Evaluate f'(x) using central differences.
%
```

```
numerator = f(3:length(f)) - f(1:length(f)-2);
denominator = x(3:length(x)) - x(1:length(x)-2);
dy = numerator./denominator;
xd = x(2:length(x)-1);
```

You may want to plot **dy** and compare it with Figure 13.

In the example discussed in this section, we assumed that we had the equation of the function to be differentiated, and thus we could generate points of the function. In many engineering problems, the data to be differentiated are collected from experiments. Thus, we cannot choose the points to be close together to get a more accurate measure of the derivative. In these cases, it might be a good solution to use the techniques from Section 2. These techniques allow us to determine an equation for a polynomial that fits a set of data and then compute points from the equation to use in computing values of the derivative.

PRACTICE!

For each of the given functions, plot the function, its first derivative, and its second derivative over the interval [−10,10]. Then use MATLAB commands to print the locations of the local minima.

1. $g_1(x) = x^3 - 5x^2 + 2x + 8$
2. $g_2(x) = x^2 + 4x + 4$
3. $g_3(x) = x^2 - 2x + 2$
4. $g_4(x) = 10x - 24$
5. $g_5(x) = x^5 - 4x^4 - 9x^3 + 32x^2 + 28x - 48$

SUMMARY

In this chapter, we explained the difference between interpolation and least-squares curve fitting. Two types of interpolation were presented: linear interpolation and cubic-spline interpolation. After presenting the MATLAB commands for performing these types of interpolations, we then turned to least-squares curve fitting using polynomials. This discussion explained how to determine the best fit to a set of data using a polynomial with a specified degree and then how to use the best-fit polynomial to generate new values of the function. Techniques for numerical integration and differentiation were also presented in this chapter. Numerical integration techniques approximate the area under a curve, and numerical differentiation techniques approximate the slope of a curve. The functions for integration are **quad** and **quadl**. The function used to compute the derivative of a function is the **diff** function, which computes differences between adjacent elements of a vector.

MATLAB SUMMARY

This MATLAB summary lists and briefly describes all of the commands and functions that were defined in this chapter.

Commands and Functions	
diff	computes the differences between adjacent values
interp1	computes linear and cubic interpolation

Commands and Functions

`polyfit`	computes a least-squares polynomial
`polyval`	evaluates a polynomial
`quad`	computes the integral under a curve (Simpson)
`quadl`	computes the integral under a curve (Lobatto)

KEY TERMS

approximation
backwards difference
central difference approximation
critical points
cubic spline
degree of a polynomial
derivative
extrema points
forward difference approximation
least-squares
linear interpolation
linear regression
quadrature
Simpson's rule
trapezoidal rule

Problems

1. Generate $f(x) = x^2$ for $x = [-3\ -1\ 0\ 2\ 5\ 6]$.
   - Compute and plot the linear and cubic-spline interpolation of the data points over the range [–3:0.05:6].
   - Compute the value of $f(4)$ using linear interpolation and cubic-spline interpolation. What are the respective errors when the answer is compared with the actual value of $f(4)$?

2. **Cylinder Head Temperatures.** Assume that the following set of temperature measurements is taken from the cylinder head in a new engine that is being tested for possible use in a race car:

TIME, s	TEMPERATURE, °F
0.0	0.0
1.0	20.0
2.0	60.0
3.0	68.0
4.0	77.0
5.0	110.0

a. Compare plots of these data, assuming linear interpolation and assuming cubic interpolation for values between the data points, using time values from 0 to 5 in increments of 0.1 s.

b. Using the data from part (a), find the time value for which there is the largest difference between its linear-interpolated temperature and its cubic-interpolated temperature.

c. Assume that we measure temperatures at three points around the cylinder head in the engine, instead of at just one point. The set of data is then the following:

TIME, s	TEMP1	TEMP2	TEMP3
0.0	0.0	0.0	0.0
1.0	20.0	25.0	52.0
2.0	60.0	62.0	90.0
3.0	68.0	67.0	91.0
4.0	77.0	82.0	93.0
5.0	110.0	103.0	96.0

Assume that these data have been stored in a matrix with six rows and four columns. Determine interpolated values of temperature at the three points in the engine at 2.6 seconds, using linear interpolation.

d. Using the information from part (c), determine the time that the temperature reached 75 degrees at each of the three points in the cylinder head.

3. **Spacecraft Accelerometer.** The guidance and control system for a spacecraft often uses a sensor called an *accelerometer*, which is an electromechanical device that produces an output voltage proportional to the applied acceleration. Assume that an experiment has yielded the following set of data:

ACCELERATION	VOLTAGE
4	0.593
2	0.436
0	0.061
2	0.425
4	0.980
6	1.213
8	1.646
10	2.158

a. Determine the linear equation that best fits this set of data. Plot the data points and the linear equation.

b. Determine the sum of the squares of the distances of these points from the line of best fit determined in part (a).

c. Compare the error sum from part (b) with the same error sum computed from the best quadratic fit. What do these sums tell you about the two models for the data?

4. Compute tan(x) for $x = [-1:0.05:1]$. Compute the best-fit polynomial of order four that approximates tan(x). Plot tan(x) and the generated polynomial on the same graph. What is the sum of square error of the polynomial approximation for the data points in x?

5. **Function Analysis.** Let the function f be defined by the following equation:

$$f(x) = 4e^{-x}$$

Plot this function over the interval [0,1]. Use numerical integration techniques to estimate the integral of (x) over [0,0.5] and over [0,1].

6. **Sounding Rocket Trajectory.** The following data set represents the time and altitude values for a sounding rocket that is performing high-altitude atmospheric research on the ionosphere:

TIME, s	ALTITUDE, m
0	60
10	2,926
20	10,170
30	21,486
40	33,835
50	45,251
60	55,634
70	65,038
80	73,461
90	80,905
100	87,368
110	92,852
120	97,355
130	100,878
140	103,422
150	104,986
160	106,193
170	110,246
180	119,626
190	136,106
200	162,095
210	199,506
220	238,775
230	277,065
240	314,375
250	350,704

a. Plot the altitude data. The velocity function is the derivative of the altitude function. Using numerical differentiation, compute the velocity values from these data, using a backward difference. Plot the velocity data. (Note that the rocket is a two-stage rocket.)

b. The acceleration function is the derivative of the velocity function. Using the velocity data determined from part (a), compute the acceleration data, using a backward difference. Plot the acceleration data.

7. **Simple Root Finding.** Even though MATLAB makes it easy to find the roots of a function, sometimes all that is needed is a quick estimate. This can be done by plotting a function and zooming in very close to see where the function equals zero. Since MATLAB draws straight lines between data points in a plot, it is good to draw circles or stars at each data point, in addition to the straight lines connecting the points. Plot the following function, and zoom in to find the roots:

```
n = 5;
x = linspace(0,2*pi,n);
y = x .* sin(x) + cos(1/2*x).^2 - 1./(x - 7);
plot (x,y,'-o')
```

Increase the value of **n** to increase the accuracy of the estimate.

Consider the data points in the following two vectors:

X = [0.1 0.3 5.0 6.0 23.0 24.0]
Y = [2.8 2.6 18.1 26.8 486.1 530.0]

8. Determine the best-fit polynomial of order 2 for the data. Calculate the sum of squares for your results. Plot the best-fit polynomial for the six data points.
9. Generate a new **X** containing 250 uniform data points in increments of 0.1 from [0.1, 25.0]. Using the best-fit polynomial coefficients from the previous problem, generate a new **Y** containing 250 data points. Plot the results.
10. Compute an estimate of the derivative using the new **X** and new **Y** generated in the previous problem. Compute the coefficients of the derivative. Plot the derivative.

12

Preparing for an Engineering Career

"The key thing that I look for when I interview students is an intuitive understanding of the material," says Tom Henderson, an on-campus interviewer for a *Fortune 500* computer manufacturer. "I'm looking for somebody who has a good feel for engineering and for the process of making good tradeoffs and decisions."

When asked how he determines whether students have a good grasp of engineering basics, Henderson stated, "I try to get them to talk about a class where they've either had big homework assignments or projects, or perhaps about a co-op experience. I ask them to explain it, and then I ask 'Why did you do that?' or 'Why didn't you do some other things?' A lot comes out when people explain what they did on a project."

"The next thing I look for," Henderson says, "is someone who has good teamwork and leadership skills, someone who can work with people and can deal with conflict—that is, someone who can work on a team of engineers. And I look for a certain amount of 'get up and go' and enthusiasm. I especially look for people who are excited about engineering and their career choices."

SECTIONS

OBJECTIVES

By reading this chapter, you will learn:

- What to do while you are in school in order to best prepare for an engineering career.
- How to land a job with a well-written resume and cover letter and by preparing for the interview.
- About the many different career positions that engineers might hold in industry, government, or academia.
- Some tips on managing your career.

How does Henderson decide which students to call for an interview? "I get a stack of resumes about three inches high," he says. "I take them home, and I pull 15 or 20 resumes that I'll call for an interview. As I scan through them, trying to make a first cut, I spend less than 30 seconds per resume looking for certain features: What's their GPA? Have they done any projects that are similar to what I'm hiring for? (That's good evidence that they're interested in doing the work I need done.) Do they have any classes that are specialized—graduate level classes, for example—or something else that makes them stand out?"

"A lot of students think that they're broadening their options by not committing to anything—by taking one digital, one power, and one analog course, for example," says Henderson. "But in some ways they're making themselves more average, so they won't stick out of the pile. It's the person who perhaps has three digital courses and a networking course that would catch my eye.

"Holding an office in any kind of organization is a real plus," he adds. "Just because a student belongs to the IEEE may not mean much, because there are always people who sit in the back row and do nothing. It's actually doing something—being the float committee chairperson, anything that shows leadership—that's important."

The thought of interviewing for a job can provoke anxiety even among the best prepared students. But Tom Henderson wants students to know that interviewers are eager to see them succeed: "On-campus interviewers are hoping to see as many good students in one day as possible, so they are rooting for everyone to do well. Students shouldn't think 'This interviewer is trying to tear me down,' but rather 'This person really wants me to do well.'"

In this chapter, we discuss the various career opportunities open to today's graduating engineering students, as well as providing pointers on what you should be doing while in school to land the job or your dreams.

1 WHILE YOU ARE IN SCHOOL

You are already well on your way to an engineering career just by being accepted to an engineering school. You must have done all the right things in high school, such as taking the appropriate math, science, and English courses. Presumably, you have an aptitude for engineering and a desire to be an engineer. Your engineering school has probably given you a wealth of material to help you plan your education and ensure you meet all requirements for the degree you are pursuing. This section should help you to understand that material better. The section also describes opportunities for work experience that you should pursue while in school, as well as engineering societies you should join.

1.1 Accreditation

In the United States, accreditation is used to ensure quality in educational institutions and programs. Accreditation is a voluntary, nongovernmental process of peer review. It requires an educational institution or program to meet certain, defined standards or criteria. There are two types of accreditation—institutional and specialized. Institutional accreditors examine the college or university as a whole educational institution. Specialized accreditors evaluate specific educational programs. The Accreditation Board for Engineering and Technology (ABET) is a specialized accrediting organization that accredits programs, not institutions. ABET accreditation assures parents and prospective students that a program has met minimum standards and assures employers that graduates are prepared to begin professional practice.

Engineering programs must demonstrate that their graduates have the following attributes:

a. an ability to apply knowledge of mathematics, science, and engineering
b. an ability to design and conduct experiments as well as to analyze and interpret data
c. an ability to design a system, component, or process to meet desired needs
d. an ability to function on multidisciplinary teams
e. an ability to identify, formulate, and solve engineering problems
f. an understanding of professional and ethical responsibility
g. an ability to communicate effectively
h. the broad education necessary to understand the impact of engineering solutions in a global and societal context
i. a recognition of the need for, and an ability to engage in, lifelong learning
j. a knowledge of contemporary issues
k. an ability to use the techniques, skills, and modern engineering tools necessary for engineering practice.

Figure 1. ABET criterion 3—program outcomes and assessment.

ABET has established new criteria for engineering program accreditation as of 2001. The standard includes eight criteria:

1. Students
2. Program Educational Objectives
3. Program Outcomes and Assessment
4. Professional Component
5. Faculty
6. Facilities
7. Institutional Support and Financial Resources
8. Program Criteria.

The first seven apply to all programs; the eighth includes specific criteria for each engineering program that ABET accredits. Criteria 3 lists the specific skills ABET wants to see all engineering graduates possess. Figure 1 lists these skills. For more informations, see ABET's Web site at http://www.abet.org/criteria.html.

It is generally important that the engineering program in which you are enrolled is accredited by ABET. An exception to this rule is when you are majoring in a relatively new or unusual engineering discipline at a respected engineering school where the other programs are accredited. Employers of engineers are well aware of the importance of accreditation. Graduate schools of law and medicine, as well as of engineering, generally require an undergraduate degree from an accredited institution or program for admission. Most state engineer licensing boards require graduation from an ABET-accredited program as the first step in the registration or certification process for professional practice.

1.2 College Education

At most engineering schools, all students take basically the same courses for the first two years. These courses are generally chosen to meet ABET standards—in particular, criteria (a) through (k) listed in Figure 1. Accredited engineering curricula always include courses in the following subjects:

- Mathematics: calculus and differential equations
- Science: physics and chemistry
- Communications: verbal and written
- General engineering: courses in other engineering disciplines and computer programming
- General education: humanities and social sciences

One basic purpose of your education is to give you an understanding of the behavior and characteristics of the natural forces and materials with which you will be working. To be successful as an engineer, for example, you must understand calculus as a description of nature. Merely learning cookbook procedures for solving standardized problems will not do. A study of science also helps you develop an intuitive feel for the world around you. Science teaches you how to examine nature and to make sense of its behavior through your knowledge of its underlying principles and structure. Your study of mathematics and science will lay the groundwork for your study of engineering, which is why math and science come first in your curriculum.

Training in communications is another important part of your engineering education. Most engineers are required to write monthly project progress reports and also to periodically describe their progress in an oral presentation to a group of managers and/or other engineers. Every project, at its end, requires that a detailed project report be written. This report often includes user instructions and enough information to enable another engineer to perform a redesign at some later date.

Beyond the math, science, and communications topics, there are two phases to your engineering studies: one dealing with general engineering and the other dealing with your engineering major. Your study of general engineering will include not only introductory courses, such as the one for which this book was written, but also courses in fields of engineering outside your major. Your understanding of these other fields and how they interact with your field will help you cooperate with other types of engineers as you work on large and complex projects as a professional engineer. Virtually all engineers use computers throughout their careers. Electrical engineers often find it useful to know a programming language, such as C, C++, or Java. Other engineers often use MATLAB or spreadsheets to accomplish much of their computer-based tasks.

Most schools are very specific about the courses engineers must take in mathematics, science, and engineering; however, they usually give considerable leeway in choices of humanities and social science courses. You should select courses that fit your goals. For example, business courses would be appropriate if you plan to go into consulting. If you expect to work internationally, you should take an appropriate foreign language. Other courses you should consider include computer science, economics, government, law, premedicine, and sociology. Planning ahead in this way is particularly important if you plan to pursue a career in a field other than engineering. Many people use an engineering degree as a starting point for other professional careers, such as business, law, and medicine. The courses engineers take in the humanities and social sciences are all the more important today as engineering-based industries become increasingly sensitive to cultural, environmental, and ethical issues. Engineers—whether they work overseas or stay at home—must have an appreciation for the history, culture, and people of the country in which they work.

1.3 Work Experience

All engineering schools encourage students to gain some relevant work experience before graduation. Most offer some assistance in the search for such experience, which might be in the form of a cooperative education job, a summer internship, or simply a part-time evening job. Cooperative education employment involves the cooperation of engineering schools and private or public industry to provide relevant work experience for students. Co-op programs enhance an engineering degree by relating theory to practice. While on co-op, students learn by doing, applying what they have learned in the classroom to a working situation. A co-op job offers the student not only valuable experience, but also an opportunity to check out a prospective employer. Likewise, the companies that hire co-op students get a chance to check out potential employees.

Most engineering schools offer cooperative education employment opportunities in some form. Typically, co-op jobs are optional, lasting for a summer, a semester, or even a full year. Some schools make a co-op a requirement for graduation and employ personnel to manage the program. Such schools often require an entire year of cooperative experience for graduation. The year is often divided into two periods, during which the student works for two different companies.

Not all engineering schools offer formal cooperative education opportunties, but most have some program that helps students gain work experience. Such experience is most often in the form of summer internships with local companies. Some schools strongly encourage seeking internships and have a list of companies seeking to hire students.

Whether or not your school offers any help in your search for a job, you should seek engineering-related work experience during your years in engineering school. Such jobs will put your engineering studies in perspective, giving you an opportunity to see how engineering is done in the real world. Even if your summer or evening jobs are not relevant to engineering, at least they allow you to document in your resume your willingness to work.

A growing trend among students seeking engineering-related work experience is taking temporary jobs in foreign countries. The increasingly global nature of the engineering profession adds considerable value to an overseas work experience. Most overseas jobs do not require that you speak a foreign language. However, the ability to speak the language of the country in which you are working is a valuable asset and might help you land your first full-time job overseas.

If you are interested in a co-op job, internship, or other engineering-related work experience in the United States or in a foreign country, ask for information from your faculty advisor, professors, department chairperson, or the dean's office. Most engineering societies also offer summer internships; check with the societies' faculty advisors or student presidents. Nearly all universities have a career services office where you can find a list of part-time and summer jobs and can receive training in resume writing, interviewing, and job searching. Career services offices also provide information on international jobs.

2 STUDENT ENGINEERING SOCIETIES

The student chapters of engineering societies have much to offer you, including the opportunity to interact with other students with common interests. At student chapter meetings, members discuss important events and developments in their area of engineering. They often invite guest speakers, including practicing engineers who can help you relate your studies to the real world. Student chapters also organize field trips to local companies so you can see engineers at work. Nearly all engineering societies offer scholarships to their student members. Financial support for student chapters of engineering societies normally comes from the host university, the national office of the host society, and from fund-raising activities. Student members typically pay dues to the national office of the host society.

All student engineering societies have student officers. The tasks of student officers include arranging the times and venues of meetings, obtaining refreshments for meetings, finding guest speakers, organizing field trips, and conducting fund-raising activities. The president or chairperson leads the meetings and delegates tasks to the other officers. A secretary takes minutes at meetings, and a treasurer handles the group's finances. Most student chapters will welcome your willingness to be an officer, giving you an opportunity to develop leadership skills that will help you succeed in your career.

If you are an exceptional student, you are likely to be invited to join one or more engineering honor societies. Each engineering field has its own honor society. The premier honor society, which covers all fields of engineering, is Tau Beta Pi. Eligibility for membership depends on your class standing in your junior and senior years. If you are invited, you should consider joining. Honor societies offer many of the same benefits as other engineering societies, including interaction with other engineering students, guest speakers, field trips and scholarships. Active involvement in honor societies—as an officer, for example will give you important experience as a leader of leaders.

Be sure you attend the meetings of the societies you join and get involved. Consider it an important part of planning for your career, your job interviews, and writing your resume. You might feel a little uncomfortable about getting involved during your freshman year, but certainly you should not wait beyond your sophomore year. When employers read resumes, they typically want to see involvement in one or more engineering societies. If they do, they are likely to ask you, during a job interview, about your experience as a member. For example, they might want to hear about what you learned from guest speakers and during field trips.

When employers examine the resumes of engineering graduates, they look at more than their grade point averages (GPAs). They want to see evidence of leadership ability and a willingness to get involved and be a team player. Membership in a student chapter of a professional engineering society gives you a chance to demonstrate these characteristics. Three or four years of societal membership and one or two years service as an officer will help convince employers you have what they want. A combination of leadership activities and a strong GPA will get an employer's attention. (See Table 1 for a list of Web sites for the engineering societies found on most campuses.)

TABLE 1 Web Sites of Engineering Societies Most Likely to Have Student Chapters on University Campuses

ACRONYM	SOCIETY	WEB SITE
ACM	Association for Computing Machinery	http://www.acm.org/
AIChE	American Institute of Chemical Engineers	http://www.aiche.org/
ASCE	American Society of Civil Engineers	http://www.asce.org/
ASME	American Society of Mechanical Engineers	http://www.asme.org/
IEEE	Institute of Electrical and Electronics Engineers	http://www.ieee.org/
IIE	Institute of Industrial Engineers	http://www.iienet.org/
NSBE	National Society of Black Engineers	http://www.nsbe.org/

TABLE 1 Web Sites of Engineering Societies Most Likely to Have Student Chapters on University Campuses (Continued)

ACRONYM	SOCIETY	WEB SITE
SHPE	Society of Professional Hispanic Engineers	http://www.shpe.org/
SWE	Society of Women Engineers	http://www.swe.org/
TBP	Tau Beta Pi Engineering Honor Society	http://www.tbp.org/TBP/pages/Main.html

3 LANDING A JOB OR INTERNSHIP

Once you have earned your engineering degree, how do you get that first job? How about getting a co-op job or an internship? This section provides details on how you start by deciding what kind of organization you want to work for, the kind of business to which you will be sending resumes. Your resume must be preceded by a cover letter that introduces yourself. The cover letter is what a potential employer reads first, so it should be flawless. The resume records your goals, lists significant work experience, and documents leadership qualities. If the employer likes both the cover letter and the resume, you may be asked to come in for an interview. If that goes well, you might have won your first job.

The process might sound simple, but it is not. Very few job applicants get it right. Most employers report amazement at the low quality of the cover letters and resumes they read, and the poor showing of many applicants in their interviews.

PROFESSIONAL SUCCESS: HOW I GOT MY FIRST JOB

So how do graduating engineers land the job of their dreams? Two successful engineers tell us:

"After receiving my undergraduate degree from Boston University, I went to work for Digital where I designed the hardware for microprocessor-based optical disk drive controllers.

"After a few years, I took a sabbatical and received my master's degree from M.I.T., with my thesis work focused on VLSI circuit design. From there, I joined Digital's Semiconductor Group, where I've been ever since."

Sharon Britton
Principal Hardware Engineer
Digital Equipment Corporation

"I decided after receiving my bachelor's degree that I didn't really know as much as I thought I should. So I thought a master's [degree] would be a good idea.

"I went to the University of Toronto, where I met a professor who was heavily involved in marine oil spills. He got me involved in the natural dispersion of oil slicks. Through his contacts, I ended up getting a job in Calgary, Alberta, which is the center of the Canadian oil industry. The job was with a company that was drilling in the Canadian arctic.

"My job was as a research engineer, dealing with prevention and cleanup of oil spills. I spent four and a half years doing lots of experiments, simulating oil spills, testing various techniques, and handling oil in open water in the Beaufort Sea, north of Alaska."

Ian Buist
Vice President
S. L. Ross Environmental Research Ltd.

3.1 Choosing a Potential Employer

Before you write your resume, you should consider the type of company, agency, or institution for which you want to work. Big, small, local, governmental, international, consulting, research and development, or manufacturing? To help you make an informed decision, throughout your time in engineering school you should read about business in general and organizations that employ engineers in particular. Read the business section of your local or regional newspaper. Read popular business magazines and newspapers like the *Wall Street Journal*. Scan the want ads in the newspapers to see what opportunities exist.

As you approach graduation, you will have to choose the specific organizations from which you will seek employment. Of course, it helps if those organizations are seeking engineers. The primary resources for engineering employment ads are engineering journals. Your engineering school and university library will have recent copies of journals that are relevant to the degrees they offer. You might also contact engineering alumni from your school and set up informational interviews to learn more about particular organizations or industries. Your deans should have a list of alumni who are willing to be contacted.

You should learn as much as possible about an organization before you send in a resume. This knowledge will help you write a quality cover letter and to perform well in an interview (both topics are covered later in this section). Most companies that hire engineers are public companies, with stock held and traded by the public. If a company in which you are interested is a public company, there will be a wealth of information on it in the Securities and Exchange Commission's *Edgar* database of corporate information and *Standard & Poor's* directories. The *Thomas Register of American Manufacturers*, which is revised annually, is the Yellow Pages of American industry and will give you important information about companies involved in all fields of engineering. All three publications should be available at your university and public libraries or online at http://www.sec.gov/edgar.shtml, http://www.standardandpoors.com/, and http://www.thomasregister.com/, respectively. You might also try the *Million Dollar Directory*, available at most university libraries. Of course, you should also visit the Web site, if one exists, of any company in which you are interested.

PROFESSIONAL SUCCESS: HOW I GOT MY FIRST JOB

So how do graduating engineers land the job of their dreams? Two more successful engineers tell us:

"I went to work for Boeing because my primary goals were staying in the Seattle area and working on large projects. (I'd spent three years working in the nuclear industry during the summer and found I enjoyed working on large projects.) I've been working at Boeing ten years now."

Clay Hess
Lead Engineer, Mechanical Hydraulic
Systems Organization
Boeing Corporation

"I had worked as a summer employee for four years—two years with Brown and Root and two with Schlumberger. My first full-time job was with Brown and Root as a construction engineer in the fabrication yard just outside of Houston."

Paul Olstad
Project Manager
Fluor Daniel

3.2 Resumes

The importance of having a quality resume cannot be overemphasized. Your resume is a sales brochure designed to sell you—that is, to land an interview. However, most employers complain about the number of resumes they receive that have misspelled words and typographical errors. Such unnecessary errors give a company an excuse for narrowing down the resumes they otherwise might seriously consider.

Do not go into writing your resume assuming you know what you are doing. If possible, attend a resume-writing workshop; most colleges offer one. Search the Web for one of its many online resume-writing tutorials. Many word-processing programs include one or more resume templates to help you get started. Once your resume is completed, be sure to have it reviewed by someone who has experience in writing resumes, perhaps a professor, engineer, or someone who regularly hires engineers.

The following is a recommended general structure for the resume of a new engineering graduate (see Figure 2):

- *Name*: Center your name in bold, large type at the top of the page. Give your address, phone number, and e-mail address.
- *Objective*: State the type of position you seek—for example, "To work as a design engineer in the construction industry." Be reasonably specific.
- *Education*: List your degree. If you received it with honors, say so. State your overall GPA if it is 3.0 (out of 4.0) or higher. State your engineering GPA, especially if it is higher than your overall GPA. List the college courses you took that support your stated objective. Also list other courses that are relevant—for example, foreign language courses if you are applying for an overseas job. List your computer hardware and software expertise.
- *Awards*: List any awards and scholarships you received in college. Include scholastic, athletic, club, and service awards.
- *Experience*: List your work experience, starting with your most recent work. Include jobs you held on campus, after school, and even while in high school. Employers like people who have worked, even when the work was unpaid or part time. It is particularly important to emphasize engineering-related jobs. Elaborate on particular achievements, such as your senior project, bringing together and leading a student committee, or helping a professor or employer install a computer network. Emphasize any computer skills you have, even if you are self-taught. Show evidence of your self-motivation, leadership abilities, and willingness to work hard.
- *Activities*: Describe your activities in your school, community, and church. Stress membership and leadership roles in engineering societies.

Do not exaggerate on your resume. For example, you should not mention a club membership if you never attended any of its meetings, since the interviewer is likely to ask for details about your involvement. On the other hand, do not be overly modest. Your resume should be accurate and truthful, but it should also present you in your best light.

New graduates often feel that they have little to put in their resumes. But if you begin to focus now on the categories listed in this section, by the time you graduate you will have plenty to offer a prospective employer.

John J. Smith

College Address:
201 Anderson Hall
Taft University
Bakersfield, CA 93309
(805) 555-0805

Permanent Address:
1234 A Street
Sacramento, CA 95606
(916) 555-1234

OBJECTIVE

Obtain an entry-level mechanical engineering position with a large manufacturing company that offers opportunities for international employment.

EDUCATION

Bachelor of Science, Mechanical Engineering, Taft University, Bakersfield, CA
Overall GPA: 3.24, Engineering GPA: 3.40
Associate of Arts, Engineering, Bakersfield Community College, Bakersfield, CA
Overall GPA: 3.75
Minor in Spanish: four semesters of conversational Spanish.
Experienced in using AutoCAD and Matlab.

AWARDS

1995	Bank of America Scholarship Award, $500.
1992 – 1996	Regent's Scholarship, covering half of tuition.
1992 – 1996	Dean's list every semester but one.

EXPERIENCE

Spring 1996	Senior Project, Taft University. Designed and built a small motorcycle powered by a chainsaw motor.
Summer, Fall 2000	Co-op, General Mills, Lodi, CA. Independently designed several packaging machines.
1998 – 2001	Lab Assistant, Taft University. Managed the engineering school computer lab 3 to 9 hours/week.
1996 – 2001	Grader, Taft University. Graded calculus, physics, and engineering homework.
1995 – 1999	Shift Manager, Pizza Hut, Bakersfield, CA. Handled sales and managed 5 workers, part time during school years, full time during summers.

ACTIVITIES

2000 – 2001 Associated Student Body Vice President
1999 – 2000 Chairperson, student chapter of the ASME.
1997 – 2001 Member, ASME.
1996 – 1999 Volunteer worker at county children's home.

REFERENCES
Available on request.

Figure 2. A sample resume.

3.3 Cover Letters

Every resume you mail should be accompanied by a unique cover letter that will call attention to your resume. Before you write the cover letter, research the organization. Determine who should receive your resume, and address your cover letter to that person. The library and online resources previously described list company phone numbers you can call and ask to whom to send your resume. Avoid simply addressing your resume to human resources or the personnel department.

Let the recipient know that you know something about his or her organization. Point out strengths in your resume that are applicable to the job you seek. Make it sound like this is the one and only resume you mailed out; never write an impersonal form letter. Keep it short, less than one page.

The following is a checklist for your cover letter:

- Is the letter unique, written expressly for the organization to which you will mail it?
- Is the letter addressed to a specific person?
- Do your opening sentences capture the reader's attention?
- Did you describe your major accomplishments, those that are relevant to the job you are seeking?
- Is the letter less than one page long and easy to read?
- Did you write in a clear, professional, businesslike manner?
- Are you positive there are no grammatical or spelling errors?
- Is the letter clean, with dark, easy-to-read print?

Figure 3 gives an example of a good cover letter. Note that the letter is addressed to a specific person, starts by getting the reader's attention, indicates knowledge of the company, and emphasizes the writer's qualities that make him a good candidate for the job he seeks.

John J. Smith
1234 Elm Street
Sacramento, CA 95606
(916) 555-1234

April 13, 1996

Ms. Jane J. Doe
Human Resources Director
Magnum Manufacturing, Inc.
Houston, TX 77707

Dear Ms. Doe:

Dr. Richard Turpin, professor of mechanical engineering at Taft University, suggested that I write you concerning a position with Magnum Manufacturing. He said that at a recent ASME conference in New Orleans you asked him to recommend graduating mechanical engineers who can help your company launch a project in Mexico. I am one of the students he recommended.

As you can see from my enclosed transcript, I have done well in my studies at Taft, and I expect to graduate with high honors. I believe my strong GPA and my elective courses in manufacturing and international studies make me a good candidate that can meet your needs.

In addition to my academic strengths, I have a strong interest in working internationally. As a teenager I lived for a year in Zimbabwe, where my father worked as an electrical engineer. I've also traveled extensively throughout Africa and Europe. While I have not yet been to Mexico, I've taken four semesters of Spanish and am able to read and speak the language fairly well.

Ms. Doe, I look forward to speaking with you personally about my qualifications and how I can serve Magnum Manufacturing. I'll phone your office on Tuesday, May 1, to inquire further about the position in Mexico. Perhaps we can arrange an interview at that time. Thank you in advance for your consideration.

Sincerely,

John J. Smith

John J. Smith

Figure 3. A sample cover letter.

PROFESSIONAL SUCCESS: HOW I GOT MY FIRST JOB

So how do graduating engineers land the job of their dreams? Two more successful engineers tell us:

"While I was in my senior year at college, I got interested in digital signal processing and communication systems. I also knew that I wanted to go to graduate school. I interviewed with Bell Laboratories in New Jersey and worked for them for three years, including a year in graduate school, which they paid for."

Jose E. Hernandez
Electrical Engineer
Lawrence Livermore National Laboratory

"For my last co-op, I worked for a food manufacturer. Then, when I graduated, they were doing a very big expansion project, and I walked in to become the project manager. It was unheard of for someone coming out of school, 25 years old, to take on a $5 million project. But thanks to my co-op work there, they knew me; I'd done projects in that facility before. The relationships were there, and I understood the business. It was a good fit. That project lasted about a year and a half."

Greg Raco
Project Manager
Ocean Spray, Inc.

3.4 Interviews

For many people the interview is the toughest part of the job-hunting process. Yet it is the most important part, so you must be well prepared. If you follow the guidelines outlined in this section, you can easily stand out as a top candidate in the eyes of a recruiter.

Recruiters will not expect you to have extensive experience or advanced engineering skills; they will be looking for potential. They will try to assess your grasp of basic engineering concepts. And they will look for positive personal traits such as self-confidence, flexibility, adaptability, and eagerness to learn.

The two most important points in an interview are the beginning and the end. The recruiter's initial impression of you is the most critical aspect of the interview. The momentum of a good start will help you relax and make the rest of the interview go more smoothly. To make a good first impression, dress well and be well groomed, be on time, and exhibit confidence. Introduce yourself, and shake the recruiter's hand with an eagerness that shows that there is no other place you would rather be.

Most recruiters mark the end of an interview with the question, "Do you have any questions about our organization?" Never say, "No." Come prepared with questions to ask. Ask questions that show an interest in the organization, not yourself. Ask questions that show that you have done some research on the organization. For example, "I know that XYZ Industries has offices in Atlanta. Are there opportunities for new engineers to work there?" or "I've read that XYZ Industries has grown 50 percent in the last two years. Do you expect such growth to continue?" During the initial interview it is generally not good form to ask, "How much will I get paid?" or "How many weeks of vacation will I get each year?"

You should walk into the interview knowing the following information, which usually can be found online:

- The history of the organization
- The size of the organization
- What the organization does or manufactures
- In what cities, states, and countries the organization operates

- The direction the organization is headed and its potential for future growth
- How well the organization is doing in the marketplace and who is its competition

Do not ask the recruiter for this information. Having it before the interview will give you confidence. The recruiter probably will ask you what you know about the organization, but you can always volunteer the information in a natural way.

Questions you might ask during the interview include

- What is the average time an engineer spends in project work before moving into project management?
- What is a typical career path in the area in which I would be working?
- What are my opportunities for travel?
- Does the organization have a formal continuing education program?

Summarizing, the following are a few good tips for doing well in an interview:

- Do some research on the company, agency, or organization. Know what it does and where it does it. Know where and how you might fit in.
- Be on time and dress appropriately.
- Look the recruiter in the eye and shake hands with confidence when you enter the room.
- Do not sit down until invited to do so.
- Remember the recruiter's name when given it, and then use it when thanking the recruiter for the interview as you leave.
- Be enthusiastic, demonstrating a positive outlook on life and your career.
- Have prepared answers for common interview questions, such as, "Tell me about yourself," "What do you know about our organization?" "Why should I hire you?" and "Where do you plan to be five years from now?"
- During the interview, occasionally look the recruiter in the eye, but not so often that it makes the recruiter uncomfortable.
- When asked if you have any questions, ask relevant questions about the organization. Use your questions to demonstrate your knowledge of the organization.

PROFESSIONAL SUCCESS: INTERVIEWING

What will those first interviews be like? One engineer passes on his insights:

"I think, when I was being interviewed myself, the biggest mistake I made was being willing to be led too much by the different interviewers. I think I was trying to make a good impression in agreeing with people when they said, 'Doesn't it sound like fun?' or, 'Wouldn't you like to do that?'

"Looking back, I think those interviewers probably ended up with a very erroneous impression of what I wanted to do."

PROFESSIONAL SUCCESS: INTERVIEWING

"Students should be frank and honest in an interview about what they want to do. I want people who have given some thought to what they want to do and who really want to come to work for me, doing the kind of stuff I do. They have to convince me that they want to work for me. That's what will make them stand out. There's a sea of people out there who want a job, so you have to stand out."
Tom Henderson

You must enter the process of finding a job with reasonable expectations and established priorities. Be flexible, willing to work in another city, state, or even country. Be willing to work in a field other than your first choice, but do not appear desperate by being "willing to do anything." Do not make money your first priority. If possible, talk to some engineers who already work for the organization and get their advice. If you follow these simple rules, your name will be much more likely to rise to the top of any recruiter's list of potential employees.

4 CAREER OPPORTUNITIES

The typical engineering degree program will train you as a designer and enable you to function in a broad range of career fields. However, only a fraction of engineering graduates actually take jobs as designers straight out of school. Those with bachelor's degrees often go into production, operations, or sales. Those with master's or doctorate degrees may take positions as researchers or teachers. Later in their careers, many engineers move into management. Some go into consulting. Your engineering education, with its requirements in mathematics, science, humanities, and social sciences, should enable you to succeed in virtually any field. In fact, schools of law and medicine typically look very favorably on a degree in engineering when choosing students for admission.

4.1 Design

As previously stated, most engineering curricula emphasize design. Designers bridge the gap between an idea and the production line. First and foremost, as a designer you must be creative. You must also have solid analytical, decision-making, and problem-solving skills. You must have strong mathematical and scientific knowledge and have an understanding of economics, being aware of the costs involved in both the design and production of a product. You must be able to work under pressure, adhering to schedules while functioning effectively as a team member and demonstrating the communication skills that are necessary for the success of the team.

Most design positions demand that the engineer take his or her design through a process that results in a working product. Therefore, as a designer you can expect to be involved in development and testing. Development takes an idea from a set of design drawings to a working prototype or final product. It includes obtaining parts and materials and interacting with technical, construction, or other specially trained personnel. Once you have developed a prototype or final product, you must test it to ensure that it meets the original specifications.

Given the broad range of skills and talents required of a design engineer, the easiest path into this career is to get a master's degree or to work your way into it through time and experience in other engineering roles. Design work is exciting and rewarding as you guide ideas into reality.

4.2 Production

While a designer typically cooperates with other engineers who design the various parts of a complex system, the production engineer coordinates the activities of the people who build the systems designers create.

Experienced production engineers often are responsible for estimating the costs of production, determining, for example, the cost of building a bridge or manufacturing 10,000 cameras. To do cost estimation, they must be able to estimate accurately the cost of fabrication materials, using various manufacturing processes and labor, as well as be able to estimate overhead and profit. As a production engineer, you might be responsible for bidding on projects and then establishing the schedules and budgets for projects.

Production engineering is a career of great responsibility, bringing together and coordinating the human, material, and monetary resources that are necessary for the creation of a product.

4.3 Operations

As an operations engineer you would be responsible for the operation of a complex system, such as a manufacturing or processing plant. Another title for an operations engineer is plant engineer. The operations engineer ensures that large systems operate efficiently, safely, and legally. For example, the piping, boilers, turbines, generators, and monitoring equipment of any power plant, whether nuclear or fossil-fuel fired, form a complex system that typically is managed by a team of operations engineers. Constant monitoring of the system is necessary. Maintenance schedules must be established and maintained. All state and federal regulations must be observed, and the safety of plant personnel also must be ensured.

An operations engineer must have a broad range of knowledge. A background in industrial engineering is most helpful, but knowledge of civil, electrical, mechanical, and chemical engineering, as well as economics and business law, can also be useful.

Operations engineering is a challenging career requiring broad knowledge, extensive communication skills, and the ability to work closely with people from many disciplines. The satisfaction of having the big picture and control over the way things are done can make this a rewarding career.

4.4 Sales

Many engineering graduates find interesting and lucrative careers in sales. Sales engineers are not salespeople. They do not knock on doors or seek sales orders. The sales engineer is a technical person who works with the sales staff, answering technical questions from potential customers and educating existing customers.

Many products created by engineers are extremely complex. A well-trained sales engineer can unravel that complexity for potential customers and convince them that a product will be an effective solution to their problem. As a sales engineer, you would train the customers how to use the product and offer technical service. You also would provide product support, seeking ways to improve the products you sell.

You must be comfortable with people and have a pleasing personality to succeed as a sales engineer. A background in psychology, sociology, and human relations also will be useful. Sales engineering offers an interesting career that always involves new places and new faces and often involves significant travel.

4.5 Research

As a researcher you would apply basic scientific principles to the discovery of new knowledge that could help solve society's engineering-related problems. You must be particularly creative. You also must be patient since a researcher can work many months or even years on one problem.

Students often assume they have to be professors to be researchers, but many government agencies and most large companies also employ researchers. Some federal agencies, such as the National Science Foundation (NSF), pay researchers to seek advancements in virtually all fields of engineering and science. Others, such as NASA, seek knowledge in more narrow areas. Although many researchers who receive support from the NSF, NASA, and other government agencies are professors, a large number work directly for federal, state, or local governments.

Both large and small companies perform research to improve their products and gain a larger segment of the market in which they compete. Most companies—those in the transportation field, for example—also perform research to find ways to increase the safety of their products. A good research and development (R&D) department can help a company remain competitive in our increasingly technological society.

Whether you seek employment as a researcher for a university, the government, or industry, the education requirements are basically the same. An advanced degree, usually a Ph.D., is a must, with a strong background in mathematics and science. You must also have a strong desire to seek and discover new knowledge. The element of discovery, coupled with solving real-world problems, can make research a particularly satisfying career.

PROFESSIONAL SUCCESS: RESEARCH

Why go into research? One engineer passes on her insights:

"I was part of a joint research project with Sandia National Labs in their combustion research facility (CRF). I took a sabbatical there, and we did a joint study working with some people who specialized in combustion engines. They were curious to see if they could get augmented heat transfer by impinging the exhaust, which is pulsating exhaust onto a flat plate.

"The team members came in with very different strengths. One person's strength was theoretical, management, project planning; he was the leader of the project. Another expertise was in combustion and fluid mechanics. I came in with expertise in conductive heat transfer and external flows. We had a blast working together, setting up the experiment, finding what went wrong, and then rerunning it until all hours of the night. It was wonderful."

Pamela Eibeck
Mechanical Engineering Department Chair
Northern Arizona University

4.6 Management

Managers manage people, materials, money, and time. They oversee the activities of the employees they supervise and help guarantee the success of projects by establishing budget and time constraints.

Managers spend much of their time reading, writing, and meeting with people. They review proposals, contracts, and specifications and keep up with new laws. They read and write letters, memos, progress reports, and personnel evaluations. Often managers have to do the bulk of their reading and writing at home because so much of their time at the office is taken up with meetings—with assistants, engineers, their own managers, clients, and government officials, to name a few.

Engineers tend to be promoted from designer to project engineer. As a new project engineer, you probably will be put in charge of a project or part of a project, with several engineers under your supervision. In this position you will oversee the design work of others on the project and will likely still do some design work yourself. The goals of your projects may or may not be initially clear; how to achieve the goals will be up to you. It will be your responsibility to bring the project in on schedule and within budget.

Over time, a competent project engineer will be given responsibility for managing increasingly large projects, or multiple projects involving the supervision of other project engineers. Depending on the size of the company, a project engineer may eventually be promoted to an executive management level, such as vice president. Vice presidents typically oversee entire sectors of their companies, including design, production, or operations.

Engineers are often viewed as having the problem-solving skills required to manage large companies. As a result, many companies that are not involved in engineering nevertheless hire engineering graduates and place them directly into management positions, usually after some training. Companies that deal with technology are even more likely to prefer to have engineers in their management positions. An engineer with a Master's in business administration (MBA) is an even more desirable candidate.

4.7 Consulting

Engineers who move into consulting typically do so after they have worked several years in industry and have developed the experience and contacts they need to strike out on their own. Frequently, two or more engineers leave a company together to form their own consulting firm. Some engineers join a consulting firm straight out of school. Larger consulting firms may employ more than 100 engineers.

In addition to engineering experience, a consultant needs business acumen to succeed. In fact, most consulting practices that fail do so because of a lack of knowledge of, or preparation for, the business end of the practice. Newcomers often face problems managing employees, dealing with administrative details, marketing their services, and handling cash flow, as clients are sometimes slow in paying for consulting services. Therefore, it is important to have ample cash reserves when starting out. Some say those reserves should be enough to last 6 to 12 months without a paying client.

Consulting is an inviting option to those who prefer to work for themselves and are willing to accept business risks that could result in great financial reward. Today the consulting field is doing well and appears to be poised for growth. Many companies are moving toward hiring fewer full-time engineers and toward hiring part-time consultants. This trend is likely to continue as companies strive to be as flexible as possible in order to compete.

PROFESSIONAL SUCCESS: CONSULTING

Why go into consulting? One engineer passes on his insights:

Joe Engel started his engineering education at Bakersfield Junior College in Bakersfield, California. He then had a double major at the University of California at Davis, receiving bachelor's degrees in mechanical and civil engineering. Today he is part owner of Engel & Company Engineers, an engineering consulting firm in Bakersfield, California. Joe Engel reflects on his 18-year consulting career:

"When I graduated from college, my dad, who owned his own consulting firm, talked me into joining the firm. Once I got out into the real world of jobs and people, I discovered I really didn't know a lot about the practical side of engineering. So I started out as basically a draftsman. But as time went on, I was taking jobs from start to finish. And that's what I've been doing ever since.

PROFESSIONAL SUCCESS: CONSULTING

"One of my biggest challenges as a consulting engineer is not only to figure out the engineering solution but also to deal with the personalities involved. I try to encourage a certain level of agreement among all members of a team so that the project will move ahead. I learned a lot from watching my father in meetings, seeing how he dealt with others. These were things I could never have learned in the classroom.

"I cannot imagine a more fulfilling occupation. When you own your own company, your position is defined in the way that you want to define it. You can work 80 hours per week, or you can work 10. In addition to the freedom, you get the satisfaction of putting together projects any way you want. And you don't have to deal with the in-fighting and jockeying for position that you see in large organizations.

"Unfortunately, I think a lot of young engineers try to go into consulting too soon, without enough experience. They just get their licenses and think they can hang out a shingle and practice engineering. They make a mistake, I think.

"My advice to the student who wants to become a consultant is to work with an older engineer for about ten years, doing the work he or she doesn't want to do. You will end up solving so many engineering problems that when you do go out on your own, you will be confident and able to provide good service.

"In any event, I think newcomers should try to start their careers in an established consulting firm. Then they can move into a partnership, becoming a consultant in a more natural way, with less risk."

Joe Engel

4.8 International Opportunities

International jobs have much to offer an engineer. Learning a new culture can be interesting and exciting. Although learning a new language may not be necessary, often it is an option that the engineer should pursue. In addition to higher pay, an international career offers interesting travel and cultural experiences in a variety of locations.

Although jobs in the less popular overseas locations can pay as much as double what you could get in the United States, you should think carefully before accepting an international position. The weather may not be to your liking. Living conditions may be less than ideal, and your travel within the host nation may be restricted. Some countries are inhospitable, or even off limits, to minorities and women. Be sure you are ready to stay for a while when you go, since a commitment to stay overseas for at least two years is a common requirement.

PROFESSIONAL SUCCESS: GLOBAL ENGINEERING

Why go into global engineering? One engineer passes on his insights:

Paul Olstad received his B.A. from Harvard University and M.S. from Rice University, in civil engineering. After graduation, he worked for Brown and Root and the Burroughs Corporation for several years before joining Fluor Daniel, where he began an international career that has lasted 14 years. Olstad describes how he came to work overseas for Fluor Daniel, and the rewards of international assignments:

"I was sent to Malaysia to assist the construction of an on-shore oil terminal. They wanted somebody who knew process, control systems, electrical, civil structural, and mechanical. Of course, I didn't know all those things, but I learned pretty fast and did what needed to be done.

PROFESSIONAL SUCCESS: GLOBAL ENGINEERING

"I'd been interested in an overseas assignment for a long time. Prior to that I had been on a few business trips and had a two-month assignment in Singapore and a two-month assignment in Denmark, but Malaysia was my first permanent assignment. It was supposed to last for five months, but it stretched into 51 weeks.

"After Malaysia, I got an assignment to Saudi Arabia. I went there in January and brought my children over in June, after they were out of school. We spent just over two years in Saudi Arabia the first time. While there, I was project manager for a number of off-shore platform projects.

"After two years, a decrease in construction activity in Saudi Arabia had virtually shut down our office there. So Fluor Daniel brought me back to Houston. Two years later, things had improved in Saudi Arabia, and I was asked if I wanted to go back and start up our office there again. Of course, I went.

"I spent about two years helping build the Saudi Arabia office from nothing to about 100 people. Then we were awarded a major program.

"A week later, Saddam Hussein invaded Kuwait. About a week after the invasion, my company evacuated everyone to Jeddah or out of Saudi Arabia, and I returned to Houston for two weeks. It was an interesting experience.

"The pay you can expect from an overseas assignment depends on the country. Almost any overseas assignment includes some increase in salary or benefits and also some assistance in accommodations. Just as a reference, for Saudi Arabia, our standard work week is 48 hours instead of 40 hours, so the engineers get a 20 percent pay increase for that. And we get another 15 percent increase as a foreign incentive. And we are provided housing, and an area increase for the cost-of-living differential.

"Another nice thing about working overseas is the opportunity to travel, which we did whenever we got our home leaves. Our children were in school in Europe, so we went to Europe often. We also went to the Far East, spent Christmas in Australia, and did a lot of things that we could never have done otherwise."

Paul Olstad
Project Manager
Fluor Daniel

4.9 Teaching

Most engineering disciplines offer numerous teaching opportunities. Although you may be able to find a teaching position at a technical school that requires that you have only an undergraduate degree, most institutions require an advanced degree. Teaching at a community college typically requires a master's degree, and teaching at a college or university requires that you earn a Ph.D. Most schools prefer that instructors have some experience as practicing engineers; however, this is not the case with most universities because they want professors to concentrate on research.

Most teachers enjoy the challenge of increasing others' knowledge and understanding, the stimulating interaction with students and colleagues, and the excitement of research. Add to these benefits a relatively flexible schedule and the variety of two new semesters every year, and it is clear that teaching can be a rewarding career.

PROFESSIONAL SUCCESS: TEACHING

Why go into teaching? One engineer passes on her insights:

Pamela Eibeck received her B.S., M.S., and Ph.D. degrees in mechanical engineering from Stanford University, then began her career as a university professor. Eibeck describes why she finds teaching so rewarding:

PROFESSIONAL SUCCESS: TEACHING

"I remember teaching a lab one time. We were measuring drag on different-shaped vehicles. I had the students read a research paper that was written by a GM engineer. The engineer happened to be at Stanford at the time for a conference. As I heard him explain his research, I remember being so excited seeing the meaningfulness of what the students were learning in school and its relationship to what is actually happening in industry.

"When I was teaching at Berkeley, I was the campus principle Investigator for a coalition of teachers from several universities whose task was to investigate innovative teaching. I discovered how much I liked having the big picture, having a sense that I could influence a strategic plan of a program.

"As chair of the Mechanical Engineering Department at NAU I'll be teaching two courses each semester. But I'll also be working on some curriculum reform, adding some new emphases to mechanical engineering, and hiring some new faculty. So I'm very much involved in teaching, in a larger, envisionary way. Yet I am still involved with the students. I would not enjoy my job if I were not involved with the students."

Pamela Eibeck
Mechanical Engineering Department Chair
Northern Arizona University

5 MAPPING YOUR CAREER

Being in control of your career takes planning that should start now. You should develop both short- and long-term goals now. Generally your long-term goals determine your short-term goals. For example, if your long-term goal is to have your own civil engineering consulting firm, your short-terms goals should include taking courses in civil engineering, economics, and business management and getting a civil engineering degree. If you plan to move into management eventually, you should consider taking some business and accounting classes; you might even want to earn an MBA (master's in business administration). If you prefer to stay involved in technical work your entire career, you might want to pursue a masters degree in engineering. If you want to teach engineering, you probably will need a Ph.D. in engineering.

Prospective employers today look for engineering-related work experience, whether cooperative or summer internship. They also seek engineers with good interpersonal skills. They want engineers who can function productively as part of a team, who have strong communication skills, and who interface well with customers. Software skills are extremely important to most employers. Business knowledge also can be beneficial. Employers complain, however, that new engineers often want too much money, are unwilling to start at the bottom of a corporate structure, and are inflexible about relocating to a new part of the country or world.

No one can confidently predict where the jobs will be in three or four years, when you graduate. However, the U.S. Bureau of Labor Statistics indicates that there will be a shortage of engineers well into the 21st century. In spite of these shortages, be aware that engineering job security is becoming an oxymoron for engineers. Many companies are moving toward hiring temporary engineers from consulting firms, allowing them to hire engineers only as needed for specific projects. As a new engineer entering the job market, you should plan for an uncertain future and be prepared to be mobile and, above all, to stay current in your field.

Chances are, as you get started as a novice engineer, you will be given relatively simple assignments. You will be expected to be a team player and to learn from the more experienced engineers. In a year or two you probably will be assigned larger projects, lasting several months or even a year or two. Within several years, you may be promoted to project engineer. If you stay on a typical career track, you eventually will be put in charge of increasingly larger projects with more engineers under your supervision. Along the way, continue to develop short- and long-term goals. Ask yourself what you want to be doing a year from now as well as ten years from now. Plan how best to achieve your goals.

Most companies will allow you to pursue a career in a purely technical role if you decide that a management role is not for you. The income and promotion opportunities typically are greater for managers in most companies; however, many companies now offer parallel career paths for those engineers who prefer a technical career to a management career. As a technical engineer you could move into positions in which you do design work as part of a team that you would also manage. Or, if you have an advanced degree, you might move into research and other more scientifically oriented work.

It is important for you to start planning your engineering career now. Remember to join one or more engineering societies and get involved in their activities. If your school has a cooperative education program, consider taking time off from your studies for a co-op job, or find work as a summer intern at an engineering company. Choose a potential employer wisely and put some time and effort into you resume and cover letter.

Whatever your career goals, you should keep them continually in mind and consciously guide your career. Do not just let your career "happen." Grasp opportunities as they present themselves. Always be a team player. Be flexible, adaptable, and a willing learner. Change is about the only constant in an engineering career, and education is your best ticket to ensuring you keep up.

KEY TERMS

consulting
cover letters
design
interviews
management
operations
production
project engineer
research
resumes
sales

Problems

1. List the required courses that all engineering students take at your school, categorized as mathematics, science, communication, engineering or computer science, humanities, or social sciences.
2. Interview a practicing engineer and report which courses he or she has found most useful during his or her career.
3. List your work experience that you would list on a resume now. List any work experience you hope to be able to add to your list by the time you graduate.
4. Attend a student engineering society meeting and write a report about the meeting, indicating the number of attendees, the person or persons who ran the meeting, the issues discussed, the plans made, and how you would contribute to the society if you were a member.
5. Describe the co-op or internship program at your school, describing what help your school offers in ensuring that its students graduate with relevant work experience.
6. List four companies at which you would you like to spend a co-op or internship and state why in each of the four cases.
7. Choose one company for which you would most like to work and then perform a Web search for information on that company. List its full legal name, the address of its corporate headquarters, the location where you might work for it, the division for which you might work, and its present stock price.

8. Using Figure 1 as a model, write your resume as you would like it to appear five years from now.
9. Using Figure 2 as a model, write a cover letter that would accompany your resume. Address it to the organization for which you would most like to work. Acquire and use information relevant to that company.
10. List the career opportunities described in Section 3 in the order of your preference for working each area.
11. How would you answer the following common interview questions: What are your short-term and long-term goals? What contribution would you make to this organization? Where do you plan to be five years from now?

13

MATLAB Environment

GRAND CHALLENGE: VEHICLE PERFORMANCE

Wind tunnels are test chambers built to generate precise wind speeds. Accurate scale models of new aircraft can be mounted on force-measuring supports in the test chamber, and then measurements of the forces acting on the models can be made at many different wind speeds and angles of the models relative to the wind direction. Some wind tunnels can operate at hypersonic velocities, generating wind speeds of thousands of miles per hour. The sizes of wind tunnel test sections vary from a few inches across to sizes large enough to accommodate a business jet. At the completion of a wind tunnel test series, many sets of data have been collected that can be used to determine the lift, drag, and other aerodynamic performance characteristics of a new aircraft at its various operating speeds and positions.

Many of the example problems in this section are related to wind tunnels and the calculations that are performed with the data collected in them.

SECTIONS

OBJECTIVES

After reading this chapter, you should be able to

- understand the MATLAB screen layout, windows, and interactive environments
- initialize and use scalars, vectors, and matrices in computations
- save and retrieve MATLAB data
- create and use script M-files

GETTING STARTED

MATLAB is one of a number of commercially available, sophisticated mathematical computation tools, such as MAPLE, Mathematica, and MathCad. Despite what their proponents may claim, no single one of these tools is "the best." They all have strengths and weaknesses. Each will allow you to perform basic mathematical computations, but they differ in the ways that they handle symbolic calculations and more complicated mathematical processes. MATLAB excels at computations involving matrices. In fact its name, MATLAB, is short for **Mat**rix **Lab**oratory. At a very basic level, you can think of these programs as sophisticated, computer-based calculators. They can perform the same functions as your scientific calculator, and **many more**. In many engineering classes, performing computations with a mathematical computation program is replacing more traditional computer programming. That doesn't mean you shouldn't learn a high-level language such as C++ or FORTRAN; but programs such as MATLAB have become a standard tool for engineers and scientists.

Today's MATLAB has capabilities far beyond the original MATLAB and is an interactive system and programming language for general scientific and technical computation. Its basic element is a matrix. Because MATLAB commands are similar to the way that we express engineering steps in mathematics, writing computer solutions in MATLAB can be much quicker than writing solutions in a high-level language. It's important to understand when to use a computational program such as MATLAB and when to use a general purpose, high-level programming language. MATLAB excels at numerical calculations, especially matrix calculations, and graphics. However, you wouldn't want to write a word processing program in MATLAB. C++ and FORTRAN are general purpose programs, and would be the programming tool of choice for large application programs such as operating systems or drafting software. (In fact, MATLAB, which is a large application program, was written in C, a precursor to C++.) Usually, high-level programs do not offer easy access to graphing. The primary area of overlap between MATLAB and high-level programs is in "number crunching"—programs that require repetitive calculations or processing of large quantities of data. Both MATLAB and high-level languages are good at processing numbers. It is usually easier to write a "number crunching" program in MATLAB, and it usually executes faster in C++ or FORTRAN. The one exception to this rule is with matrices. Because MATLAB is optimized for matrices, if a problem can be formulated with a matrix solution, MATLAB executes substantially faster than a similar program in a high-level language.

MATLAB is available in both a professional version and a student version. The professional version is probably installed in your college or university computer laboratory, but you may enjoy having a student version at home.

Student Edition of MATLAB

In this section, we explain the differences between the professional and student versions of MATLAB, and introduce you to the MATLAB environment. A number of examples are presented. We encourage you to type the example problems into MATLAB as you read the book, and observe the results.

Hint: You may think some of the examples are too simple to type in yourself—that just reading the material is sufficient. However, you will remember the material better if you both read it and type it!

The MathWorks provides an inexpensive student version of MATLAB, for the Microsoft Windows, McIntosh, and Linux operating systems. The student version of MATLAB includes the following components of the professional version:

- The basic MATLAB engine and development environment
- The MATLAB notebook
- Simulink
- The symbolic math toolbox functions

You probably won't be able to tell the difference between the student and professional versions. Matrix sizes are unlimited in both; the amount of memory in your computer is the limiting factor. The Simulink toolbox for the student version is limited to 300 modeling blocks, but that is usually more than adequate.

Other toolboxes besides the included symbolic math toolbox must be purchased separately; however, most problems can be solved with the standard software. Not all toolboxes are available for the student version. For more information, please see the MATLAB website, www.themathworks.com.

The only difference you should notice is the command prompt. In the professional version the prompt is >>, but in the student version it is **EDU>>.**

MATLAB Windows

To begin MATLAB, use your mouse to click on the MATLAB icon (which should be located on the desktop) or use the start menu. If you are using a UNIX operating system, type **matlab** at the shell prompt. You should see the MATLAB prompt (>> or **EDU**>>), which tells you that MATLAB is waiting for you to enter a command. To exit MATLAB, type **quit** or **exit** at the MATLAB prompt, choose **EXIT MATLAB** from the file menu, or select the close icon (x) from the upper right-hand corner of the screen. (See Figure 1.)

MATLAB uses several display windows. The default view includes a large **command window** on the right, and stacked on the left are the **current directory, workspace**, and **command history windows**. Notice the tabs at the bottom of the windows on the left, which allow you to access the hidden windows. Older versions of MATLAB also included a **launch pad** window, which has been replaced by the **start** button in the lower left-hand corner. In addition, **document windows, graphics windows**, and **editing windows** will automatically open when needed.

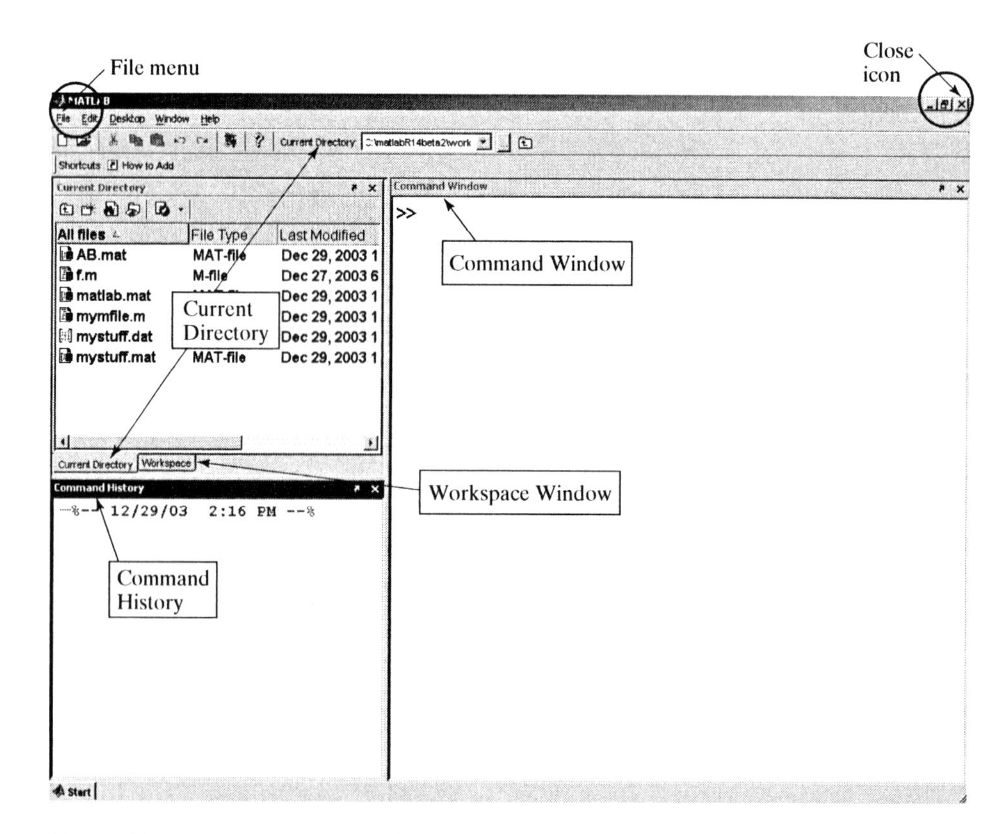

Figure 1. MATLAB opening window.

Command Window

You can use MATLAB in two basic modes. The command window offers an environment similar to a scratch pad. Using the command window allows you to save the values you calculate, but not the commands used to generate those values. If you want to save the command sequence, you'll need to use the editing window to create an **M-file**. (M-Files are MATLAB files that contain programming code. An M-File is an ASCII text file similar to a C or FORTRAN source code file.) Both approaches are valuable. Here, we will concentrate on using the command window.

You can perform calculations in the command window in a manner very similar to the way you perform calculations on a scientific calculator. Most of the syntax is even the same. For example, to compute the value of 5 squared, type the command

```
5^2
```

The following output will be displayed:

```
ans =
       25
```

Or, to find the value of $\cos(\pi)$, type

```
cos(pi)
```

which results in the following output:

```
ans =
      -1
```

MATLAB uses the standard algebraic rules for order of operation, which becomes important when you chain calculations together.

Hint: You may find it frustrating to discover that when you make a mistake, you can't just overwrite your command after you have executed it. This is because the command window is creating a list of all the commands you've entered. You can't "un-execute" a command, or "un-create" it. What you can do is enter the command correctly, and then execute your new version. MATLAB offers several ways to make this easier for you. One way is to use the arrow keys, usually located on the right-hand side of your keyboard. The up arrow, ↑, allows you to move through the list of commands you have executed. Once you find the appropriate command, you can edit it, and then execute your new version. This can be a real time-saver. However, you can also always just retype the command.

Command History

The command history window records the commands you issued in the command window. When you exit MATLAB, or when you issue the `clc` command, the command window is cleared. However, the command history window retains a list of all of your commands. You may clear the command history using the file menu if you need to. If you work on a public computer, as a security precaution MATLAB's defaults may be set to clear the history when you exit MATLAB. If you entered the example commands above, notice that they are repeated in the command history window. This window is valuable for a number of reasons. It allows you to review previous MATLAB sessions, and it can be used to transfer commands to the command window. For example, in the command window, type

```
clc
```

This should clear the command window, but leave the data in the command history window intact. You can transfer any command from the command history window to the command window by double clicking (which also executes the command) or by clicking and dragging the line of code into the command window. Try double clicking

```
cos(pi)
```

which should return

```
ans =

    -1
```

Click and drag

```
5^2
```

from the command history window into the command window. The command won't execute until you hit enter, and then you'll get the following result:

```
ans =
    25
```

You'll find the command history useful as you perform more and more complicated calculations in the command window.

Workspace Window

The workspace window keeps track of the variables you have defined as you execute commands in the command window. As you do the examples, the workspace window should just show one variable, **ans**, and tell us that it has a value of 25 and is a double array:

Name	Value	Class
ans	25	double array

Set the workspace window to show us more about this variable by right-clicking on the bar with the column labels. (This is new to MATLAB 7.) Check **size** and **bytes**, in addition to **name, value**, and **class**. Your workspace window should now display:

Name	Value	Size	Bytes	Class
ans	25	1 × 1	8	double array

The yellow grid-like symbol indicates the variable **ans** is an array. The size, 1 × 1, tells us that it is a single value (one row by one column) and therefore a scalar. The array uses 8 bytes of memory. MATLAB was written in C, and the class designation tells us that in the C language **ans** is a double precision, floating point array. For our needs it is enough to know that the variable **ans** can store a floating point number (one with a decimal point). MATLAB considers every number you enter to be a floating point number, whether you put a decimal in the number or not.

You can define additional variables in the command window and they will be listed in the workspace window. For example, type

```
A = 5
```

which returns

```
A =
    5
```

Notice that the variable A has been added to the workspace window, which lists variables in alphabetical order. Variables beginning with capital letters are listed first, followed by variables starting with lowercase letters:

Name	Value	Size	Bytes	Class
A	5	1 × 1	8	double array
ans	25	1 × 1	8	double array

Entering matrices into MATLAB is not discussed in detail in this section. However, you can enter a simple one-dimensional matrix by typing

```
B = [1, 2, 3, 4]
```

which returns

```
B =
    1      2      3      4
```

The commas are optional. You'd get the same result with

```
B = [ 1  2  3  4]
B =
    1      2      3      4
```

Notice that the variable B has been added to the workspace window and that its size is a 1 × 4 array:

Name	Value	Size	Bytes	Class
A	5	1 × 1	8	double array
B	[1 2 3 4]	1 × 4	32	double array
ans	25	1 × 1	8	double array

You define two-dimensional matrices in a similar fashion. Semicolons are used to separate rows. For example,

```
C = [ 1 2 3 4; 10 20 30 40; 5 10 15 20]
```

returns

```
C =
    1      2      3      4
    10     20     30     40
    5      10     15     20
```

Notice that C appears in the workspace window as a 3 × 4 matrix. You can recall the values for any variable by just typing in the variable name. For example, entering

```
A
```

returns

```
A =
    5
```

Name	Value	Size	Bytes	Class
A	5	1 × 1	8	double array
B	[1 2 3 4]	1 × 4	32	double array
C	<3 × 4 *double*>	3 × 4	96	double array
ans	25	1 × 1	8	double array

Although we have only introduced variables that are matrices, other types of variables, such as symbolic variables, are possible.

If you prefer to have a less cluttered desktop, you may close any of the windows (except the command window) by selecting the x in the upper right-hand corner of each window. You can also personalize which windows you prefer to keep open by selecting **View** from the menu bar and checking the appropriate windows. If you suppress the workspace window, you can still find out what variables have been defined by using the command

```
whos
```

which returns

```
  Name       Size        Bytes      Class
  A          1x1            8       double array
  B          1x4           32       double array
  C          3x4           96       double array
  ans        1x1            8       double array
Grand total is 18 elements using 144 bytes
```

Current Directory Window

When MATLAB either accesses files or saves information onto your computer, it uses the current directory. The default for the current directory varies, depending on your version of the software and how it was installed. However, the current directory is listed at the top of the main window. The current directory can be changed by selecting another directory from the drop-down list located next to the directory listing, or by browsing through your computer files using the browse button located next to the drop-down list (circled on Figure 2).

Document Window

Double clicking on any variable listed in the workspace window automatically launches a document window containing the **array editor**. Values stored in the variable are displayed in a spreadsheet format. You can change values in the array editor, or you can add new values. For example, if you haven't already entered the two-dimensional matrix C, enter the following command in the command window:

```
C = [ 1 2 3 4; 10 20 30 40; 5 10 15 20];
```

Placing a semicolon at the end of the command suppresses the output so that it is not repeated back in the command window; however, C should now be listed in the workspace window. Double click it. A document window will open above the command window, as shown in Figure 3.

You can now add additional values to the C matrix, or change existing values.

The document window that displays the array editor can also be used in conjunction with the workspace window to create entirely new arrays. Run your mouse slowly over the icons in the shortcut bar at the top of the workspace window. The function of each icon should appear, if you are patient. The new-variable icon looks like a page with a large asterisk behind it. Select the new-variable icon. A new variable called **unnamed** should appear on the variable list. You can change its name by right-clicking and selecting **rename** from the pop-up menu. To add values to this new variable, double click on it and add your data from the document window.

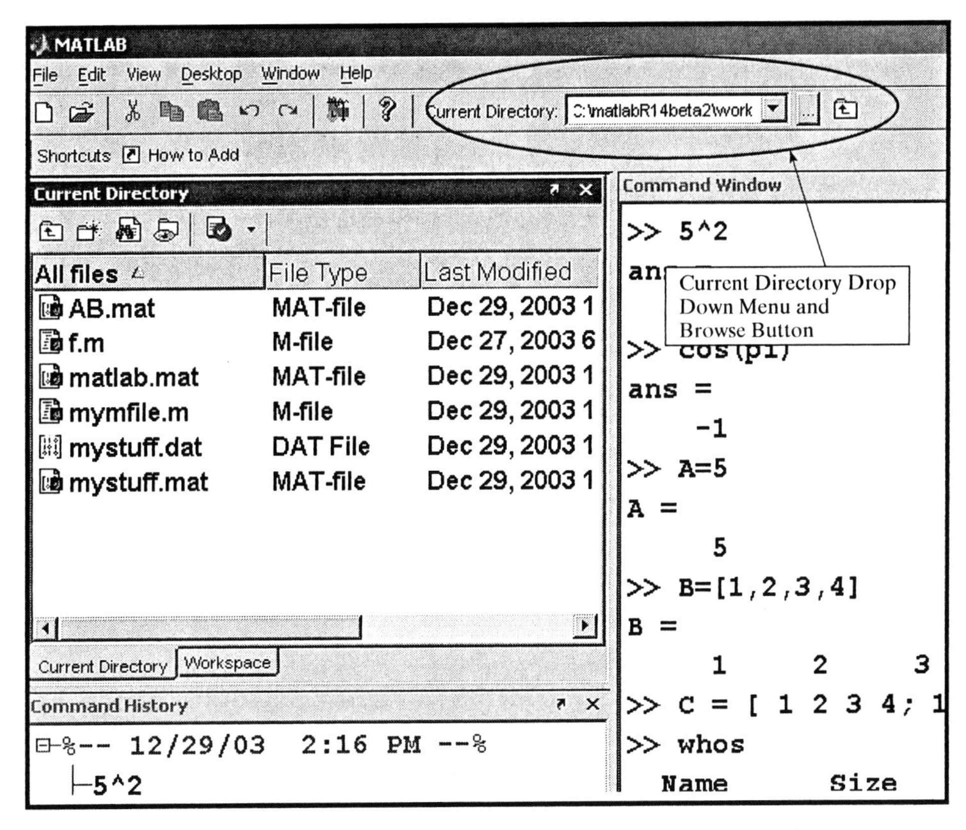

Figure 2. The **Current Directory Window** lists all the files in the current directory.

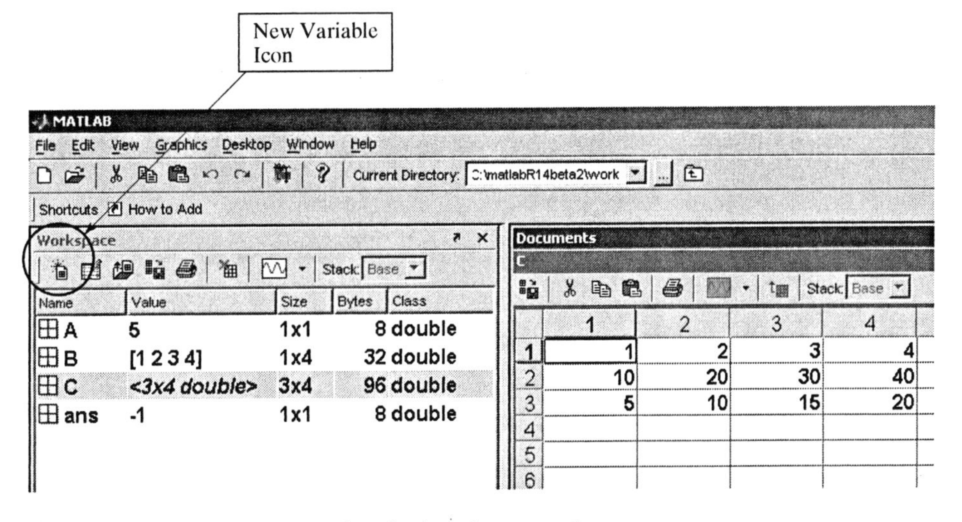

Figure 3. The document window displays the array editor.

Graphics Window

The graphics window(s) launches automatically when you request a graph. To create a simple graph first, create an array of *x* values:

```
x = [ 1 2 3 4 5];
```

(Remember, the semicolon suppresses the output from this command; however, a new variable **x**, appears in the workspace window.) Now create a list of **y** values:

```
y = [10 20 30 40 50];
```

To create a graph, use the plot command:

```
plot(x,y)
```

The graphics window opens automatically. (See Figure 4.) Notice that a new window label also appears on the task bar at the bottom of the windows screen. It will either be titled **<Student Version> Figure**..., or simply **Figure 1**, depending on whether you are using the student or professional version of the MATLAB software. Any additional graphs you create will overwrite Figure 1 unless you specifically command MATLAB to open a new graphics window.

MATLAB makes it easy to modify graphs by adding titles, x and y labels, multiple lines, and more.

Edit Window

The editing window is opened by choosing **File** from the menu bar, then **New**, and finally **m-file** (**File → New → m-file**). This window allows you to type and save a series of commands without executing them. You may also open the edit window by typing **edit** at the command prompt.

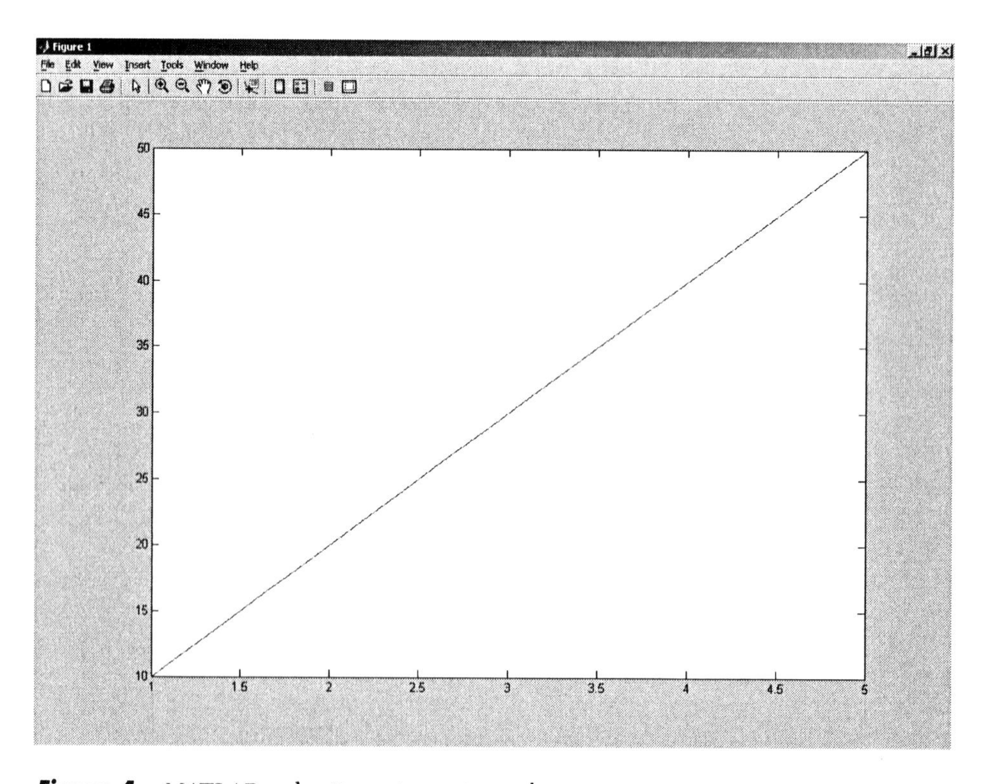

Figure 4. MATLAB makes it easy to create graphs.

Start Button

The start button is located in the lower left-hand corner of the MATLAB window. It offers alternative access to the MATLAB toolboxes and to the various MATLAB windows, help function, and Internet products. Toolboxes provide additional MATLAB functionality for specific content areas. The start button is new to MATLAB 7 and replaces the launch pad window used in MATLAB 6.

SOLVING PROBLEMS IN MATLAB

The command window environment is a powerful tool for solving engineering problems. To use it effectively, you'll need to understand more about how MATLAB works.

Variables

In MATLAB we assign names to the scalars, vectors and matrices we use. The following rules apply to these variable names:

- Variable names must start with a letter.
- Variable names are case sensitive. The names **time, Time**, and **TIME** all represent different variables.
- Other than the first letter, variable names can contain letters, digits, and the underscore (_) character. To test whether a name is a legitimate variable name, use the isvarname command. The answer 1 means true, and the answer 0 means false. For example,

  ```
  isvarname  Vector
  ans =
          1
  ```

  means that Vector is a legitimate variable name.
- Variable names can be any length, but only the first *N* characters are used by MATLAB. The value of *N* varies, depending on the version of MATLAB that you are using. For Version 7, Release 14, the value of *N* is 63. You can see the value of *N* on your system by typing

  ```
  namelengthmax
  ```

- Variables cannot have the same name as any of MATLAB's keywords. To see a list of all MATLAB keywords, type

  ```
  iskeyword
  ```

- MATLAB allows you to use the names of its built-in functions as variable names. This is a dangerous practice, since you can overwrite the meaning of a function, such as **sin**. To check whether a name is a built-in function, use the **which** command. For example, typing

  ```
  which sin
  ```

  returns

  ```
  sin is a built in function.
  ```

Working with Matrices

When solving engineering problems, it is important to visualize the data related to the problem. Sometimes the data is just a single number, such as the radius of a circle. Other times, the data may be a coordinate on a plane that can be represented as a pair of numbers, with one number representing the x-coordinate and the other number representing the y-coordinate. In another problem, we might have a set of four x-y-z coordinates that represent the four vertices of a pyramid with a triangular base in a three-dimensional space. We can represent all of these examples using a special type of data structure called a matrix. A matrix is a set of numbers arranged in a rectangular grid of rows and columns. Thus, a single point can be considered a matrix with one row and one column—often referred to as a scalar. An x-y coordinate can be considered a matrix with one row and two columns, and is often called a vector. A set of four x-y-z coordinates can be considered a matrix with four rows and three columns:

$$\mathbf{A} = [3.5] \qquad \mathbf{B} = [1.5 \quad 3.1]$$

$$\mathbf{C} = \begin{bmatrix} -1 & 0 & 0 \\ 1 & 1 & 0 \\ 1 & -1 & 0 \\ 0 & 0 & 2 \end{bmatrix}$$

Note that the data within a matrix are written inside brackets.

Scalar Operations

The arithmetic operations between two scalars are shown in Table 1. They include addition, subtraction, multiplication, division, and exponentiation. The command

```
a = 1 + 2
```

should be read as **a** is assigned a value of 1 plus 2, which is the addition of two scalar quantities. Assume, for example, that you have defined **a** in the previous statement and that **b** has a value of 5:

```
b = 5
```

Then

```
x = a + b
```

will return the following result:

```
x =
    8
```

A single equals sign (=) is known in MATLAB as the assignment operator. The assignment operator causes the result of your calculations to be stored in a computer memory

TABLE 1 Arithmetic Operations Between Two Scalars

Operation	Algebraic Form	MATLAB Form
Addition	$a + b$	**a + b**
Subtraction	$a - b$	**a - b**
Multiplication	$a \times b$	**a * b**
Division	$\frac{a}{b}$	**a / b**
Exponentiation	a^b	**a ^ b**

location. In the example above, **x** is assigned a value of eight, and is stored in computer memory. If you enter the variable name

```
x
```

into MATLAB, you get the result

```
x =
     8
```

which should be read as "**x** is assigned a value of 8." If we interpret assignment statements in this way, we are not disturbed by the valid MATLAB statement

```
x = x + 1
```

which, since the value stored in **x** was originally 8, returns

```
x =
     9
```

indicating that the value stored in the memory location named **x** has been changed to 9. Clearly, this statement is not a valid algebraic statement, but is understandable when viewed as an assignment rather than as a statement of equality. The assignment statement is similar to the familiar process of saving a file. When you first save a word processing document, you assign it a name. Subsequently, when you've made changes, you resave your file, but still assign it the same name. The first and second versions are not equal; you've just assigned a new version of your document to an existing memory location.

Precedence of Arithmetic Operations

Because several operations can be combined in a single arithmetic expression, it is important to know the order in which operations are performed. Table 2 contains the precedence of arithmetic operations performed in MATLAB. Note that this precedence follows the rules of standard algebraic precedence.

Assume that we want to calculate the area of a trapezoid, where the base is horizontal and the two edges are vertical. We know that the equation for the area of this trapezoid is

```
area = 0.5 * base * (height_1 + height_2)
```

There are two equally valid approaches to solving this problem. First, assume some values for base, height_1, and height_2, and enter them into MATLAB:

```
base = 5;
height_1 = 12;
height_2 = 6;
```

Now you can solve the problem by entering the equation for area in MATLAB:

```
area = 0.5 * base * (height_1 + height_2)
```

TABLE 2 Precedence of Arithmetic Operations

Precedence	Operation
1	Parentheses, innermost first
2	Exponentiation, left to right
3	Multiplication and division, left to right
4	Addition and subtraction, left to right

This equation returns

```
area =
    45
```

Understanding the order of operation is important. MATLAB will first add the two height values together:

```
height_1 + height_2
```

Then the program will perform the multiplication operations, starting from the left. An alternative approach would be to simply enter the numerical values directly into the formula:

```
area = 0.5 * 5 * (12 + 6)
```

This will return

```
area =
    45
```

In either case, neglecting the parentheses will result in the wrong answer. For example,

```
area = 0.5 * base * height_1 + height_2
```

gives

```
area =
    36
```

In this case, MATLAB will first perform the multiplications, working from left to right:

```
0.5 * base * height_1
```

Then it will add the result to height_2. Clearly, it is important to be very careful when converting equations into MATLAB statements. Adding extras parentheses is an easy way to ensure that computations are performed in the order you want.

If an expression is long, break it into multiple statements. For example, consider the equation

$$f = \frac{x^3 - 2x^2 + x - 6.3}{x^2 + 0.05005x - 3.14}$$

The value of f could be computed with the following MATLAB statements:

```
numerator = x^3 - 2*x^2 + x - 6.3;
denominator = x^2 + 0.05005*x - 3.14;
f = numerator/denominator;
```

It is better to use several statements that are easy to understand than to use one statement that requires careful thought to figure out the order of operations.

Hint: MATLAB does not read "white space," so it doesn't matter if you add spaces to your commands. It is easier to read a long expression if you add a space before and after plus (+) and minus (−) signs, but not multiplication (*) and division (/) signs.

EXAMPLE 1

SCALAR OPERATIONS

Wind tunnels are used to evaluate high performance aircraft. (See Figure 5.) To interpret wind tunnel data, the engineer needs to understand how gases behave. The basic equation describing gas properties is the ideal gas law,

$$PV = nRT$$

Figure 5. Wind tunnels are used to test aircraft designs.

where

P = pressure, kPa

V = volume, m^3

n = number of kmoles of gas in the sample

R = ideal gas constant, 8.314 kPa m^3/kmole K

T = temperature, expressed on an absolute scale (i.e., in degrees K)

In addition, we know that the number of kmoles of gas is equal to the mass of gas divided by the molar mass (also known as the molecular weight); that is,

$$n = m/\mathrm{MW}$$

where

m = mass, kg

MW = molar mass, kg/kmole

Different units can be used in the equations, if the value of R is changed accordingly. Assume that the volume of air in the wind tunnel is 1000 m^3. Before the wind tunnel is turned on, the temperature of the air is 300 K and the pressure is 100 kPa. The molar mass (molecular weight) of air is approximately 29 kg/kmole. Find the mass of air in the wind tunnel.

SOLUTION

To solve this problem, use the following problem-solving methodology:

1. State the Problem

When you solve a problem, it is a good idea to restate it in your own words:

Find the mass of air in the wind tunnel.

2. Describe the Input and Output

Input

$$V = 1000 \text{ m}^3$$
$$T = 300 \text{ K}$$
$$P = 100 \text{ kPa}$$
$$\text{MW} = 29 \text{ kg/kmole}$$
$$R = 8.314 \text{ kPa m}^3\text{/kmole K}$$

Output

mass kg

3. Hand Example

Working the problem by hand (or with a calculator) allows you to outline an algorithm, which you can translate to MATLAB code later. You should choose simple data that make it easy to check your work.

Solve the ideal gas law for n, and plug in the given values. This results in

$$\begin{aligned} n &= PV/RT \\ &= (100 \text{ kPa} \times 1000 \text{ m}^3)/(8.314 \text{ kPa m}^3\text{/kmole K}) \times 300 \text{ K}) \\ &= 40.0930 \text{ kmoles} \end{aligned}$$

Convert moles to mass by multiplying by the molar mass:

$$m = n \times \text{MW} = 40.0930 \text{ kmoles} \times 29 \text{ kg/kmole}$$
$$m = 1162.70 \text{ kg}$$

4. Develop a MATLAB solution

```
P = 100
P =
     100
T = 300
T =
     300
V = 1000
V =
        1000
MW = 29
MW =
     29
R = 8.314
R =
     8.3140
n = (P*V)/(R*T)
n =
     40.0930
m = n*MW
m =
       1.1627e+003
```

There are several things you should notice about this MATLAB solution. Because there were no semicolons used to suppress the output, the variable values are repeated back to

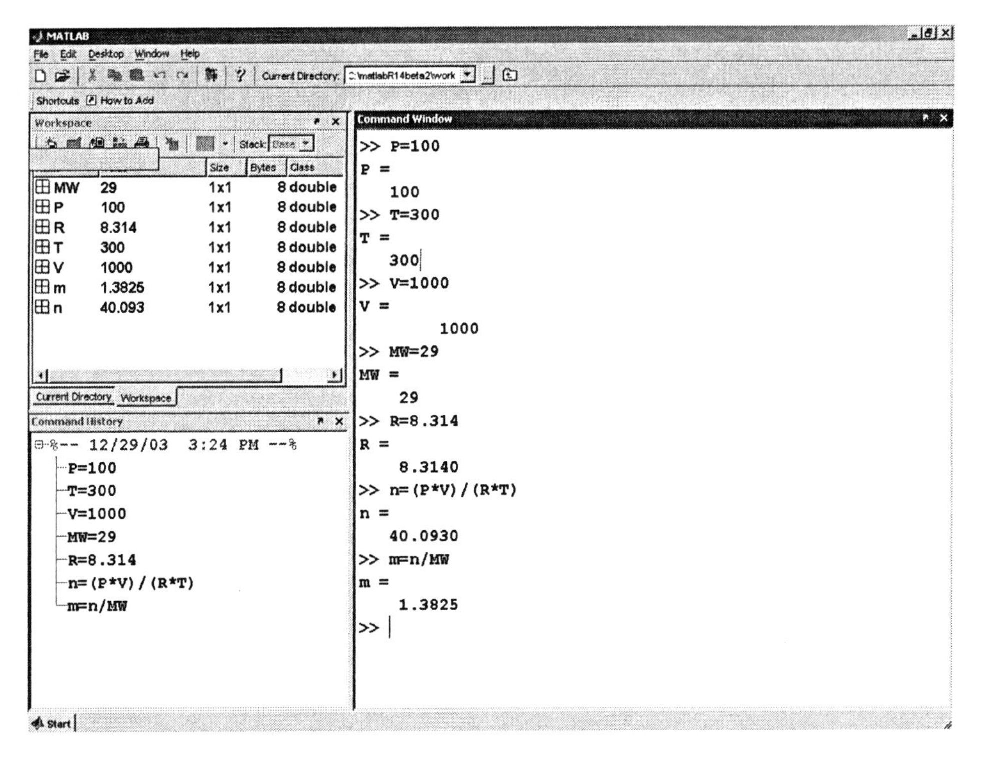

Figure 6. MATLAB screen used to solve the ideal gas problem.

us after each assignment statement. Notice also the use of parentheses in the calculation of n. They are necessary for the denominator, but not for the numerator; however, using parentheses in both makes it easier to read.

5. Test the Solution

In this case, comparing the result to the hand result is sufficient. More complicated problems solved in MATLAB should use a variety of input data to confirm that your solution works in a variety of cases. A picture of the MATLAB screen used to solve this problem is shown in Figure 6.

Notice that the variables defined in the command window are listed in the workspace window. Also notice that the command history lists the commands executed in the command window. If you were to scroll up in the command history window, you would see commands from previous MATLAB sessions. All of these commands are available for you to move to the command window. ■

Array Operations

Using MATLAB as a glorified calculator is okay, but its real strength is in matrix manipulations. As described previously, the simplest way to define a matrix is to use a list of numbers called an explicit list. The command

```
X = [1 2 3 4]
```

returns the row vector

```
X =
    1 2 3 4
```

Recall that when defining this vector, you may either list the values with or without commas. A new row is indicated by a semicolon, so that a column vector is specified as

```
Y = [ 1; 2; 3; 4]
```

and a matrix that contains both rows and columns would be created with the statement

```
A = [ 1 2 3 4; 2 3 4 5 ; 3 4 5 6]
```

which would return

```
A =
      1 2 3 4
      2 3 4 5
      3 4 5 6
```

Hint: It's easier to keep track of how many values you've entered into a matrix if you enter each row on a separate line:

```
A = [1 2 3 4;
2 3 4 5;
3 4 5 6]
```

While a complicated matrix might have to be entered by hand, evenly spaced matrices can be entered much more readily. The command

```
B = 1:5
```

or the command

```
B = [1:5]
```

returns a row matrix

```
B =

  1 2 3 4 5
```

(The square brackets are optional.) The default increment is 1, but if you want to use a different increment, put it between the first and final values. For example,

```
C = 1:2:5
```

indicates that the increment between values will be 2 and returns

```
C =

      1     3     5
```

If you want MATLAB to calculate the spacing, you must use the **linspace** command. Specify the initial value, the final value, and how many total values you want. For example,

```
D = linspace(1,10,3)
```

returns a vector with three values, evenly spaced between 1 and 10, as follows:

```
D =

      1     5.5    10
```

Matrices can be used in many calculations with scalars. If **A = [1 2 3]**, we can add 5 to each value in the matrix with the calculation

```
B = A + 5
```

which returns

```
B =
      6     7     8
```

This works well for addition and subtraction; however, multiplication and division are slightly different. In matrix mathematics the multiplication operator (*) has a very specific meaning. If you want to do an element-by-element multiplication, the operator .* is used. For example,

```
A .* B
```

results in

element #1 of matrix **A** being multiplied by element #1 of matrix *B*,
element #2 of matrix **A** being multiplied by element #2 of matrix *B*, etc., and
element #*n* of matrix **A** being multiplied by element #n of matrix *B*.

For the particular case of our **A** (which is [1 2 3]) and our **B** (which is [6 7 8]),

```
A .* B
```

returns

```
ans =
     6      14      24
```

(Be sure to do the math to convince yourself why these are the correct answers.)

Just using * implies a matrix multiplication, which in this case would return an error message, because this particular **A** and **B** do not meet the rules for multiplication in matrix algebra. Just be careful to use the correct operator when you mean element-by-element (also called array) multiplication.

The same syntax holds for element-by-element division (./) and exponentiation (.^) of individual elements:

```
A ./B
A .^2
```

As an exercise, predict the values resulting from the preceding two expressions, then test out your predictions by executing the commands in MATLAB.

The matrix capability of MATLAB makes it easy to do repetitive calculations. For example, assume you have a list of angles in degrees that you would like to convert to radians. First, put the values into a matrix. For angles of 10, 15, 70, and 90, enter

```
D = [ 10 15 70 90];
```

To change the values to radians, you must multiply by $\pi/180$:

```
R = D*pi/180;
```

This command returns a matrix **R**, with the values in radians. (Try it!)

Hint: The value of π is built into MATLAB as a floating point number, called pi. Because π is an irrational number, it cannot be expressed exactly with a floating point representation, and the MATLAB constant, pi, is really an approximation. You can see this when you find sin(pi). Based on trigonometry, the answer should be 0. However, MATLAB returns a very small number. The actual value depends on your version of the program—our version returned 1.2246e-016. In most calculations this won't make a difference in the final result.

Another useful matrix operator is transposition. The transpose operator basically changes rows to columns or vice versa. For example,

```
D'
```

returns

```
ans =
      10
      15
      70
      90
```

This makes it easy to create tables. For example, to create a table of degrees to radians, enter

```
table =[D',R']
```

which tells MATLAB to create a matrix named **table**, where column #1 is `D'`, and column #2 is `R'`:

```
table =
         10.0000    0.1745
         15.0000    0.2618
         70.0000    1.2217
         90.0000    1.5708
```

EXAMPLE 2

MATRIX CALCULATIONS WITH SCALARS

Scientific data, such as that collected from wind tunnels, are usually in SI (system international) units. However, much of the manufacturing infrastructure in the United States has been tooled in English (sometimes called American Engineering or American Standard) units. Engineers need to be fluent in both systems, and especially careful when sharing data with other engineers. Perhaps the most notorious example of unit confusion problems is the *Mars Climate Orbiter*, which was the second flight of the NASA Mars Surveyor Program. (See Figure 7.) The spacecraft burned up in the orbit of Mars in Sep-

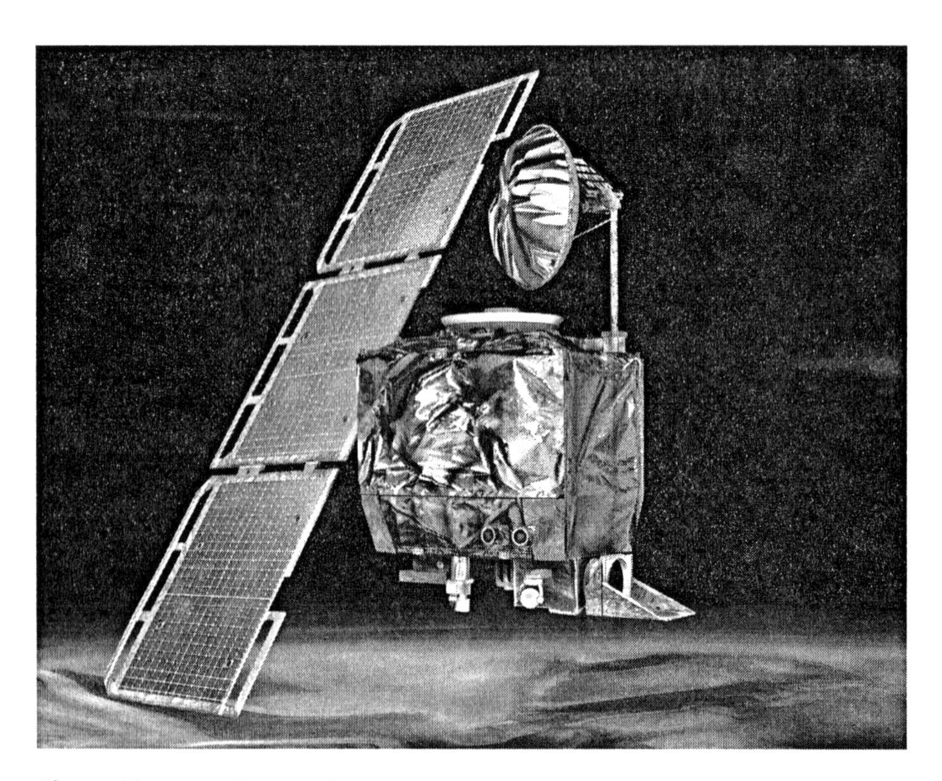

Figure 7. Mars Climate Orbiter.

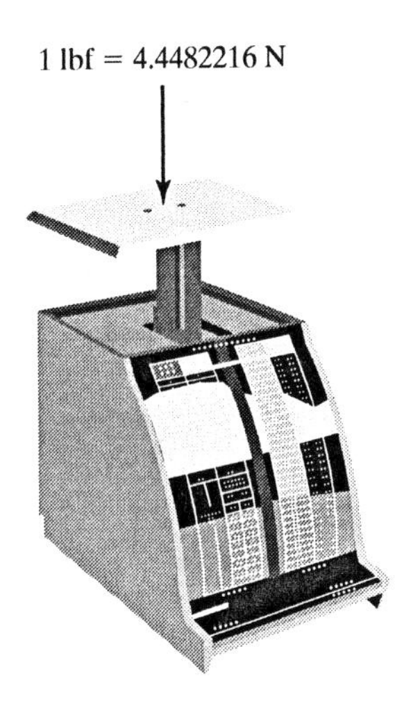

Figure 8. A scale measures the applied force.

tember 1999 because of a look-up table embedded in the spacecraft's software. The table, probably generated from wind tunnel testing, used pounds force (lbf), when the program expected values in Newtons (N). (See Figure 8.)

Use MATLAB to create a conversion table of pounds force (lbf) to Newtons (N). Your table should start at 0 and go to 1000 lbf, at 100 lbf intervals. Use the conversion

$$1 \text{ lbf} = 4.4482216 \text{ N}$$

1. State the Problem

   Create a table converting pound force (lbf) to Newtons (N).

2. Describe the Input and Output

Input

The starting value in the table is: 0 lbf
The final value in the table is: 1000 lbf
The increment between values is: 100 lbf
The conversion from lbf to N is: 1 lbf = 4.4482216 N

Output

Table listing pound force (lbf) and Newtons (N)

3. Hand Example

$$0 \times 4.4482216 = 0$$
$$100 \times 4.4482216 = 444.82216$$
$$1000 \times 4.4482216 = 4448.2216$$

4. Develop a MATLAB Solution

```
lbf = [0:100:1000];
N = lbf * 4.44822;
[lbf',N']
```

```
ans =
  1.0e+003 *
         0         0
    0.1000    0.4448
    0.2000    0.8896
    0.3000    1.3345
    0.4000    1.7793
    0.5000    2.2241
    0.6000    2.6689
    0.7000    3.1138
    0.8000    3.5586
    0.9000    4.0034
    1.0000    4.4482
```

It is always a good idea to clear the workspace and the command window before starting a new problem. Notice in the workspace window that lbf and N are 1 × 11 matrices, and that **ans** (which is where the table we created is stored) is an 11 × 2 matrix. The output from the first two commands was suppressed by adding a semicolon at the end of each line. It would be very easy to create a table with more entries by changing the increment to 10 or even to 1. Also notice that you'll need to multiply the table results by 1000 to get the correct answers. MATLAB tells you this is necessary directly above the table, as shown in Figure 9.

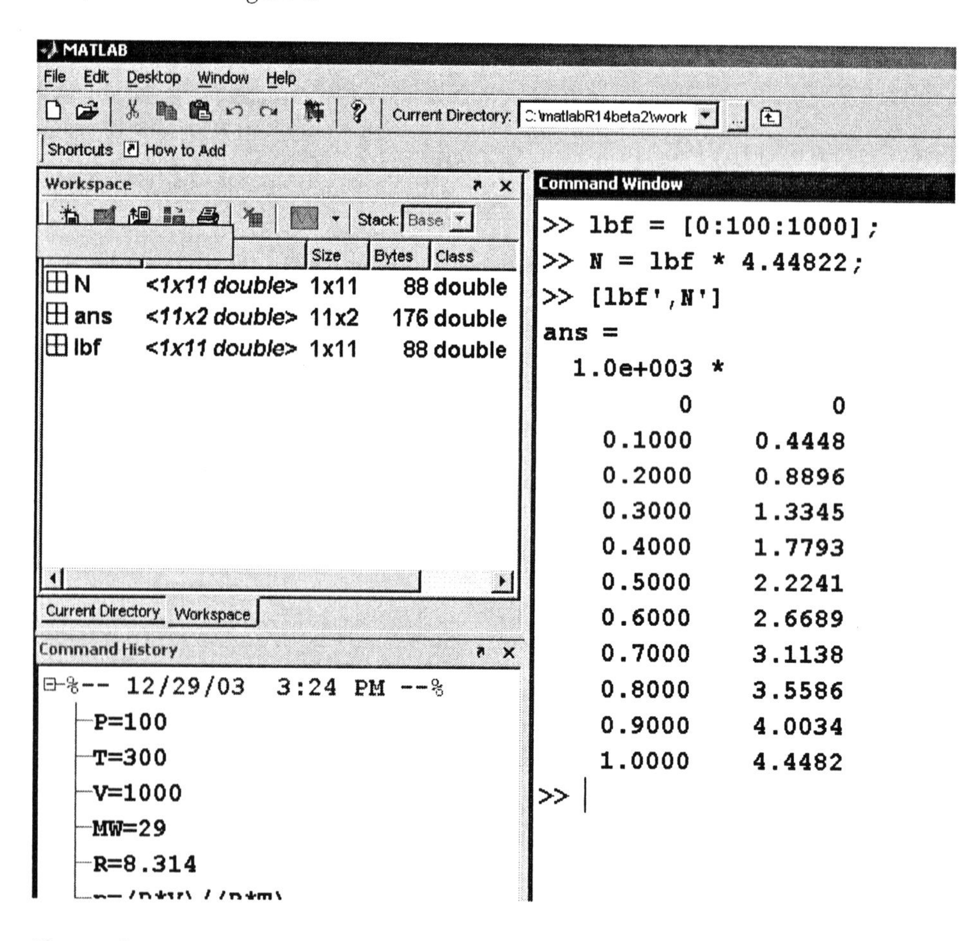

Figure 9. The MATLAB workspace window shows the variables as they are created.

5. Test the Solution

Comparing the results of the MATLAB solution to the hand solution shows the same results. Once we've verified that our solution works, it's easy to use the same algorithm to create other conversion tables. For example, modify this example to create a conversion table of Newton (N) to pound force, with an increment of 10 N, from 0 N to 1000 N. ■

EXAMPLE 3

CALCULATING DRAG

One performance characteristic that can be determined in a wind tunnel is drag. The friction related to drag on the Mars Climate Observer (caused by Mars' atmosphere), resulted in its burning up during course corrections. Drag is extremely important in the design of terrestrial aircraft as well.

Drag is the force generated as an object, such as an airplane, moves through a fluid. (See Figure 10.) Of course, in the case of a wind tunnel, air moves past a stationary model, but the equations are the same. Drag is a very complex force, depending on many factors. One factor is skin friction, which depends on the surface properties of the aircraft, the properties of the moving fluid (air in this case), and the flow patterns caused by the shape of the aircraft (or in the case of the Mars Climate Observer, by the spacecraft). Drag can be calculated with the drag equation

$$\text{Drag} = C_d \frac{rV^2A}{2}$$

where

C_d = drag coefficient, which is determined experimentally, usually in a wind tunnel
r = air density
V = velocity
A = reference area

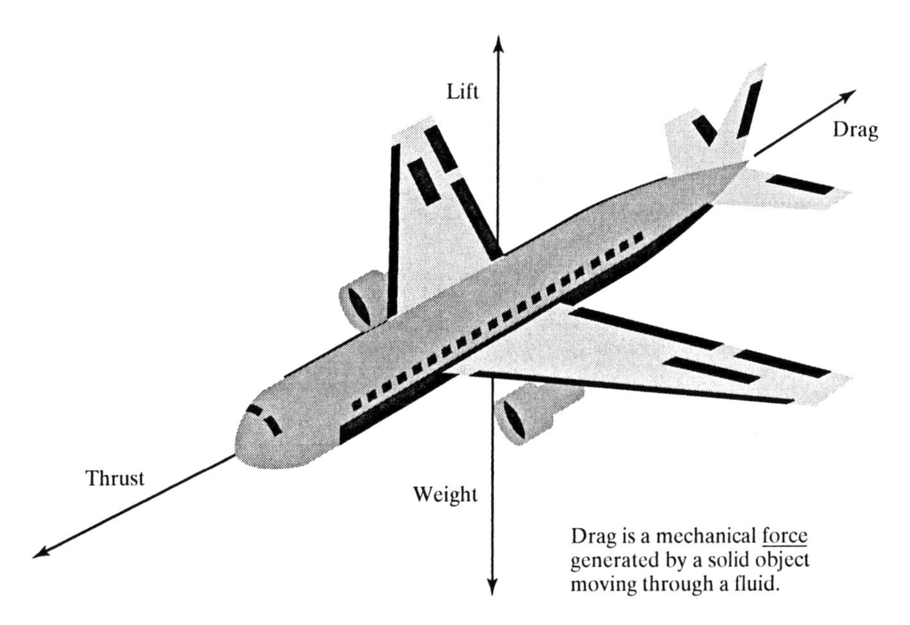

Figure 10. Drag is a mechanical force generated by a solid object moving through a fluid.

Although the drag coefficient is not a constant, it can be used as a constant at low speeds (less than 200 mph). Assume the following data were measured in a wind tunnel:

drag	20,000 N
r	1×10^{-6} kg/m^3
V	100 mph (you'll need to convert this to meters per second)
A	1 m^2

Calculate the drag coefficient. Finally, use this experimentally determined drag coefficient to predict how much drag the aircraft will experience at velocities from 0 mph to 200 mph.

1. State the Problem

Calculate the drag coefficient
Use the drag coefficient to determine the drag at a variety of velocities

2. Describe the Input and Output

Input

drag	20,000 N
r	1×10^{-6} kg/m^3
V	100 mph
A	1 m^2

Output

drag coefficient
drag at a velocities from 0 to 200 mph

3. Hand Example

First find the drag coefficient from the experimental data:

$$C_d = \text{drag} \times 2/(r \times V^2 \times A) = 2.0019\text{ e7}$$

Use the drag coefficient to find the drag at different velocities:

$$\text{drag} = C_d \times \text{r} \times \text{V}^2 \times \text{A}/2$$

Calculate the value of drag with $V = 200$ mph, using a calculator

$$\text{drag} = 80{,}000 \text{ N}$$

4. Develop a MATLAB Solution

```
drag = 20000;                 Define the variables, and change
r = 0.000001;                   V to SI units
V = 100*0.4470;
A = 1;
cd = drag*2/(r*V^2*A)         Calculate the coefficient of drag
cd =
   2.0019e+007
V = 0:20:200;                 Redefine V as a matrix
V = V*0.4470;                 Change it to SI units, and
drag = cd*r*V.^2*A/2;           calculate the drag
table = [V', drag']
```

```
table =
  1.0e+004 *
       0           0
    0.0009      0.0800
    0.0018      0.3200
    0.0027      0.7200
    0.0036      1.2800
    0.0045      2.0000
    0.0054      2.8800
    0.0063      3.9200
    0.0072      5.1200
    0.0080      6.4800
    0.0089      8.0000
```

(See Figure 11.) Notice that the equation for the drag,

```
Drag = cd * r * V.^2 * A/2;
```

uses the **.^** operator, because we intend that each value in the matrix **V** be squared, not that the entire matrix **V** be multiplied by itself. Using just the exponentiation operator **(^)** would result in an error message. Unfortunately, it is possible to compose problems where using the wrong operator does not give us an error message—but does give us a wrong answer. This makes Step 5 in our problem solving methodology especially important.

5. Test the Solution

By comparing the hand solution to the MATLAB solution, we see that both give the same results. Once we have confirmed with sample data that our algorithm works, we can substitute in new data with confidence that the results will be correct. Ideally, the results should also be compared to experimental data to confirm that the equations we are using accurately model the real physical process. ■

Number Display

Scientific Notation

Although you can enter any number in decimal notation, it isn't always the best way to represent very large or very small numbers. For example, a number that is used frequently in chemistry is Avogadro's constant, whose value to four significant digits is 602,200,000,000,000,000,000,000. The diameter of an iron atom is approximately 140 picometers, which is .000000000140 meters. Scientific notation expresses a value as a number between 1 and 10 (the mantissa) multiplied by a power of 10 (the exponent). In scientific notation, Avogadro's number becomes 6.022×10^{23}, and the diameter of an iron atom becomes 1.4×10^{-10} meters. In MATLAB, values in scientific notation are designated with an e between the mantissa and the exponent. For example,

```
Avogadros_constant = 6.022e23;
Iron_diameter = 140e-12;  or
Iron_diameter = 1.4e-10;
```

It is important to omit blanks between the mantissa and the exponent. For example, MATLAB will interpret

```
6.022      e23
```

as two values (6.022 and 10^{23}).

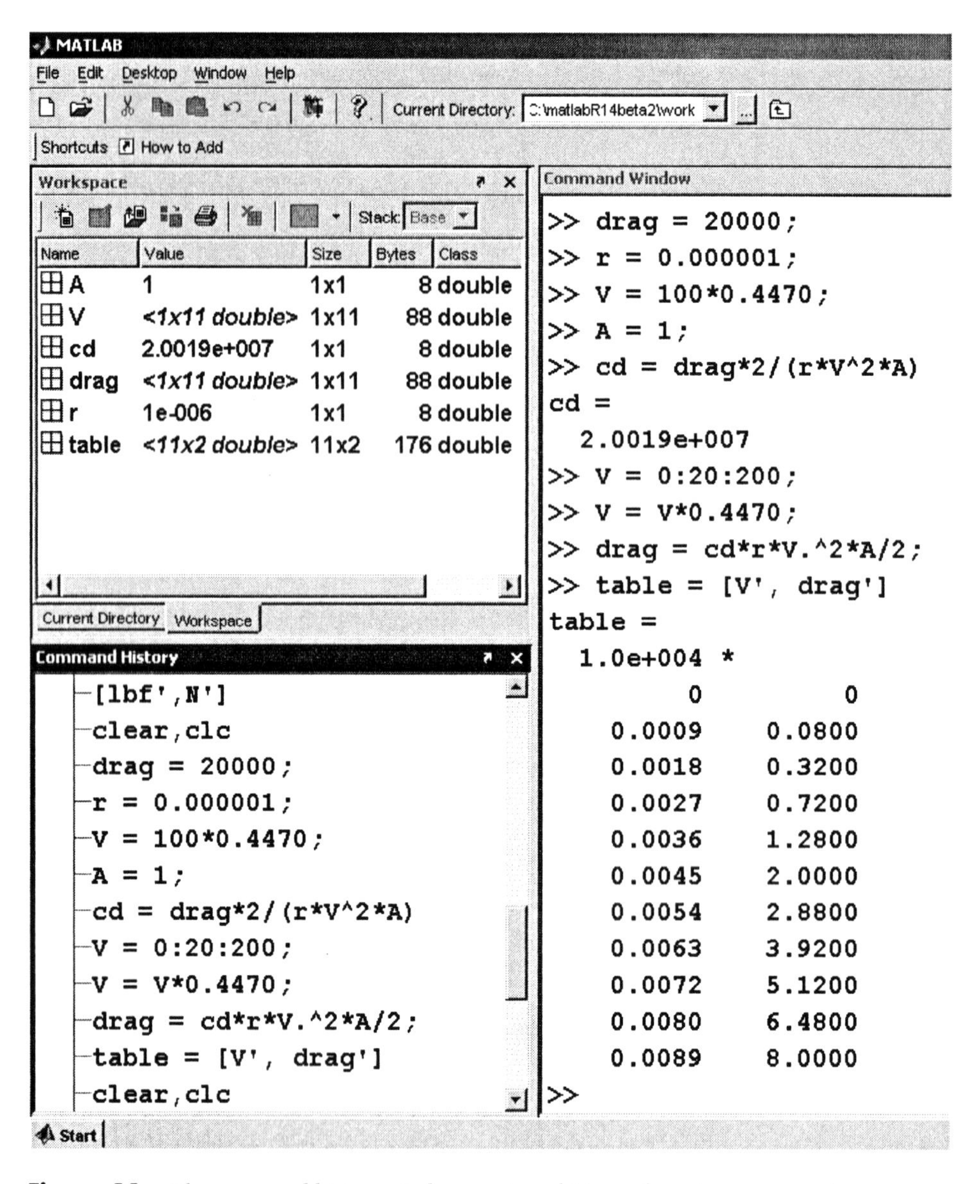

Figure 11. The command history window creates a history of previous commands.

Display Format

When elements of a matrix are displayed in MATLAB, integers are always printed as integers. However, values with decimal fractions are printed using a default format that shows four decimal digits. Thus,

```
A = 5
```

returns

```
A =
     5
```

but

```
A = 5.1
```

returns

```
A =
    5.1000
```

and

```
A = 51.1
```

returns

```
A =
    51.1000
```

MATLAB allows you to specify other formats that show more significant digits. For example, to specify that we want values to be displayed in a decimal format with 14 decimal digits, we use the command

```
format long
```

which changes all subsequent displays. For example,

```
A
```

now returns

```
A =
    51.10000000000000
```

We can return the format to four decimal digits by using the command

```
format short
A
A =
    51.1000
```

Two decimal digits are displayed when the format is specified as **format bank**. No matter what display format you choose, MATLAB uses double precision, floating-point numbers in its calculations. Exactly how many digits are used in these calculations depends upon your computer. However, changing the display format does not change the accuracy of your results.

When numbers become too large or too small for MATLAB to display using the default format, the program automatically expresses them in scientific notation. For example, if you enter Avogadro's constant into MATLAB in decimal notation,

```
a = 602000000000000000000000
```

the program returns

```
a =
    6.0200e+023
```

You can force MATLAB to display all numbers in scientific notation with **format short e** (with 5 significant digits) or **format long e** (with 14 significant digits). Thus,

```
format short e
    x = 10.356789
```

returns

```
x =
    1.0357e+001
```

TABLE 3 Numeric Display Formats

MATLAB Command	Display	Example
`format short`	4 decimal digits	15.2345
`format long`	14 decimal digits	15.23453333333333
`format short e`	14 decimal digits	1.5234e+01
`format long e`	15 decimal digits	1.523453333333333e+01
`format bank`	2 decimal digits	15.23
`format +`	+, −, blank	+

Another format command is **`format +`**. When a matrix is displayed with this format, the only characters printed are plus and minus signs. If a value is positive, a plus sign will be displayed; if a value is negative, a minus sign will be displayed. If a value is zero, nothing will be displayed. This format allows us to view a large matrix in terms of its signs:

```
format +
B = [1, -5, 0,12; 10005, 24, -10,4]
B =
     +- +
     ++-+
```

For long and short formats, a common scale factor is applied to the entire matrix if the elements become very large or very small. This scale factor is printed along with the scaled values. For example, when the command window is returned to

```
format short
```

the results from Example 3 are displayed as

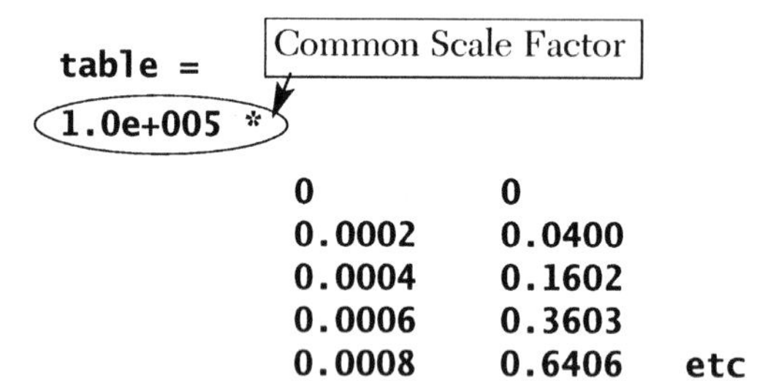

Finally, the command **`format compact`** suppresses many of the line feeds that appear between matrix displays and allows more lines of information to be seen together on the screen. The command **`format loose`** will return the command window to the less compact display mode. The examples in this text use the compact format to save space (see Table 3 for numeric display formats).

SAVING YOUR WORK

Working in the command window is similar to performing calculations on your scientific calculator. When you turn off the calculator, or when you exit the program, your work is gone. It *is* possible to save the values of the variables that you defined in the command window and that are listed in the workspace window. Although this may be useful, it is more likely that you will want to save the list of commands that generated your results. In this section, we will first show you how to save and retrieve variables (the results of the assignments you made and the calculations you performed) to MAT-files or to DAT-files.

Then, we'll introduce script M-files, which are created in the edit window. Script M-files allow you to save a list of commands and to execute them later. You will find script M-files especially useful for solving homework problems.

Saving Variables

To preserve the variables you created in the **command window** (check the **workspace window** on the left-hand side of the MATLAB screen for the list of variables) between sessions, you must save the contents of the **workspace window** to a file. The default format is a binary file called a MAT-file. To save the workspace (remember, this is just the set of variables, not the list of commands in the command window) to a file, at the prompt type

```
save < file_name >
```

Although **save** is a MATLAB command, **file_name** is a user defined file name. In this text, we'll indicate user defined names by placing them inside pointed brackets (< >). The file name can be any name you choose, as long as it conforms to the variable naming conventions for MATLAB. Actually, you don't even need to supply a file name. If you don't, MATLAB names the file **matlab.mat**. You could also choose **File → Save Workspace As** from the menu bar, which will then prompt you to enter a file name for your data. To restore a workspace, type

```
load < file_name >
```

Again, **load** is a MATLAB command, but **file_name** is the user defined file name. If you just type **load**, MATLAB will look for the default **matlab.mat** file.

The file you save will be stored in the current directory.

For example, type

```
clear, clc
```

This will clear the workspace and the command window. Verify that the work space is empty by checking the workspace window, or by typing

```
whos
```

Now define several variables, such as:

```
A = 5;
B = [1,2,3];
C = [ 1, 2; 3,4];
```

Check the workspace window once again to confirm that the variables have been stored. Now, save the workspace to a file called **my_example_file**:

```
save my_example_file
```

Confirm that a new file has been stored in the current directory. If you prefer to save the file to another directory (for instance, onto a floppy drive), use the browse button (refer to Figure 2) to navigate to the directory of your choice. Remember that in a public computer lab, the current directory is probably purged after each user logs off of the system.

Now, clear the workspace and command window by typing

```
clear, clc
```

The workspace window should be empty. Now load the file back into the workspace:

```
load my_example_file
```

Again, the file you want to load must be in the current directory, or else MATLAB won't be able to find it. In the command window, type

```
A
```

which returns

```
A =
     5
```

Similarly,

```
B
```

returns

```
B =
     1   2   3
```

and typing

```
C
```

returns

```
C =
        1     2
        3     4
```

MATLAB can also store individual matrices or lists of matrices into the current directory via the command

```
save <file_name>  <variable_list >
```

where **file_name** is the user-defined file name where you wish to store the information, and **variable_list** is the list of variables to be stored in the file. For example,

```
save  my_new_file  A B
```

would save just the variables **A** and **B**, into **my_new_file.mat**.

If your saved data will be used by a program other than MATLAB (such as C or C++), the .mat format is not appropriate, because .mat files are unique to MATLAB. The ASCII format is standard between computer platforms and is more appropriate if you need to share files. MATLAB allows you to save files as ASCII files by modifying the save command:

```
save <file_name>  <variable_list>  -ascii
```

The command **-ascii** tells MATLAB to store the data in a standard 8-digit text format. ASCII files should be saved into a .dat file instead of a .mat file; just be sure to add .dat to your file name—if you don't, it will default to .mat. If more precision is needed, the data can be stored with a 16-digit text format:

```
save file_name  variable_list  -ascii  -double
```

It is also possible to delimit the elements (numbers) with tabs:

```
save <file_name>   <variable_list>  -ascii -double -tabs
```

You can retrieve the data from the current directory with the load command:

```
load <file_name>
```

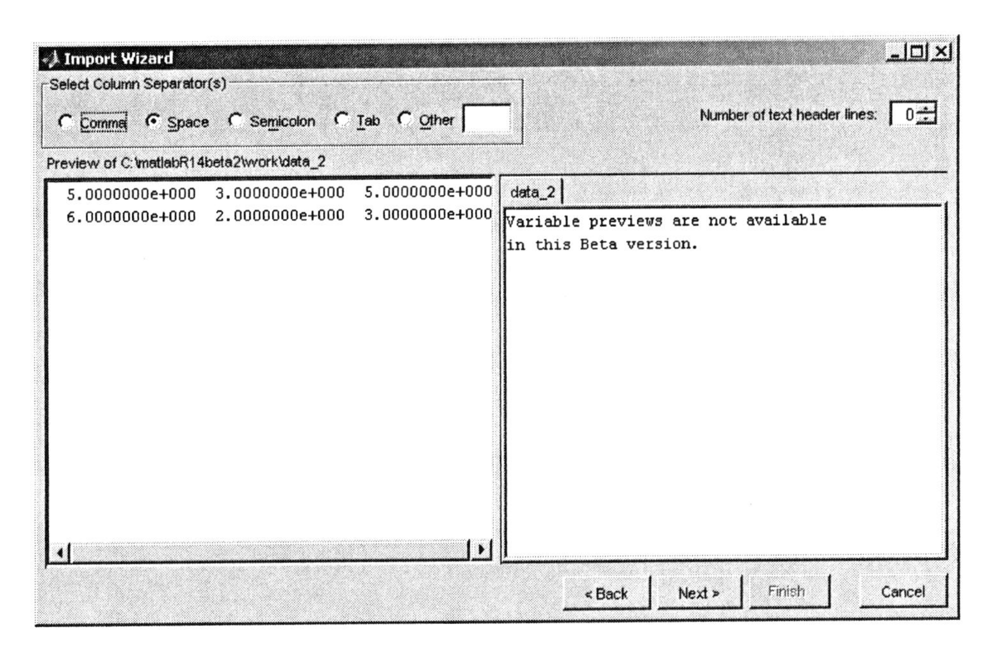

Figure 12. Double clicking the file name in the command directory launches the import wizard.

For example, to create the matrix **Z** and save it to the file **data_2.dat** in 8-digit text format, use the following commands:

```
Z = [5 3 5; 6 2 3];
save data_2.dat Z -ascii
```

This command causes each row of the matrix **Z** to be written to a separate line in the data file. You can view the data_2.dat file by double clicking the file name in the current directory window. (See Figure 12.) Follow the directions in the import wizard, which will automatically launch, to load the data into the workspace with the same name as the data file. You can use this same technique to import data from other programs, including Excel spreadsheets, or you can select **File** → **import data**... from the menu bar.

Perhaps the easiest way to retrieve data from an ASCII. dat file is to enter the **load** command followed by the file name. This will cause the information to be read into a matrix with the same name as the data file.

Script M-Files

In addition to providing an interactive computational environment (using the command window as a scratch pad), MATLAB contains a powerful programming language. As a programmer, you can create and save code in files. The MATLAB files that contain programming code are called M-files. An M-file is an ASCII text file similar to a C or FORTRAN source code file. An M-file can be created and edited using the MATLAB M-file Editor/ Debugger, or you can use another text editor of your choice. The MATLAB editing window is shown in Figure 13.

If you choose a different text editor, make sure the files you save are ASCII files. NotePad is an example of a text editor that defaults to an ASCII file structure. Other word processors, such as WordPerfect or Word, will require you to specify the ASCII structure when you save the file. These programs default to proprietary file structures that are not ASCII compliant, and may result in some unexpected results if

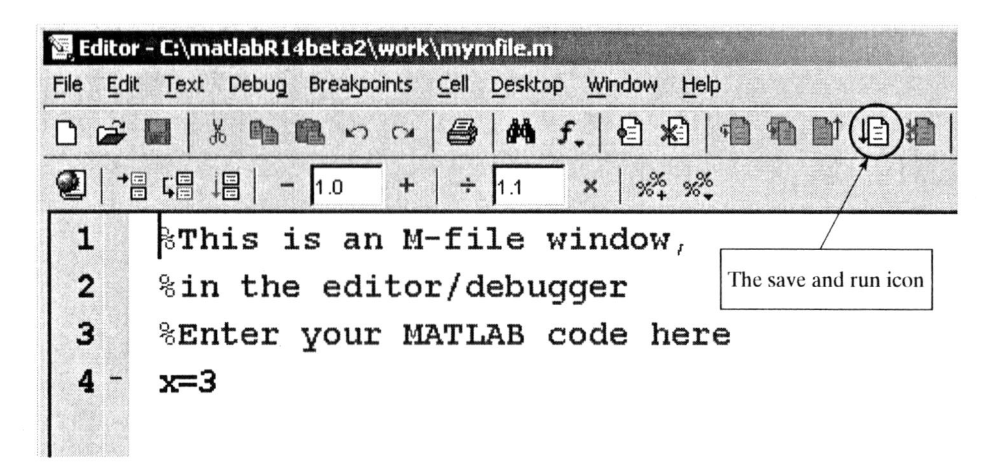

Figure 13. The editing window—also called the Editor/Debugger.

you try to use code written in them without specifying that the files are to be saved in ASCII format.

When you save an M-file, it is stored in the current directory. You'll need to name your file with a "legal" MATLAB variable name; that is, one that starts with a letter and contains only letters, numbers, and the underscore (_). Spaces are not allowed.

There are two types of M-files, called scripts and functions. A script M-file is simply a list of MATLAB statements that are saved in a file (typically with a .m file extension). The script has access to workspace variables. Any variables created in the script are accessible to the workspace when the script finishes. A script created in the MATLAB editor window can be executed by selecting the save and run icon from the menu bar. (See Figure 13.) Alternately, a script can be executed by typing a filename or by using the run command from the command window.

Assume you have created a script file named myscript.m. You can either run the script from the edit window or use one of the following three ways of executing the script from the command window:

MATLAB Command	Comments
`myscript`	Type the file name. The .m file extension is assumed.
`run myscript`	Use the run command with the file name.
`run('myscript')`	This method uses the functional form of the run command.

All three techniques are equivalent. Which one you choose is strictly a personal preference.

You can find out what M-files and MAT files are in the current directory by typing

```
what
```

into the command window. You can also simply browse through the current directory by looking in the current directory window.

Using script M-files allows you to work on a project and to save the list of commands for future use. Because you will be using these files in the future, it is a good idea to comment them liberally. MATLAB will not execute any code on a commented line. The comment operator is the percentage sign:

```
% This is a comment
```

You can also add comments after a command, but it has to be on the same line:

```
A = 5        %The variable A is defined as 5
```

The MATLAB code that could be used to solve Example 3, if it were entered into an M-file, is shown next. It could be run either from the M-file or from the command window. The results will appear in the command window in either case, and the variables will be stored in the workspace. The code is as follows:

```
clear, clc
% A Script M-file to find Drag
%  First define the variables
drag = 20000;             %Define drag in Newtons
r = 0.000001;             %Define air density in kg/m^3
V = 100*0.4470;           %Define velocity in m/s
A = 1;                    %Define area in m^2
% Calculate coefficient of drag
cd = drag *2/(r*V^2*A)
% Find the drag for a variety of velocities
V = 0:20:200;             %Redefine velocity
drag = cd*r*V.^2*A/2;     %Calculate drag
table = [V',drag']        %Create a table of results
```

Example 4 uses a script M-file to find the velocity and acceleration of an aircraft using a UDF engine (unducted fan) at different time values.

EXAMPLE 4 UDF ENGINE PERFORMANCE

An advanced turboprop engine, called an unducted fan (UDF), is one of the promising new propulsion technologies being developed for future transport aircraft.

Turboprop engines, which have been in use for decades, combine the power and reliability of jet engines with the efficiency of propellers. They are a significant improvement over earlier piston-powered propeller engines. Their application has been limited to smaller commuter-type aircraft, however, because they are not as fast or powerful as the fanjet engines used on larger airliners. The UDF engine employs significant advancements in propeller technology, narrowing the performance gap between turboprops and fanjets. New materials, blade shapes, and higher rotation speeds enable UDF-powered aircraft to fly almost as fast as fanjets, and with greater fuel efficiency. The UDF is also significantly quieter than the conventional turboprop.

During the test flight of a UDF-powered aircraft, the test pilot has set the engine power level at 40,000 Newtons, which causes the 20,000 kg aircraft to attain a cruise speed of 180 m/s. The engine throttles are then set to a power level of 60,000 Newtons, and the aircraft begins to accelerate. As the speed of the plane increases, the aerodynamic drag increases in proportion to the square of the air speed. Eventually, the aircraft reaches a new cruise speed, where the thrust from the UDF engines is just offset by the drag. The equations used to estimate the velocity and acceleration of the aircraft from the time the throttle is reset to the time the plane reaches new cruise speed (at approximately 120 s) are the following:

$$\text{velocity} = 0.00001\ \text{time}^3 - 0.00488\ \text{time}^2 + 0.75795\ \text{time} + 181.3566$$

$$\text{acceleration} = 3 - 0.000062\ \text{velocity}^2$$

Figure 14. An unducted fan engine (UDF).

Write a MATLAB program, using a script M-file, that calculates the velocity and acceleration of the aircraft at times from 0 to 120 seconds, and at increments of 10 seconds. Assume that time zero represents the point at which the power level was increased. Display the results in a table of time, velocity, and acceleration.

1. State the Problem

Calculate the velocity and acceleration, using a script M-file.

2. Describe the Input and Output

Input

Start time is	0 seconds
Final time is	120 seconds
Time increment is	10 seconds

Output

velocity
acceleration

3. Hand Example

Solve the equations stated in the problem for time = 100 seconds;

$$\begin{aligned} \text{velocity} &= 0.00001\ \text{time}^3 - 0.00488\ \text{time}^2 + 0.75795\ \text{time} + 181.3566 \\ &= 218.35\ \text{m/sec} \\ \text{acceleration} &= 3 - 0.000062\,\text{velocity}^2 \\ &= 0.04404\ \text{m/sec}^2 \end{aligned}$$

4. Develop a MATLAB Solution

Create a new script M-file, using the **File → New → m-file** menu selection. Enter these commands:

```
clear, clc
%Example 4
%These commands generate velocity and acceleration
%values for a UDF aircraft test
%Define the time matrix
time = 0:10:120;
%Calculate the velocity matrix
velocity = 0.00001*time.^3 - 0.00488*time.^2 ...
              + 0.75795*time + 181.3566;
%Use the calculated velocities to find the acceleration
acceleration = 3 - 6.2e-5*velocity.^2;
%Present the results in a table
[time', velocity', acceleration']
```

Save the file with a name of your choice, using the file selection from the menu bar. Remember that the file name needs to be a legitimate variable name. For example, save the file as **example_4**.

Execute the file by selecting the run icon from the menu bar. The results will be displayed in the command window.

```
ans =
            0          181.3566     0.9608
            10.0000    188.4581     0.7980
            20.0000    194.6436     0.6511
            30.0000    199.9731     0.5207
            40.0000    204.5066     0.4070
            50.0000    208.3041     0.3098
            60.0000    211.4256     0.2286
            70.0000    213.9311     0.1625
            80.0000    215.8806     0.1105
            90.0000    217.3341     0.0715
            100.0000   218.3516     0.0440
            110.0000   218.9931     0.0266
            120.0000   219.3186     0.0178
```

Figure 15 is a picture of the MATLAB environment, after the script M-file was executed. Notice the list of variables in the workspace window and the list of files in the current directory window. The current directory window was moved out from under the workspace window by clicking and dragging, so that both could be viewed at the same time. Notice that the command history window *does not* reflect the commands issued and executed in the script M-file.

5. Test the Solution

Compare the MATLAB results to the hand example results. Notice that the velocity and acceleration calculated from the hand example and the MATLAB solution match. Now that you have a MATLAB program that works, you can modify it for other equations chosen to model aircraft behavior. ■

SUMMARY

In this chapter, we introduced you to the MATLAB environment. In particular, we explored the window structure and solved problems in the command window. The primary data structure in MATLAB is a matrix, which can be a single point (a scalar), a

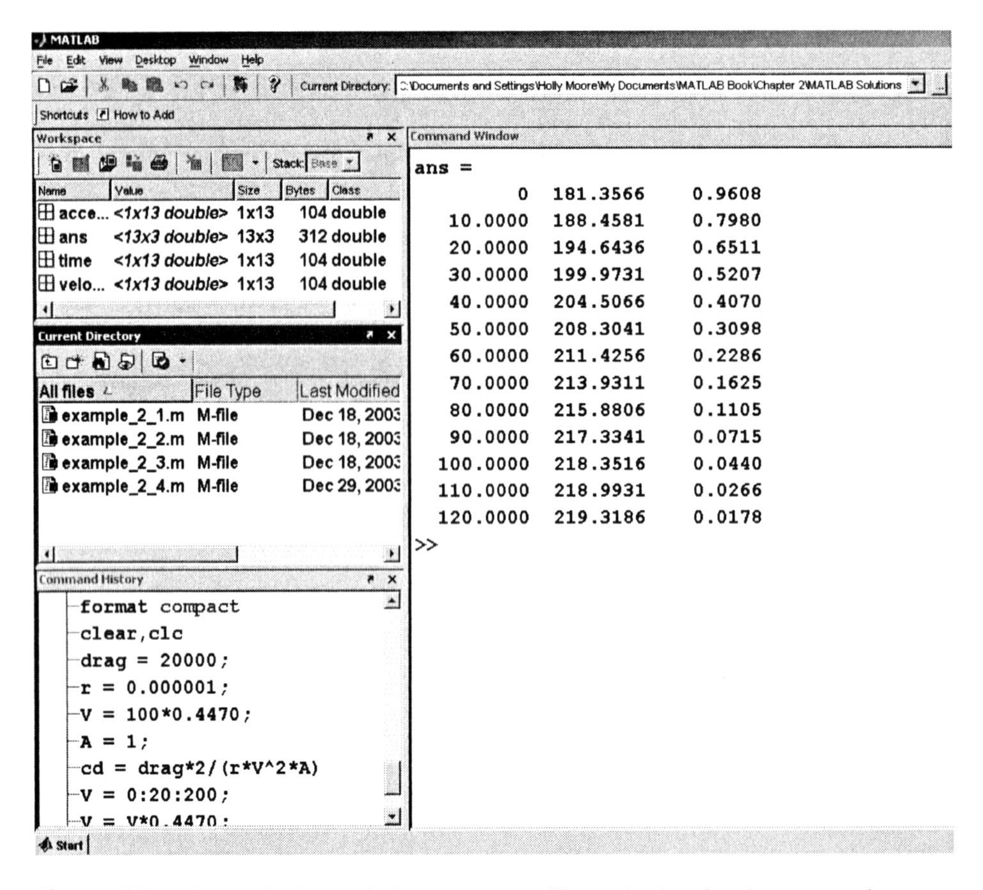

Figure 15. The results from calculations in an M-file are displayed in the command window.

list of values (a vector), or a rectangular grid of values with rows and columns. Values can be entered into a matrix by explicitly listing the values or by loading them from MAT files or ASCII files. In addition, we learned how to save values into both MAT files and ASCII files. We explored the various mathematical operations that are performed in an element-by-element manner. Finally, we learned how to use a script M-file to record the sequence of commands used to solve a MATLAB problem.

MATLAB SUMMARY

This MATLAB summary lists all of the special characters, commands, and functions that were defined in this chapter:

Special Characters	
[ ]	forms matrices
( )	used in statements to group operations used with a matrix name to identify specific elements
,	separates subscripts or matrix elements
;	separates rows in a matrix definition suppresses output when used in commands
:	used to generate matrices indicates all rows or all columns

=	assignment operator—assigns a value to a memory location—not the same as an equality
%	indicates a comment in an M-file
+	scalar and array addition
−	scalar and array subtraction
*	scalar multiplication
.*	array multiplication
/	scalar division
./	array division
^	scalar exponentiation
.^	array exponentiation

Commands and Functions

`ans`	default variable name for results of MATLAB calculations
`clc`	clears command screen
`clear`	clears workspace
`exit`	terminates MATLAB
`format +`	sets format to plus and minus signs only
`format compact`	sets format to compact form
`format long`	sets format to 14 decimal places
`formal long e`	sets format to 14 exponential places
`format loose`	sets format back to default, non-compact form
`format short`	sets format back to default, four decimal places
`format short e`	sets format to four exponential places
`help`	invokes help utility
`linspace`	linearly spaced vector function
`load`	loads matrices from a file
`pi`	numeric approximation of the value of π
`quit`	terminates MATLAB
`save`	saves variables in a file
`who`	lists variables in memory
`whos`	lists variables and their sizes

KEY TERMS

arguments
array editor
ASCII
assignment operator
command history
command window
current directory
DAT-file
document window
edit window
function
graphics window
M-file
MAT-file
matrix
operator
prompt
scalar
scientific notation
script
start button
transpose operator
vector
workspace

Problems

1. Which of the following are legitimate variable names in MATLAB?

   a. 3vars
   b. global

c. help
d. My_var
e. sin
f. X + Y
g. _input
h. input
i. tax-rate
j. example1.1
k. example1_1

Test your answers by trying to assign a value to each name by using, for example,

```
3vars = 3
```

or by using **isvarname**, as in

```
isvarname 3vars
```

Remember, **isvarname** returns a 1 if the name is legal and a 0 if it is not. Although it is possible to reassign a function name as a variable name, it's not a good idea. Use **which** to check whether the preceding names are function names, as in

```
which sin
```

In what case would MATLAB tell you that **sin** is a variable name, not a function name?

2. Predict the outcome of the following MATLAB calculations:

$$1 + 3/4$$
$$5 \times 6 \times 4/2$$
$$5/2 \times 6 \times 4$$
$$5\hat{}2 \times 3$$
$$5\hat{}(2 \times 3)$$
$$1 + 3 + 5/5 + 3 + 1$$
$$(1 + 3 + 5)/(5 + 3 + 1)$$

Check your results by entering the calculations into the command window.

3. Create MATLAB code to perform the following calculations:

$$5^2$$
$$\frac{5+3}{5 \cdot 6}$$
$$\sqrt{4 + 6^3}$$

Hint: A square root is the same thing as a $\frac{1}{2}$ power.

$$9\frac{6}{12} + 7 \cdot 5^{3+2}$$
$$1 + 5 \cdot 3/6^2 + 2^{2-4} \cdot 1/5.5$$

Check your code by entering it into MATLAB and performing the calculations on your scientific calculator.

4. a. The area of a circle is πr^2. Define r as 5, and then find the area of a circle, using MATLAB.
   b. The surface area of a sphere is $4\pi r^2$. Find the surface area of a sphere with a radius of 10 ft.
   c. The volume of a sphere is $\frac{4}{3}\pi r^3$. Find the volume of a sphere with a radius of 2 ft.

5. a. The volume of a cylinder is $\pi r^2 h$. Define r as 3 and **h** as the matrix

```
h = [1,5,12]
```

   find the volume of the cylinders.
   b. The area of a triangle is $\frac{1}{2}$ base $\times$ height. Define the base as the matrix

```
b = [2,4,6]
```

   and the height h as 12, and find the area of the triangles.
   c. The volume of any right prism is base $\times$ vertical_dimension. Find the volume of the triangles in problem (b), for a vertical dimension of 10.

6. a. Generate an evenly spaced vector of values from 1 to 20, in increments of 1.
   b. Generate a vector of values from zero to 2π in increments of $\pi/100$.
   c. Generate a vector containing 15 values, evenly spaced between 4 and 20.

   Hint: Use the linspace command. If you can't remember the syntax, type

```
help linspace
```

7. Generate a table of conversions from degrees to radians. The first line should contain the values for 0°, the second line should contain the values for 10°, and so on. The last line should contain the values for 360°.

8. Generate a table of conversions from centimeters to inches. Start the centimeters column at 0 and increment by 2 centimeters. The last line should contain the value 50 cm.

9. Generate a table of conversions from mi/h to ft/s. The initial value in the mi/h column should be 0 and the final value should be 100. Print 14 values in your table.

10. The general equation for the distance that a free falling body has traveled (neglecting air friction) is

$$d = \frac{1}{2}gt^2.$$

Assume that $g = 9.8$ m/s^2. Generate a table of time versus distance traveled.

Hint: Be careful to use the correct operators: t^2 is an array operation!

11. Newton's law of universal gravitation tells us that the force exerted by one particle on another is

$$F = G\frac{m_1 m_2}{r^2}$$

where the universal gravitational constant is found experimentally to be

$$G = 6.673 \times 10^{-11} \text{ N } m^2/\text{kg}^2.$$

The mass of each object is m_1 and m_2, respectively, and r is the distance between the two particles. Use Newton's law of universal gravitation to find the force exerted by the earth on the moon, assuming that

the mass of the earth is approximately 6×10^{24} kg,
the mass of the moon is approximately 7.4×10^{22} kg, and
the earth and the moon are an average of 3.9×10^{8} m apart.

12. We know the earth and the moon are not always the same distance apart. Find the force the moon exerts on the earth for 10 distances between 3.8×10^{8} m and 4.0×10^{8} m.

13. Your instructor will provide you with a file called volatage.dat, which represents data collected during an experiment. We know from Ohm's law that

$$V = I \cdot R.$$

If the resistance in the circuit is constant at 4 ohms, use MATLAB to find the current corresponding to each voltage. First you'll need to load the data into MATLAB, then perform the calculations, and finally create a table of results. Save your table of results into an ASCII file called current.dat.

Index

D

T

Z